W9-DFR-316

Applied Probability and Statistics (Continued)

BROWNLEE · Statistical Theory and Methodology in Science and Engineering, *Second Edition*
BUSH and MOSTELLER · Stochastic Models for Learning
CHERNOFF and MOSES · Elementary Decision Theory
CHEW · Experimental Designs in Industry
CLARK · An Introduction to Statistics
COCHRAN · Sampling Techniques, *Second Edition*
COCHRAN and COX · Experimental Designs, *Second Edition*
CORNELL · The Essentials of Educational Statistics
COX · Planning of Experiments
DEMING · Sample Design in Business Research
DEMING · Some Theory of Sampling
DODGE and ROMIG · Sampling Inspection Tables, *Second Edition*
FRYER · Elements of Statistics
GOLDBERGER · Econometric Theory
GOULDEN · Methods of Statistical Analysis, *Second Edition*
GUTTMAN and WILKS · Introductory Engineering Statistics
HALD · Statistical Tables and Formulas
HALD · Statistical Theory with Engineering Applications
HANSEN, HURWITZ, and MADOW · Sample Survey Methods and Theory, Volume I
HAUSER and LEONARD · Government Statistics for Business Use, *Second Edition*
HOEL · Elementary Statistics
JOHNSON and LEONE · Statistics and Experimental Design: In Engineering and the Physical Sciences, Volumes I and II
KEMPTHORNE · An Introduction to Genetic Statistics
MEYER · Symposium on Monte Carlo Methods
PRABHU · Queues and Inventories: A Study of Their Basic Stochastic Processes
RICE · Control Charts in Factory Management
SARHAN and GREENBERG · Contributions to Order Statistics
TIPPETT · Technological Applications of Statistics
WILLIAMS · Regression Analysis
WOLD and JURÉEN · Demand Analysis
YOUDEN · Statistical Methods for Chemists

Tracts on Probability and Statistics

BILLINGSLEY · Ergodic Theory and Information

Ergodic Theory and Information

Ergodic Theory and Information

PATRICK BILLINGSLEY

The University of Chicago

John Wiley & Sons, Inc., New York · London · Sydney

Ruth
Frances
Patricia
Julia
Martha
Paul

Foreword

It is a great pleasure to be allowed a few words in which to introduce Patrick Billingsley's monograph, the first in a new Series of *Tracts on Probability and Mathematical Statistics.*

This book originated in a lively series of lectures which Professor Billingsley gave to one of the London Mathematical Society's Instructional Conferences, lectures which we felt should be made available to a wider public. It is particularly fitting that this book should initiate the new Series, because the *Tracts* and the London Mathematical Society's Conferences are both intended to make new mathematical developments generally accessible while the pulse of life still beats in them, and before they have acquired a chilling permanence.

We hope to keep the tracts to the moderate length of the present book. Most prospective authors feel appalled by the thought of writing, typing, and correcting proof of many hundreds of pages of mathematics, and there can be no doubt that some excellent mathematical books are never written for this reason and because those who would be their authors find it impossible to detach themselves from teaching and research for the length of time required to write a comprehensive treatise.

We also hope through this series to make a contribution to the improvement of current standards in the design and printing of mathematical books. A book is useless unless it is read. It is the conviction of the editors that an exciting subject and a masterly touch are not enough; the text must be attractively presented in a manner which positively aids the comprehension of the argument. This is not a matter of aesthetics but of communication, and we think that it deserves greater attention.

Cambridge, England   *David Kendall*

Preface

This book grew out of a survey* of ergodic theory and information theory designed to follow a brief course in measure-theoretic probability.

Chapter 1 centers on the ergodic theorem. Chapter 2 treats the Kolmogorov-Sinai application of Shannon's entropy to the isomorphism problem of ergodic theory. In reverse of the historical order, these ideas are only later applied (in Chapters 4 and 5) to information theory and to coding theory. The results on coding do not go deep; my aim here has been to link coding theory as closely as possible to ergodic theory and to avoid technicalities. The connection between the two theories forms a thread running through the whole book.

It is assumed from the outset that the reader knows about $(\Omega, \mathscr{F}, P)$. To reduce the measure-theoretic prerequisites though, I have included an account (Chapter 3) of conditional probability and expectation with respect to a σ-field, and I have "starred" a number of topics that the reader may omit (of course, a star attaches to the book as a whole).

I have tried to write not for experts, but for those to whom the subject is new. And I have tried to follow the excellent example of Hardy and Wright, who wrote their *Introduction to the Theory of Numbers* with the avowed aim, as they say in the preface, of producing an interesting book.

Copenhagen, December 1964   *Patrick Billingsley*

---

* A course of lectures delivered at the London Mathematical Society's Instructional Conference on Mathematical Probability, held at the Durham Colleges, March 28 to April 11, 1963.

Acknowledgments

For various facts and viewpoints, I am indebted to many people, particularly to L. E. Baum, J. R. Blum, T. A. Brown, D. A. Edwards, D. L. Hanson, K. Jacobs, R. A. Leibler, R. Ranga Rao, Ya. G. Sinai, L. Sucheston, and D. R. Weck. Special thanks go to Paul Halmos, through whom I became acquainted with the theory set out in Chapter 2; and to David Kendall and Inge Henningsen, whose comments on the manuscript led me to clear up many obscurities and to remove a number of blunders.

The writing of this book was supported in part by the Statistics Branch, Office of Naval Research, and in part by Research Grant No. 609 from the Division of Mathematical, Physical, and Engineering Sciences of the National Science Foundation.

Contents

CHAPTER 1   ERGODIC THEORY,   1

Section 1   *Measure-preserving transformations*   1

Introduction 1, Definitions 2, Some examples 3,
Ergodicity 7, Ergodicity of rotations 9, Ergodicity of
the dyadic transformation 11, Mixing 12, Statement
of the ergodic theorem 13, Consequences of the ergodic
theorem 15, Tests for ergodicity 16, A more
complicated shift 18

Section 2   *Proof of the ergodic theorem*   20

First proof 20, The maximal ergodic theorem 24,
Second proof 27

Section 3   *Further examples*   29

Other shifts 30, Measures on the interval 34, An
existence theorem 37, Ergodicity and extreme points 38

Section 4   *Application to continued fractions*   40

The transformation 40, Gauss's measure 43,
Application to Diophantine approximation 47, Mixing
and Gauss's problem 49

CHAPTER 2   ENTROPY   51

Section 5   *The problem of isomorphism*   51

Isomorphism 52, Invariants 57, Entropy 60,

Isomorphism vs. conjugacy 66, Isomorphism vs. spectral equivalence 73

Section 6   *Properties of $H(\mathscr{A})$ and $H(\mathscr{A}, T)$*   77

Properties of $H(\mathscr{A})$ and $H(\mathscr{A} \mid \mathscr{B})$ 78, Properties of $h(\mathscr{A}, T)$ 81

Section 7   *Properties of $h(T)$*   84

The Kolmogorov-Sinai theorem 84, Calculation of entropy 85, Some extensions 87

Section 8   *The completeness problem*   90

Some open problems 90, Kolmogorov shifts 92

CHAPTER 3. CONDITIONAL PROBABILITY AND EXPECTATION 95

Section 9   *Conditional probability*   95

The finite case 95, The general case 97, Properties of conditional probability 103, Functions vs. measures 105

Section 10 *Conditional expectation*   106

Definition 106, Basic properties 109, Iterated conditional expectations 110, Jensen's inequality 112, A special formula 112

Section 11 *A convergence theorem*   115

The theorem 115, Examples 118, Decreasing σ-fields 120

CHAPTER 4 CONVERGENCE OF ENTROPY 123

Section 12 *A generalization of conditional entropy*   123

Definition 123, Properties of $H(\mathscr{A} \mid \mathscr{G})$ 124, Two special formulas 126

Section 13 *The Shannon-McMillan-Breiman theorem*   129

The result 129, Other versions of the theorem 133, The equipartition property 135

Section 14 *A connection with dimension theory* 136

The classical definition 136, Dimension in the unit
interval 138, The generalized definition 139, The main
result 141

CHAPTER 5 CODING 146

Section 15 *The coding theorem for the noiseless channel* 146

Some notation 146, The noiseless channel 147,
Coding theorems 150

Section 16 *The noisy channel* 152

Definitions 152, The channel without memory 153,
The input-output measure 154, Rate of transmission 155,
Channel capacity 160, Ergodicity of the input-output
process 161

Section 17 *The coding theorem for the noisy channel* 162

The problem 162, A simple converse 164, Comments
on the direct theorem for the channel without memory
164, A refinement of the converse 166

Section 18 *Feinstein's theorem* 168

The decision scheme 169, Application 174

Section 19 *Block codes* 175

Definition 175, The direct theorem by block codes 176

Bibliography, 181
Index of Examples, 187
General Index, 191

CHAPTER 1

Ergodic Theory

1. MEASURE-PRESERVING TRANSFORMATIONS

Introduction

Even though chance necessarily involves the notion of change, the laws governing the change may themselves remain fixed as time passes: if time does not alter the roulette wheel, the gambler's fortunes fluctuate according to constant probability laws. Ergodic theory is a key to understanding these fluctuations.

Tossing a coin, rolling a die, observing the length of a queue, determining the number of molecules in a given volume—imagine any such chance experiment or observation. The state space of the experiment is the set ρ of possible outcomes: ρ comprises the faces of the coin, or the sides of the die, or the like, as appropriate. Suppose the experiment is performed once each minute (say), and that this has been going on forever and will continue forever.

We can regard the whole doubly infinite sequence of experiments as one grand experiment; its outcome is represented by a doubly infinite sequence $\omega = (. . . , \omega_{-1}, \omega_0, \omega_1, . . .)$ of elements of ρ. The probability structure of this grand experiment is described by a probability measure P on the space Ω of such sequences ω.*

---

* It is hard to see how to fit P into the frequency theory of probability: the grand experiment cannot be repeated, since one replication uses up all of time. No matter: although the infiniteness of the sequence of component experiments is mathematically crucial, it must not be taken literally in real applications.

While allowing for the possibility that the outcome of each experiment strongly influences the outcomes of its successors, we want to reflect mathematically the idea that passage of time does not affect the set of joint probability laws governing the experimentation. Shifting the sequence ω to the left one place produces a new sequence $\omega' = (\ldots, \omega_0, \omega_1, \omega_2, \ldots)$, in which ω_1 stands now in the 0th place. Since ω and ω' are identical realizations of the grand experiment, apart from a change in the origin of the time scale, if the probability laws are to be constant in time then P should assign the same probability to ω' as to ω. Actually, ω and ω' will generally have probability 0, and what we must require is that P be preserved by the transformation T that carries ω to ω', in the sense that $P(A) = P(TA)$ for sets A. This leads us to study measure-preserving transformations—ergodic theory.

In this section, after setting out the first definitions, examples (some from probability, some from other parts of mathematics), and principles, we state the ergodic theorem, which is the central result of the theory, and illustrate it by applications. Section 2 contains proofs of the ergodic theorem, and further examples and applications follow in Sections 3 and 4.

Definitions

In ergodic theory, one studies transformations that preserve the structure of measure spaces. Since we shall be concerned with ergodic theory as it relates to probability theory and to information theory, we shall confine our attention to probability measure spaces.

Let $(\Omega, \mathscr{F}, P)$ be a probability space,* and let T be a transformation of Ω into itself that is *measurable* in the sense that $A \in \mathscr{F}$ implies $T^{-1}A = \{\omega: T\omega \epsilon A\} \in \mathscr{F}$. If T is also one-to-one, if $T\Omega = \Omega$, and if $A \in \mathscr{F}$ implies $TA = \{T\omega: \omega \epsilon A\} \in \mathscr{F}$, then we say T is *invertible*. In case $P(T^{-1}A) = P(A)$ for every A in $\mathscr{F}$, T is said to be *measure preserving*; if T is invertible, an equivalent requirement is that $P(TA) = P(A)$.

---

* That is to say, Ω is a space of points ω, $\mathscr{F}$ is a σ-field (that is, σ-algebra) of subsets of Ω, and P is a probability measure on $\mathscr{F}$. For the measure-theoretic basis of probability, see, for example, Chapter X of Halmos (1950), or Kolmogorov's monograph (1933).

(Even if a measure-preserving transformation is not invertible, its range $T\Omega$ is essentially all of Ω, since $T\Omega \subset A \in \mathscr{F}$ implies $T^{-1}A = \Omega$ and hence $P(A) = 1$; in particular, if $T\Omega$ happens to lie in $\mathscr{F}$ then $P(T\Omega) = 1$.)

Some Examples

Consider first two probabilistic examples.

Example 1.1.* Let ρ be a finite set of r elements. The general probability measure on ρ—on the σ-field of all subsets of ρ, really—is specified by assigning nonnegative probabilities p_i to the elements i of ρ in such a way that $\Sigma_{i\epsilon\rho}p_i = 1$. Let $(\Omega, \mathscr{F}, P)$ be the product of a doubly infinite sequence of copies of the resulting measure space. The general element of Ω is a doubly infinite sequence $\omega = (\ldots, \omega_{-1}, \omega_0, \omega_1, \ldots)$ of elements of ρ. Let x_n be the nth coordinate function—the mapping from Ω to ρ whose value $x_n(\omega)$ at the point ω is the nth coordinate ω_n of ω.† The σ-field $\mathscr{F}$ is generated by the (finitely additive) field consisting of the cylinders, or sets of the form

$$\{\omega : (x_n(\omega), \ldots, x_{n+k-1}(\omega)) \in E\} = \{\omega : (\omega_n, \ldots, \omega_{n+k-1}) \in E\}$$

with E a subset of the Cartesian product ρ^k of k copies of ρ. The σ-field $\mathscr{F}$ is also generated by what may be called "thin" cylinders, that is, sets of the form $\{\omega : x_l(\omega) = i_l, n \le l < n + k\}$, where the i_l are elements of ρ; indeed, each cylinder is a finite, disjoint union of thin cylinders. Finally, P is specified by its values on thin cylinders:

$$(1.1) \qquad P\{\omega : x_l(\omega) = i_l, n \le l < n + k\} = \prod_{l=n}^{n+k-1} p_{i_l}.\ddagger$$

---

* At the end of the book there is a separate descriptive index of these examples.

† Although $x_n(\omega)$ is nothing other than ω_n, if we used ω_n as a name for the function $\omega \to \omega_n$, the argument ω would be one of the two symbols making up this name, which would be inconvenient if only because the argument could not then be suppressed; hence we give the function $\omega \to \omega_n$ a special name.

‡ These characterizations of Ω and of $\mathscr{F}$ can be taken as definitions. We have appealed to the general theory of product measures for the theorem that says there exists on $\mathscr{F}$ a unique probability measure P satisfying (1.1). This follows also from the Kolmogorov (or Daniell-Kolmogorov) existence theorem. An elementary direct proof appears in Section 3.

Thus $\{\ldots, x_{-1}, x_0, x_1, \ldots\}$ is an independent sequence of random variables with values in ρ. Let $T\colon \Omega \to \Omega$ be the mapping that carries $(\ldots, \omega_{-1}, \omega_0, \omega_1, \ldots)$ to $(\ldots, \omega_0, \omega_1, \omega_2, \ldots)$. More precisely, T is defined by $(T\omega)_n = \omega_{n+1}$, or, what is the same thing, by $x_n(T\omega) = x_{n+1}(\omega)$. Since $x_n(\omega) = x_0(T^n\omega)$, any statement about the random variables x_n can be converted into a statement about x_0 and T. If A is any cylinder then clearly $T^{-1}A$ is also a cylinder and hence lies in $\mathscr{F}$, and $P(T^{-1}A) = P(A)$. That T is then measurable and measure preserving is a consequence of the following general result.

THEOREM 1.1   *Let $\mathscr{F}_0$ be a field generating $\mathscr{F}$. If $T^{-1}A \in \mathscr{F}$ and $P(T^{-1}A) = P(A)$ for all A in $\mathscr{F}_0$, then T is a measure-preserving transformation.*
Proof.   If $\mathscr{G}$ is the collection of sets A in $\mathscr{F}$ for which $T^{-1}A \in \mathscr{F}$ and $P(T^{-1}A) = P(A)$, then $\mathscr{G}$ is a monotone class and contains the field $\mathscr{F}_0$ and hence coincides with $\mathscr{F}$.*

Example 1.1 is intended to provide a mathematical model for a doubly infinite sequence of Bernoulli trials. Imagine a simple chance experiment with finite state space ρ, with p_i for the probability of outcome i. The example is a model for the conceptual experiment that consists of a doubly infinite sequence of independent repetitions of the simple experiment represented by ρ. Suppose one repetition is made each day; a point $\omega = (\ldots, \omega_{-1}, \omega_0, \omega_1, \ldots)$ of Ω specifies completely the outcome of this complicated experiment, ω_n being the outcome of the component experiment made on the nth day.

But now there arises a point of interpretation which is at first confusing. A knowledge of the outcome $x_5(\omega)$ for the fifth day, say, is not supposed to help one predict the outcome $x_6(\omega)$ for the sixth day. But $x_5(\omega)$ is not determined unless ω itself is determined, in which case $x_6(\omega)$ is also completely determined. The randomness seems to have evaporated. To put it slightly differently, the coordinates of ω are determined simultaneously, so to speak; how, then, can they provide a model for experiments done sequentially in time?

The following allegorical way of looking at the model may help.

---

* See Halmos (1950, p. 27).

Tyche* draws a point ω from Ω according to the probability distribution P. She does this before the beginning of time and then reveals the coordinates ω_n to the experimenter one by one—one each day. The dynamic aspects of the model are conveniently studied by means of the transformation T because this is the transformation that makes time go by. (The mathematics itself fortunately depends on no such interpretations.)

Remark on invertibility. An application of Theorem 1.1 to the inverse point-mapping T^{-1} shows that Example 1.1 is invertible. A technical point is involved here. In some cases, the inverse point-mapping is well defined (that is, the original transformation is one-to-one and has all of Ω as its range) and yet fails to be measurable. This is true, for example, of the transformation T on $(\Omega, \mathscr{F}', P')$, where T and Ω are as in Example 1.1, $\mathscr{F}'$ is the σ-field generated by $x_0, x_1, x_2, \ldots$, and P' is the restriction of P to $\mathscr{F}'$. To prove T^{-1} measurable thus requires an argument. If this is established, however, that T^{-1} preserves measure then follows directly from the corresponding fact for T.

Example 1.2. Let Ω and $\mathscr{F}$ be as in the first example, but now let P be *any* measure that is preserved by the transformation T defined there. To say that T preserves P is (by Theorem 1.1) exactly to say that $P\{\omega: (x_n(\omega), \ldots, x_{n+k-1}(\omega)) \in E\}$ is independent of n, which is just the definition of the stationarity of the stochastic process $\{\ldots, x_{-1}, x_0, x_1, \ldots\}$ that the coordinate variables constitute. The transformation T is called the *shift* associated with the process.

Since the finite disjoint unions of thin cylinders form a field which generates $\mathscr{F}$, a measure P on $\mathscr{F}$ is uniquely determined by the values

(1.2) $p_k(i_1 \cdots i_k) = P\{\omega: x_n(\omega) = i_1, \ldots, x_{n+k-1}(\omega) = i_k\}$,

it gives such cylinders. If functions p_k of k-long sequences of elements of ρ are defined by (1.2) then

(1.3) $\begin{cases} p_k(i_1, \ldots, i_k) \geq 0 \\ \sum_i p_{k+1}(i_1, \ldots, i_k, i) = p_k(i_1, \ldots, i_k) \\ \sum_i p_1(i) = 1, \end{cases}$

---

* Goddess of chance; see Graves (1955) for an account. Her appearance in this book always signals a time-out for heuristics.

and, since T preserves measure,

$$(1.4) \qquad p_k(i_1, \ldots, i_k) = \sum_i p_{k+1}(i, i_1, \ldots, i_k).$$

Conversely, corresponding to a given set of functions p_k satisfying (1.3) and (1.4), there is just one probability measure P on $\mathscr{F}$ that satisfies (1.2) and is preserved by T.* If $p_k(i_1, \ldots, i_k) = p_{i_1} p_{i_2} \cdots p_{i_k}$, the p_i being nonnegative numbers adding to 1, then (1.3) and (1.4) hold; we have again Example 1.1, which we shall call the *Bernoulli shift*. Various other special cases are worked out in detail in Section 3. Note that the transformation T, qua point transformation on Ω, is the same in Examples 1.1 and 1.2. A measure-preserving transformation, however, is the point transformation together with the σ-field with respect to which it is measurable and the measure it preserves.

Example 1.2 provides a model for trials that, while not necessarily independent, are made under constant conditions—this is the idea behind stationarity, or the requirement that T preserve P. Since stationary processes are of wide occurrence, and since any property of the process is really a property of the associated shift, it is profitable to study the shift itself. The best way to study the shift is to study measure-preserving transformations in general, because then a variety of examples, many of them substantially simpler than the two already given, present themselves. The following four illustrate some of the different kinds of behavior possible.

Example 1.3.   Suppose that Ω is the five-point space $\{a, b, c, d, e\}$, that $\mathscr{F}$ consists of all subsets of Ω, and that T is the permutation $T = (a, b, c)(d, e)$, a product of two cycles. If T preserves P, then P must assign equal masses to a, b, and c, and equal masses to d and e.

Example 1.4.   With Ω and $\mathscr{F}$ as in the preceding example, take T to be cyclic: $T = (a, b, c, d, e)$. All five masses must be $\frac{1}{5}$.

Example 1.5.   Let Ω be the unit circle in the complex plane, with $\mathscr{F}$ consisting of the ordinary Borel subsets of Ω ($\mathscr{F}$ is the σ-field generated

---

* This is a special case of Kolmogorov's existence theorem; a special proof is given in Section 3.

by the arcs), and let P be circular Lebesque measure on Ω, so normalized that $P(\Omega) = 1$. For a fixed element c of Ω, let $T\omega = c\omega$. Since T is effectively a rotation of the circle through the angle arg c, T preserves P. We shall see that T has radically different properties according as c is a root of unity or not.

Example 1.6. Let $\mathscr{F}$ consist of the Borel subsets of the half-open unit interval $\Omega = [0, 1)$, with Lebesgue measure for P, and let $T\omega = 2\omega \pmod{1}$ (that is, $T\omega$ is 2ω on $[0, \frac{1}{2})$ and $2\omega - 1$ on $[\frac{1}{2}, 1)$). The transformation T is closely associated with the base-2 expansion of a point of the unit interval; in fact, if $f(\omega)$ is 0 for $\omega < \frac{1}{2}$ and 1 for $\omega \geq \frac{1}{2}$, then $f(T^{n-1}\omega)$ is the nth digit of the dyadic (base-2) expansion of $\omega = \sum_{n=1}^{\infty} f(T^{n-1}\omega)/2^n$ (if ω is a dyadic rational, the expansion is the one that terminates). Therefore, if ω has the expansion $\omega = .\omega_1\omega_2\ldots$, then $T\omega = .\omega_2\omega_3\ldots$. An application of Theorem 1.1 shows that T preserves measure. Although the preceding examples are all invertible, this one, which we may call the *dyadic transformation*, is not.

Sufficient specimen transformations have been given to motivate and illustrate the general considerations that follow. A number of additional examples are set out in Section 3.

Ergodicity

We are interested in discovering which transformations T have the property for almost every ω the *orbit* $\{\omega, T\omega, T^2\omega, \ldots\}$* of ω is a sort of replica of Ω itself. In Example 1.4 every orbit resembles Ω in the primitive sense of being equal to Ω as a set, while this is not true in Example 1.3, the trouble being that the set $A = \{a, b, c\}$ is sent into itself by T and so is the complimentary set $\{d, e\}$: $T^{-1}A = A$. Observe that in Example 1.4 not only does each orbit equal Ω as a set, but each one even contains the elements of Ω in the right proportions: the asymptotic relative frequency of occurrence of a (or b, . . .) in the orbit is just $P(a) = \frac{1}{5}$ (or $P(b) = \frac{1}{5}$, . . .).

---

* We take this sequence as the orbit of ω, even if T is invertible (when it might more properly be called the half-orbit, and $\{\ldots, T^{-1}\omega, \omega, T\omega, \ldots\}$ the orbit).

The surprising thing is that if we assume of a general measure-preserving transformation T that there exist no sets A such that $T^{-1}A = A$—apart from such uninteresting ones as $A = 0$ and $A = \Omega$—then the orbits replicate Ω in the sense that for each A the orbit of almost every ω enters A with asymptotic relative frequency $P(A)$:

$$\lim_{n \to \infty} \frac{1}{n} \sum_{k=0}^{n-1} I_A(T^k \omega) = P(A) \qquad \text{a.e.*}$$

This fact, to be further described and illustrated in this section and proved in the next, is the central fact of ergodic theory.

Let us then define a set† A to be *invariant* (under T) in case $T^{-1}A = A$; if T is invertible, this is equivalent to $TA = A$. And let us define T to be *ergodic*‡ if each invariant set is trivial in the sense of having measure either 0 or 1. Then Example 1.4 is ergodic and Example 1.3 is not (unless the mass concentrates on one of the two cycles). It will turn out that if T is ergodic then the orbits have the desirable property just described.

For technical reasons it is convenient to modify slightly the definition of invariance; we shall say that A is invariant if $P(A + T^{-1}A) = 0$.§ For example, if the points d and e in Example 1.3 have mass 0, then $A = \{a, b, c, d\}$ is invariant in the new sense but not in the old one. For any set A, however, the set $B = \limsup_n T^{-n}A$ is invariant in the old sense, and if A is invariant in the new sense, then A and B have the same measure. Therefore, if there is a nontrivial set that is invariant in the new sense, there is also a nontrivial set that is invariant in the old sense, so the definition of ergodicity is unaffected. A set invariant old sense we shall call *strictly* invariant. In proving ergodicity, it is

---

* Here I_A is the indicator, or characteristic function, of the set A; thus $\sum_{k=0}^{n-1} I_A(T_k \omega)$ is the number of elements of the sequence $\{\omega, T\omega, \ldots, T^{n-1}\omega\}$ that lie in A. The "a.e." stands for "almost everywhere" and means "except for ω lying in a set of measure 0."

† Unless the contrary is stated, any set mentioned is assumed to lie in $\mathscr{F}$.

‡ *Metrically transitive* or *indecomposable* are substitutes for *ergodic*.

§ The $+$ here stands for symmetric difference: $A + B = (A - B) \cup (B - A)$. We shall often use the facts that $A + B \subset (A + C) + (C + B)$ and $P(A + B) \leq P(A + C) + P(C + B)$.

enough to check that the strictly invariant sets have measure either 0 or 1.

Remark. Since T preserves measure,

$$P(A - A \cap T^{-1}A) = P(A) - P(A \cap T^{-1}A)$$
$$= P(T^{-1}A) - P(A \cap T^{-1}A) = P(T^{-1}A - A \cap T^{-1}A),$$

and hence

$$P(A + T^{-1}A) = 2P(A - T^{-1}A) = 2P(T^{-1}A - A).$$

Therefore A is invariant if and only if one or the other of $P(A - T^{-1}A)$ and $P(T^{-1}A - A)$ vanishes. In particular, if T is ergodic, then neither of the relations $A \subset T^{-1}A$ and $T^{-1}A \subset A$ is possible for a nontrivial A: in addition to being unable to leave a nontrivial set fixed, an ergodic transformation can neither "expand" nor "contract" such a set.

It is easy to see that if T is invertible, then T is ergodic if and only if T^{-1} is ergodic.

Ergodicity of Rotations

In Example 1.5, if the number c defining the rotation is -1 then the set consisting of the first and third quadrants is a nontrivial invariant set, and hence T is not ergodic. A similar construction shows that T is not ergodic if c is any root of unity.

The following Fourier-analytic argument shows that T is ergodic in the opposite case. Let $e_n(\omega) = \omega^n$ be the circular functions; let the Fourier series for I_A be $I_A(\omega) \sim \sum_n a_n e_n(\omega)$. Since $e_n(T\omega) = c^n e_n(\omega)$, it follows by a change of variable* that

$$a_n = \int_A e_{-n}\, dP = c^{-n} \int_{T^{-1}A} e_{-n}\, dP,$$

whence $I_{T^{-1}A}(\omega) \sim \sum_n c^n a_n e_n(\omega)$. If A is invariant, then $I_A(\omega)$ and

---

* A function $f(\omega)$ is integrable over A if and only if $f(T\omega)$ is integrable over $T^{-1}A$, in which case $\int_{T^{-1}A} f(T\omega)P(d\omega) = \int_A f(\omega)P(d\omega)$. To prove this, it suffices to treat the case $A = \Omega$, since the general case then follows upon replacement of f by $I_A f$. If f is an indicator, $\int f(T\omega)P(d\omega) = \int f(\omega)P(d\omega)$ holds just because T preserves measure; the formula follows easily for a simple function f and then, by the usual approximation argument, for the general f.

$I_{T^{-1}A}(\omega)$ are equal a.e. and hence have the same Fourier coefficients: $a_n = c^n a_n$ for all n. If c is not a root of unity, then $a_n = 0$ for all $n \neq 0$ and hence, by the uniqueness theorem for Fourier coefficients, $I_A(\omega)$ equals some constant a.e., so that $P(A)$ must be either 0 or 1. Thus T is ergodic.

It is an old number-theoretic fact, due to Jacobi, that if c is not a root of unity then the orbit of every ω is dense in the unit circle Ω, another of the primitive notions of ergodicity. (Note that in this case it is too much to ask that an orbit equal Ω as a set, the former being countable and the latter uncountable.) To prove Jacobi's result it is clearly enough to show that the orbit $\{1, c, c^2, \ldots\}$ of 1 is dense. But if c is not a root of unity then the elements of this orbit are all distinct and hence, by compactness, have a limit point ω_0. For any positive ϵ, therefore, there are distinct points c^n and c^{n+k} within $\epsilon/2$ of ω_0 (measuring distance along the arc) and hence within ϵ of one another. Since the distance from c^{n+lk} to $c^{n+(l+1)k}$ is the same as that from c^n to c^{n+k}, it is clear that for some m the points $c^n, c^{n+k}, \ldots, c^{n+mk}$ form a chain which extends all the way around the circle and in which the distance from one point to the next is less than ϵ. Thus any point on the circle is within ϵ of some point of the orbit $\{1, c, c^2, \ldots\}$; hence, since ϵ was arbitrary, this orbit is dense.

We can use Jacobi's result to give a second proof that the rotation T is ergodic (still assuming of course that c is not a root of unity). This proof is more elementary in that it does not involve the uniqueness theorem for Fourier coefficients. Let A be a strictly invariant set with $P(A) > 0$; we shall prove $P(A) = 1$.

We first show that for any ϵ with $0 < \epsilon < 1$, there is a nondegenerate arc I, of length at most ϵ, such that $P(A \cap I) \geq (1 - \epsilon)P(I)$. In fact, by the definition of (circular) Lebesgue measure, A can be covered by a sequence $I_1, I_2, \ldots$ of arcs such that $P(A)/(1 - \epsilon) \geq \Sigma_n P(I_n)$ (we have assumed $P(A) > 0$); we may take these arcs to be disjoint and each of length less than ϵ. Since $\Sigma_n P(A \cap I_n) = P(A) \geq (1 - \epsilon) \Sigma_n P(I_n)$, we must have $P(A \cap I_n) \geq (1 - \epsilon)P(I_n)$ for some value of n—take $I = I_n$.

Now, from the invariance of A and the fact that T is invertible and preserves P, we obtain $P(A \cap T^n I) \geq (1 - \epsilon)P(T^n I)$. If $n_1, \ldots, n_k$ are integers for which $T^{n_1}I, \ldots, T^{n_k}I$ are disjoint, then

$$P(A) \geq \sum_{i=1}^{k} P(A \cap T^{n_i}I) \geq (1 - \epsilon)P\left(\bigcup_{i=1}^{k} T^{n_i}I\right).$$

If $\{1, c, c^2, \ldots\}$ is dense, then so is the orbit of either of the endpoints of I. Since $P(I) \leq \epsilon$, it is clear that there exist integers $n_1, \ldots, n_k$ such that the sets $T^{n_1}I, \ldots, T^{n_k}I$ are sufficient in number and, while disjoint, so nearly abutting as to cover the circle to within a set of measure 2ϵ. Since $P(\bigcup_{i=1}^{k}T^{n_i}I) \geq 1 - 2\epsilon$ in this case, we have

$$P(A) \geq (1 - \epsilon)(1 - 2\epsilon),$$

and hence, since ϵ was arbitrary, $P(A) = 1$. Again T is ergodic.

The strictly invariant sets are the unions of complete orbits (sets $(\ldots, T^{-1}\omega, \omega, T\omega, \ldots)$), which gives rise to the illusion that one can construct a nontrivial invariant set by taking "half" the complete orbits. This procedure works if c is a root of unity, but fails otherwise: we have seen that if c is not a root of unity then any strictly invariant Borel set has measure either 0 or 1, and it follows that the same is true of any strictly invariant Lebesgue set.*

Ergodicity of the Dyadic Transformation

Consider the transformation $T\omega = 2\omega \,(\text{mod } 1)$ (Example 1.6). If $\omega = .\omega_1\omega_2 \cdots$ and $\omega' = \omega + \frac{1}{2} \,(\text{mod } 1)$ then $\omega' = .\omega_1'\omega_2\omega_3 \cdots$ with $\omega_1' = 1 - \omega_1$. Therefore, assuming $A = T^{-1}A$, $\omega \in A$ is equivalent to $T\omega \in A$, and $\omega' \in A$ is equivalent to $T\omega' \in A$; since $T\omega = T\omega' = .\omega_2\omega_3 \ldots$, $\omega \in A$ if and only if $\omega' \in A$. Therefore, if $E = [0, \frac{1}{2})$, the set† $A \cap E^c$ is just the set $A \cap E$ translated to the right a distance $\frac{1}{2}$.

---

* There do exist strictly invariant nonmeasurable sets if c is not a root of unity; such a set automatically has inner measure 0 and outer measure 1. Order by inclusion the family of strictly invariant sets containing no pairs of elements ω_1 and ω_2 that are equivalent in the sense that ω_1/ω_2 is a root of unity. By Zorn's lemma, the family contains a maximal element A. Any ω is equivalent to some element of A, since otherwise A could be enlarged by adding to it the complete orbit of ω. It follows by the usual argument that A is nonmeasurable.

† We use E^c to denote the complement of E.

It follows that these two sets have the same measure (P is Lebesgue measure here), and hence $P(A) = 2P(A \cap E) = P(A \cap E)/P(E)$. Thus A and E are independent. An elaboration of this argument shows that the same thing is true if E is any dyadic interval, or disjoint union of dyadic intervals. Given a positive ϵ, choose such a union E with $P(A + E) < \epsilon$. Then $|P(A) - P(E)| < \epsilon$ and $|P(A) - P(A)P(E)| = |P(A) - P(A \cap E)| < \epsilon$, so that $|P(A) - P(A)^2| < 2\epsilon$. Since ϵ was arbitrary, $P(A) = P(A)^2$, and hence $P(A)$ must be 0 or 1. Therefore T is ergodic.

Mixing

Now Example 1.1 turns out to be ergodic, but it is best to prove this by showing that it has an even stronger property. A measure-preserving transformation T is said to be *mixing* if

$$(1.5) \qquad \lim_{n \to \infty} P(A \cap T^{-n}B) = P(A)P(B)$$

holds for every pair of sets A and B.* If T is invertible, an equivalent requirement is that (1.5) hold with $T^{-n}B$ replaced by $T^n B$. Since (1.5) is equivalent to $P(T^{-n}B \mid A) - P(T^{-n}B) \to 0$, the property of mixing has to do with the wearing off of initial conditions.

If the set B in (1.5) is invariant, then $P(A \cap B) = P(A)P(B)$, and, if we take $A = B$, it follows that $P(B)$ is 0 or 1. Therefore *mixing implies ergodicity*. The mixing property can in many instances be verified by using the following result.

THEOREM 1.2   *Let $\mathscr{F}_0$ be a field generating $\mathscr{F}$. If (1.5) holds for A and B in $\mathscr{F}_0$, then T is mixing.*
Proof. Given A and B in $\mathscr{F}$ and a positive ϵ, choose sets A_0 and B_0 in $\mathscr{F}_0$ for which $A + A_0$ and $B + B_0$ have measure less than ϵ. Then $T^{-n}B + T^{-n}B_0 = T^{-n}(B + B_0)$ has measure less than ϵ, and hence $(A \cap T^{-n}B) + (A_0 \cap T^{-n}B_0)$ has measure less than 2ϵ, for all n. Thus

---

* This is sometimes called *strong mixing*, to distinguish it from a related concept called *weak mixing*, in which one requires only

$$n^{-1} \textstyle\sum_{k=0}^{n-1} |P(A \cap T^{-k}B) - P(A)P(B)| \to 0.$$

See Halmos (1956, p. 38.)

$P(A \cap T^{-n}B)$ is within 2ϵ of $P(A_0 \cap T^{-n}B_0)$ and hence has limits superior and inferior within 2ϵ of $\lim_n P(A_0 \cap T^{-n}B_0) = P(A_0 \cap B_0)$, which is in turn within 2ϵ of $P(A \cap B)$. Since ϵ was arbitrary, the result follows.

In Example 1.1, if A and B are cylinders, then A and $T^{-n}B$ are cylinders depending on sets of coordinates which are disjoint if n is large enough. Thus $P(A \cap T^{-n}B) = P(A)P(B)$ for large n so that (1.5) holds for all A and B in the field $\mathscr{F}_0$ of cylinders. By Theorem 1.2, T is mixing and hence ergodic.

Example 1.3 is of course not mixing, since it is not ergodic. Example 1.4 is ergodic but not mixing (take $A = B = \{a\}$). A more interesting example of a transformation which is ergodic but not mixing is provided by the rotation (Example 1.5) with c not a root of unity. Take $A = B$ to be the upper half-arc; since $\{c^n\}$ is dense, A and $T^{-n}A$ very nearly coincide for infinitely many values of n, so that (1.5) is impossible. Thus mixing is definitely a stronger property than ergodicity.

Another application of Theorem 1.2 shows that the dyadic transformation (Example 1.6), in addition to being ergodic, is mixing.

Statement of the Ergodic Theorem

We turn now to the principal consequence of ergodicity. A function $g(\omega)$ (assumed to be measurable $\mathscr{F}$) is said to be *invariant* if $g(T\omega) = g(\omega)$ a.e. A set is invariant if and only if its indicator is. If g is an invariant function which is not trivial in the sense of being a.e. constant, then for some α the invariant set $\{\omega: g(\omega) \leq \alpha\}$ has measure strictly between 0 and 1. Thus T is ergodic if and only if each invariant function is a.e. constant. We can now state the ergodic theorem.

THEOREM 1.3 *If f is integrable, then there exists an integrable, invariant function $\hat{f}$ such that* $E\{\hat{f}\} = E\{f\}$ *and*

$$(1.6) \qquad \lim_{n \to \infty} \frac{1}{n} \sum_{k=0}^{n-1} f(T^k\omega) = \hat{f}(\omega) \quad \text{a.e.}$$

If T is ergodic then $\hat{f}(\omega) = E\{f\}$ a.e.

---

* We use $E\{f\}$, $\int f(\omega)P(d\omega)$, and $\int f \, dP$ interchangeably.

We give at this point a proof of a very special case, with the conclusion very much weakened: we shall show that if T is mixing and if f is the indicator of a set A then $n^{-1} \sum_{k=0}^{n-1} f(T^k \omega)$ converges in probability to $E\{f\} = P(A)$. If

$$c_{i,k} = E\{(f(T^i \omega) - P(A))(f(T^k \omega) - P(A))\}$$

$$= P(T^{-i} A \cap T^{-k} A) - P(A)P(A),$$

then, since T preserves measure, we have $c_{i,k} = \rho_{|k-i|}$ where $\rho_n = P(A \cap T^{-n} A) - P(A)P(A) \to 0$ as $n \to \infty$, by the mixing hypothesis. But

$$E\left\{\left[\frac{1}{n} \sum_{k=0}^{n-1} f(T^k \omega) - P(A)\right]^2\right\} = \frac{1}{n^2} \sum_{i=0}^{n-1} \sum_{k=0}^{n-1} c_{i,k}$$

$$= \frac{1}{n} \rho_0 + \frac{2}{n^2} \sum_{k=1}^{n-1} (n - k)\rho_k$$

$$\leq \frac{1}{n} |\rho_0| + \frac{2}{n} \sum_{k=1}^{n-1} |\rho_k| \to 0$$

by the theorem on arithmetic means of convergent sequences. That $n^{-1} \sum_{k=0}^{n-1} f(T^k \omega)$ converges in probability to $P(A)$ now follows via Chebyshev's inequality. For the general proof—it bears no resemblance to this one—see the next section.

If the limit (1.6) does exist a.e. then certainly the limit function $\hat{f}(\omega)$ is invariant and hence, in the ergodic case, is constant a.e. If $E\{\hat{f}\} = E\{f\}$, then clearly this constant value is $E\{f\}$. If T is ergodic, the ω-set where the limit (1.6) exists is, being invariant, of measure either 0 or 1— but to prove that it is 1 is difficult even in this case. If T is not ergodic, the limit $\hat{f}$ need not be constant, for if f is a nontrivial invariant function (the indicator of a nontrivial invariant set, say) then the averages in (1.6) are just f itself, so that $\hat{f} = f$ is nonconstant.

In Section 10 (Example 10.2) we shall identify $\hat{f}$ as a conditional expected value (the conditional expected value of f with respect to the σ-field of invariant sets).

Consequences of the Ergodic Theorem

If T is ergodic then, taking $f = I_A$ in (1.6), we have

(1.7)
$$\lim_{n \to \infty} \frac{1}{n} \sum_{k=0}^{n-1} I_A(T^k \omega) = P(A) \quad \text{a.e.}$$

This is the sense in which the orbits of an ergodic transformation were to replicate Ω.

An application of the ergodic theorem to the Bernoulli shift (Example 1.1) yields the strong law of large numbers for Bernoulli trials. In fact, let $f(\omega)$ be 1 or 0 according as $x_1(\omega)$ is the element i of ρ or not (f is just the indicator of the cylinder $\{\omega : x_1(\omega) = i\}$). Then $\sum_{k=0}^{n-1} f(T^k \omega)$ is the number of occurrences of i among $x_1(\omega), \dots, x_n(\omega)$, so that the limit (assuming it exists) of $n^{-1} \sum_{k=0}^{n-1} f(T^k \omega)$ is the asymptotic relative frequency of occurrence of outcome i in the trials at positive time-points in the unending sequence of trials represented by ω. According to the ergodic theorem, this limit exists and equals $E\{f\} = p_i$ a.e., which is the strong law of large numbers.

Taking $f(\omega)$ to be 1 or 0 according as $x_1(\omega) = i$ and $x_2(\omega) = j$ or not, we see that the asymptotic relative frequency of outcomes i and j at successive trials is $p_i p_j$ a.e. Note that the ergodic theorem for the Bernoulli shift is stronger than statements like these, since f may be taken to be some complicated function of *all* the coordinate variables.

Borel's theorem about normal numbers follows by an application of the ergodic theorem to the dyadic transformation (Example 1.6). A number ω in the unit interval is normal (to the base 2) if the relative frequency of 1 in the first n places of the dyadic expansion of ω converges to $\frac{1}{2}$. By the ergodic theorem with $f(\omega) = 0$ for $\omega < \frac{1}{2}$ and $f(\omega) = 1$ for $\omega \geq \frac{1}{2}$, it follows that almost all numbers are normal.

Another application of the ergodic theorem to this example, with $f(\omega) = \omega$, shows that $n^{-1} \sum_{k=0}^{n-1} \{2^k \omega\} \to \frac{1}{2}$ a.e., where $\{x\}$ denotes the fractional part of the real number x.

Consider now the rotation of the circle (Example 1.5) with c not a root of unity. Since T is ergodic, it follows by the ergodic theorem that for almost all ω the orbit $\{\omega, c\omega, c^2\omega, \dots\}$ of ω enters any given arc I with the "right" asymptotic relative frequency, namely $P(I)$. Let $I_1, I_2, \ldots$ be all the arcs that have their endpoints in some fixed countable, dense subset of Ω, say the set of all roots of unity. Then for almost all ω the orbit of ω enters each I_n with the proper frequency; it is not hard to show that the orbit of any such ω is *uniformly distributed* in the sense that it enters *every* arc of the circle with the right asymptotic relative frequency.* Thus the orbits of almost all points are uniformly distributed, and hence, since the orbits are rotations of each other, every orbit is uniformly distributed. Of course, any uniformly distributed orbit is dense, which leads us back to Jacobi's theorem.

Each of these consequences of the ergodic theorem (except, of course, the general result (1.7)) was proved by special methods before the ergodic theorem itself was discovered.

Tests for Ergodicity

In discussing the ergodicity and mixing properties of the various examples just given, we avoided any confrontation with the general shift of Example 1.2. There is no effective criterion for deciding whether or not a given shift is ergodic, or mixing; each case, or class of cases, must be decided separately.

There is a construction that shows that Example 1.2 is really a very general one. Let $\tilde{T}$ be an invertible measure-preserving transformation on a probability space $(\tilde{\Omega}, \tilde{\mathscr{F}}, \tilde{P})$, and let $\tilde{A}$ be some set in $\tilde{\mathscr{F}}$. Take $(\Omega, \mathscr{F})$ to be the product space in Example 1.2, with $\rho = \{0, 1\}$, and define a mapping ϕ of $\tilde{\Omega}$ into Ω by $(\phi(\tilde{\omega}))_n = I_{\tilde{A}}(\tilde{T}^n \tilde{\omega})$. If $P = \tilde{P}\phi^{-1}$, then the shift T on Ω preserves P. Shifts of more or less arbitrary complexity can be constructed in this way.

The following theorem is sometimes useful in establishing the ergodicity of shifts and other transformations (applications are made in

---

* One can even show (by using the theory of weak convergence) that a uniformly distributed orbit enters an arbitrary Borel set A with limiting relative frequency $P(A)$ if the boundary of A has measure 0. For each ω, though, there is some set which the orbit of ω does not enter with the correct frequency, for example, the orbit itself.

Section 3). If (1.7) holds, let us say that T *respects* A; thus an ergodic T respects each A. If T respects a set B then we have

$$\lim_{n \to \infty} \frac{1}{n} \sum_{k=0}^{n-1} I_A(\omega) I_B(T^k \omega) = I_A(\omega) P(B) \quad \text{a.e.}$$

for each set A; if we integrate to the limit,

$$(1.8) \qquad \lim_{n \to \infty} \frac{1}{n} \sum_{k=0}^{n-1} P(A \cap T^{-k}B) = P(A)P(B)$$

results. Thus (1.8) holds whatever A may be, provided that T respects B. On the other hand, if (1.8) holds for all A and B, then it follows easily that any invariant set has measure either 0 or 1, and hence T is ergodic. Finally, if (1.8) holds for all A and B in a field $\mathscr{F}_0$ generating $\mathscr{F}$, then it holds for all A and B in $\mathscr{F}$, by an argument analogous to that used to establish Theorem 1.2. Thus we have the following criterion.

THEOREM 1.4 *If T is ergodic then it respects every set A and so* (1.8) *holds for all A and B. Let $\mathscr{F}_0$ be a field generating $\mathscr{F}$. If T respects every A in $\mathscr{F}_0$, or if (apparently more generally) (1.18) holds for all A and B in $\mathscr{F}_0$, then T is ergodic.*

A comparison of (1.5) with (1.8) shows that mixing is a much stronger property than ergodicity.

Even if T is not ergodic, we have

$$\lim_{n \to \infty} \frac{1}{n} \sum_{k=0}^{n-1} I_B(T^k \omega) = \hat{I}_B(\omega) \qquad \text{a.e.,}$$

where $\hat{I}_B$ is the "hat function" corresponding to I_B. Integrating to the limit over A leads to

$$\lim_{n \to \infty} \frac{1}{n} \sum_{k=0}^{n-1} P(A \cap T^{-k}B) = E\{I_A \hat{I}_B\}.$$

The right-hand member of this equation has a different form that is symmetric in A and B. In fact, the function $(I_A \hat{I}_B)^\wedge$ corresponding to

$I_A \hat{I}_B$ has a.e. the value

$$\lim_{n \to \infty} \frac{1}{n} \sum_{k=0}^{n-1} I_A(T^k\omega)\hat{I}_B(T^k\omega) = \lim_{n \to \infty} \frac{1}{n} \sum_{k=0}^{n-1} I_A(T^k\omega)\hat{I}_B(\omega) = \hat{I}_A(\omega)\hat{I}_B(\omega),$$

where the first equality holds a.e. because of the invariance of $\hat{I}_B$. Therefore, since $I_A\hat{I}_B$ and $(I_A\hat{I}_B)^{\wedge}$ have the same integral,

(1.9) $$\lim_{n \to \infty} \frac{1}{n} \sum_{k=0}^{n-1} P(A \cap T^{-k}B) = E\{\hat{I}_A\hat{I}_B\}.$$

In any case, the limit in (1.8) always exists.

*A More Complicated Shift**

Our final illustration extends the ideas of Example 1.2.

Example 1.7. Let Ω consist of doubly infinite sequences $\omega = (\cdots \omega_{-1}, \omega_0, \omega_1, \ldots)$ of real numbers; let $\mathscr{F}$ be the σ-field generated by the cylinders, or sets of the form $\{\omega : (x_n(\omega), \ldots, x_{n+k-1}(\omega)) \in E\}$ with E a k-dimensional Borel set (here the x_n are the coordinate variables: $x_n(\omega) = \omega_n$); and let P be any measure preserved by the shift T defined by $x_n(T\omega) = x_{n+1}(\omega)$. The measure P is determined by the finite-dimensional measures

$$\mu_k(E) = P\{\omega : (x_n(\omega), \ldots, x_{n+k-1}(\omega)) \in E\}$$

it induces. The transformation T is the shift corresponding to the real-valued stochastic process $\{\ldots, x_{-1}, x_0, x_1, \ldots\}$.

If each μ_k is the k-fold product of μ_1, the process $\{x_n\}$ is independent. It follows in this case, by Theorem 1.2, that T is mixing and hence ergodic. Taking $f(\omega) = x_0(\omega)$ in the ergodic theorem, we see that if $E\{|x_0|\} < \infty$ then

$$\lim_{n \to \infty} \frac{1}{n} \sum_{k=0}^{n-1} x_k(\omega) = E\{x_0\} \qquad \text{a.e.}$$

---

* The rest of this section may be omitted.

The ergodic theorem thus contains the strong law of large numbers for independent, identically distributed random variables with finite first moments.

Example 1.7 is so general that to know the ergodic theorem for each transformation of this form is to know the ergodic theorem for any invertible transformation. Indeed, to prove the ergodic theorem for a given integrable function $\tilde{f}$ and invertible measure-preserving transformation $\tilde{T}$ on a probability space $(\tilde{\Omega}, \tilde{\mathscr{F}}, \tilde{P})$, take $(\Omega, \mathscr{F})$ to be as in Example 1.7, and define P on $\mathscr{F}$ by $P = \tilde{P}\phi^{-1}$, where $\phi(\tilde{\omega}) = (\ldots, \tilde{f}(\tilde{T}^{-1}\tilde{\omega}), \tilde{f}(\tilde{\omega}), \tilde{f}(\tilde{T}\tilde{\omega}), \ldots)$. Then $x_0(\omega)$ is integrable on Ω. If A is the ω-set where $n^{-1} \sum_{k=0}^{n-1} x_k(\omega)$ converges to $\int x_0 \, dP$ and $\tilde{A}$ is the set where $n^{-1} \sum_{k=0}^{n-1} \tilde{f}(\tilde{T}^k\tilde{\omega})$ converges to $\int \tilde{f} d\tilde{P}$, then $\tilde{A} = \phi^{-1}A$. If the ergodic theorem holds for the shift T on Ω, then $P(A) = 1$, so that $\tilde{P}(\tilde{A}) = 1$. (If $\tilde{T}$ is not necessarily invertible, there is an analogous analysis involving a space of one-sided sequences of real numbers.)

A similar argument shows that the ergodic theorem for the shift in Example 1.2 implies that any invertible ergodic transformation respects each set in the space on which it is defined.

There is another way in which Example 1.7 serves as a standard of comparison. Let $\{\ldots, \tilde{x}_{-1}, \tilde{x}_0, \tilde{x}_1, \ldots\}$ be a stochastic process, defined on a space $(\tilde{\Omega}, \tilde{\mathscr{F}}, \tilde{P})$, which is stationary: $\tilde{P}\{\tilde{\omega} : (\tilde{x}_n(\tilde{\omega}), \ldots, \tilde{x}_{n+k-1}(\tilde{\omega})) \in E\}$ is independent of n. Here $\tilde{\Omega}$ need not be a product space, and the $\tilde{x}_n$ need not be coordinate variables. Define a mapping ψ from $\tilde{\Omega}$ into the space Ω of Example 1.7 by $\psi(\tilde{\omega}) = (\ldots, \tilde{x}_{-1}(\tilde{\omega}), \tilde{x}_0(\tilde{\omega}), \tilde{x}_1(\tilde{\omega}), \ldots)$ and let $P = \tilde{P}\psi^{-1}$. Then the shift T on Ω preserves P because of the assumed stationarity of the process $\{\tilde{x}_n\}$. All definitions and questions concerning $\{\tilde{x}_n\}$ can be formulated in terms of the coordinate variables x_n on Ω and the measure P. For example, the process $\{\tilde{x}_n\}$ is said to be ergodic or mixing according as the shift T is; if $\{\tilde{x}_n\}$ is ergodic in this sense and if $\int |\tilde{x}_0| \, d\tilde{P} < \infty$, then it follows by an application of the ergodic theorem to T that $n^{-1} \sum_{k=0}^{n-1} \tilde{x}_k(\tilde{\omega}) \to \int \tilde{x}_0 \, d\tilde{P}$ with probability one.

Remarks. This introduction to ergodic theory ignores its origins in statistical mechanics; see Kac (1959).

Halmos (1956), Hopf (1937), and Jacobs (1960 and 1962–1963) contain general accounts of ergodic theory.

2. PROOF OF THE ERGODIC THEOREM

The ergodic theorem deserves more than one proof. In this section, we first reduce it to the so-called maximal ergodic theorem (Theorem 2.4 below) by arguments involving the function spaces L^1 and L^2. We next prove the maximal ergodic theorem without reference to L^1 and L^2. Finally, we prove the ergodic theorem once again, deducing it this time directly from the maximal ergodic theorem by a proof not involving L^1 and L^2.*

First Proof

The measure-preserving transformation T on $(\Omega, \mathscr{F}, P)$ induces in a natural way an operator $\hat{T}$ on the Hilbert space L^2 of real-valued, square-integrable functions on Ω. If $f(\omega)$ is any real function on Ω, let $\hat{T}f$ denote the function whose value at ω is $f(T\omega)$. If f is measurable (as are all functions considered below) then so is $\hat{T}f$, since T is measurable; if f lies in L^2 then so does $\hat{T}f$, since T is measure preserving. Thus $\hat{T}$ maps L^2 into itself; clearly it is linear. By the change-of-variable formula,†

$$(\hat{T}f, \hat{T}g) = \int \hat{T}f \cdot \hat{T}g \, dP = \int f(T\omega)g(T\omega)P(d\omega)$$

$$= \int f(\omega)g(\omega)P(d\omega) = (f, g).$$

Thus inner products and lengths are preserved: $\hat{T}$ is an isometry.‡

The space of square-integrable functions over the five-point space $\{a, b, c, d, e\}$ of Examples 1.3 and 1.4 can be identified with the space R^5 of five-demensional (column) vectors. With this identification, the isometries $\hat{T}$ induced by the transformations in these two examples are

---

* It is possible to skip directly to Theorem 2.4, omitting entirely the first proof of the ergodic theorem. But this first proof, though round-about, is instructive.

† We write (f, g) for the inner product and $\|f\|_2 = \sqrt{(f, f)}$ for the norm in L^2.

‡ Quite a bit can be learned about the original measure-preserving transformation T by a study of the induced isometry $\hat{T}$, only the very simplest properties of which are used here. See the end of Section 5 for further information about $\hat{T}$.

given respectively by

$$
\begin{bmatrix}
0 & 1 & 0 & 0 & 0 \\
0 & 0 & 1 & 0 & 0 \\
1 & 0 & 0 & 0 & 0 \\
0 & 0 & 0 & 0 & 1 \\
0 & 0 & 0 & 1 & 0
\end{bmatrix}
\quad \text{and} \quad
\begin{bmatrix}
0 & 1 & 0 & 0 & 0 \\
0 & 0 & 1 & 0 & 0 \\
0 & 0 & 0 & 1 & 0 \\
0 & 0 & 0 & 0 & 1 \\
1 & 0 & 0 & 0 & 0
\end{bmatrix},
$$

the permutation matrices corresponding to $(a, b, c)(d, e)$ and to (a, b, c, d, e). The rotation of the circle (Example 1.5) induces an isometry which carries the function with Fourier series $\Sigma_n a_n e_n(\omega)$ onto the function with series $\Sigma_n c^n a_n e_n(\omega)$.

The ergodic theorem states that if f is integrable then

$$
\frac{1}{n} \sum_{k=0}^{n-1} f(T^k \omega) \to \hat{f}(\omega) \qquad \text{a.e.}
$$

for a suitable function $\hat{f}$. We first prove the following weaker result, known as the mean ergodic theorem, or the L^2 ergodic theorem.* It will be convenient to denote by A_n the averaging operator

$$
A_n f = \frac{1}{n} \sum_{k=0}^{n-1} \hat{T}^k f.
$$

Note that

$$
(2.1) \qquad \qquad \|A_n f\|_2 \le \|f\|_2.
$$

THEOREM 2.1 *For any f in L^2 there is an invariant $\hat{f}$ in L^2 such that $A_n f \to \hat{f}$ in the L^2 sense ($\|A_n f - \hat{f}\|_2 \to 0$).*
Proof. If $A_n f$ converges to an element of L^2 at all, the limit is certainly invariant. Let E^2 be the collection of f in L^2 for which $\{A_n f\}$ converges. We shall show that E^2 coincides with L^2 by showing that it is closed and that it contains a subset spanning L^2.

Suppose $f_k \in E^2$ and $\|f_k - f\|_2 \to 0$. To prove $f \in E^2$, it is enough to show that the averages $A_n f$ form a fundamental sequence. If

---

* The ergodic theorem itself (Theorem 1.3) is sometimes called the individual, or pointwise, ergodic theorem to distinguish it from other ones.

$\|f_k - f\|_2 < \epsilon$, then, by (2.1),

$$\|A_m f - A_n f\|_2 \leq \|A_m f - A_m f_k\|_2$$
$$+ \|A_m f_k - A_n f_k\|_2 + \|A_n f_k - A_n f\|_2 < \|A_m f_k - A_n f_k\|_2 + 2\epsilon.$$

Since $\|A_m f_k - A_n f_k\|_2 \to 0$ as $m, n \to \infty$, $\{A_n f\}$ is indeed fundamental. Thus E^2 is closed.

If $f = \hat{T}f$, then of course $f \in E^2$ (with $\hat{f} = f$). If f has the form $f = g - \hat{T}g$, then $A_n f = (g - \hat{T}^n g)/n$, so that $\|A_n f\|_2 \leq 2 \|g\|_2/n \to 0$ and hence $f \in E^2$ (with $\hat{f} = 0$). Thus E^2 contains the class E_0^2 consisting of all invariant functions and all functions of the form $g - \hat{T}g$.

The proof will be complete if we show that E_0^2 spans L^2, or that 0 is the only function orthogonal to E_0^2. For this it is enough to show that any function h orthogonal to every function of the form $g - \hat{T}g$ satisfies $h = \hat{T}h$ (since then if it is also orthogonal to every invariant function, it is orthogonal to itself and hence is 0). From the defining property $(f_1, \hat{T}f_2) = (\hat{T}^* f_1, f_2)$ of the adjoint operator $\hat{T}^*$, we have the identity $(h, g - \hat{T}g) = (h - \hat{T}^* h, g)$. Therefore $(h, g - \hat{T}g) = 0$ for all g implies $h = \hat{T}^* h$. Now* $\|h - \hat{T}h\|_2^2 = \|h\|_2^2 - (h, \hat{T}h) - (\hat{T}h, h) + \|\hat{T}h\|_2^2$. Of course, $\|\hat{T}h\|_2^2 = \|h\|_2^2$ and, if $h = \hat{T}^* h$, $(h, \hat{T}h) = (\hat{T}^* h, h) = \|h\|_2^2$, and similarly $(\hat{T}h, h) = \|h\|_2^2$, so that $\|h - \hat{T}h\|_2^2 = 0$, or $h = \hat{T}h$. Thus $h = \hat{T}h$ does follow if h is orthogonal to each $g - \hat{T}g$, which completes the proof.

Note that the operator carrying f to $\hat{f}$ is the orthogonal projection on the subspace of invariant functions.

The next step is to prove the L^1 analogue of Theorem 2.1. Since $P(\Omega) = 1$, L^2 is a subspace of L^1. If $f(\omega)$ is integrable then so is $f(T\omega)$, and hence the operator $\hat{T}$ is defined on the space L^1 of integrable functions. From now on we regard $\hat{T}$ as an operator on L^1 which carries the subspace L^2 into itself. If $\|f\|_1 = \int |f| \, dP$ denotes the L^1-norm, we have $\|\hat{T}f\|_1 = \|f\|_1$, and (using A_n as before to denote the average $n^{-1} \sum_{k=0}^{n-1} \hat{T}^k$, but on L^1 now) $\|A_n f\|_1 \leq \|f\|_1$.

---

* If $\hat{T}$ is invertible, then, being an isometry, it is unitary, so that $h = \hat{T}^* h = \hat{T}^{-1} h$ implies the desired conclusion $h = \hat{T}h$. But $\hat{T}$ need not be invertible, which is the reason for the argument that follows.

THEOREM 2.2   *For any f in L^1 there is an invariant $\hat{f}$ in L^1 such that $A_n f \to \hat{f}$ in the L^1 sense ($\|A_n f - \hat{f}\|_1 \to 0$).*

Proof.   Denote by E^1 the set of f in L^1 that satisfy the conclusion of the theorem. In the proof of Theorem 2.1, the argument showing that E^2 is L^2-closed shows also that E^1 is L^1-closed—we need only replace the L^2-norms by L^1-norms throughout the argument. If f lies in L^2, then, by the preceding theorem, there is an $\hat{f}$ in L^2 such that $\|A_n f - \hat{f}\|_2 \to 0$. Of course this $\hat{f}$ lies in L^1; by Hölder's inequality $\|A_n f - \hat{f}\|_1 \le \|A_n f - \hat{f}\|_2 \to 0$, so that $f \in E^1$. Thus $L^2 \subset E^1$. Any f in L^1 is the limit in the sense of L^1 of functions in L^2—indeed, of bounded functions—so that the L^1-closure of L^2 is all of L^1. Since $L^2 \subset E^1$ and E^1 is closed, it follows that $E^1 = L^1$.

Of course, $\int A_n f \, dP = \int f \, dP$ so that, since $A_n f \to \hat{f}$ in the L^1 sense,

$$(2.2) \qquad \int \hat{f} \, dP = \int f \, dP.$$

Let us now try to construct a proof of the individual ergodic theorem along the lines of the preceding two proofs. Let G be the set of elements f of L^1 for which there exists a function $\hat{f}$ such that

$$\lim_{n \to \infty} \frac{1}{n} \sum_{k=0}^{n-1} f(T^k \omega) = \hat{f}(\omega) \qquad \text{a.e.}$$

If such an $\hat{f}$ exists at all, it must coincide with the $\hat{f}$ of Theorem 2.2 and hence must be an invariant element of L^1 satisfying (2.2). We can prove the individual ergodic theorem by showing that G (i) is L^1-closed and (ii) contains a subset that spans L^1.

Assuming the truth of (i), which is the hard part to prove, let us prove (ii). If $f = \hat{T} f$ then certainly $f \in G$ (with $\hat{f} = f$). If $f = g - \hat{T} g$, where $g(\omega)$ is bounded (by K, say), then

$$|A_n f(\omega)| = |g(\omega) - g(\hat{T}^n \omega)|/n \le 2K/n \to 0$$

for each ω, so that $f \in G$ (with $\hat{f} = 0$). If $f = g - \hat{T} g$ with $g \in L^1$, choose bounded functions g_k such that $\|g_k - g\|_1 \to 0$; because of the continuity of the operator $\hat{T}$, f is then the L^1-limit of $g_k - \hat{T} g_k$ and hence (if we assume (i) above) lies in G. Therefore G contains the class E_0^2—consisting of all invariant elements of L^2 and all elements of the form $g - \hat{T} g$ with g in L^2—that was introduced into the proof of Theorem

2.1. It was shown there that the L^2-closure of E_0^2 is L^2. By Hölder's inequality, any L^2-limit of elements of E_0^2 is an L^1-limit of them as well; thus the set G, assumed to be L^1-closed, contains L^2 and hence coincides with L^1.

It remains to show that G is closed in the sense of L^1. We carry through the proof assuming the following result.

THEOREM 2.3 *If $f \in L^1$ and $\lambda > 0$, then*

$$P\{\omega: \sup_{n \geq 1} |A_n f(\omega)| > \lambda\} \leq \frac{1}{\lambda} \|f\|_1.$$

Suppose that $f_k \in G$ and that $\|f_k - f\|_1 \to 0$. For each ω,

$$(2.3) \quad |A_m f(\omega) - A_n f(\omega)| \leq |A_m f_k(\omega) - A_n f_k(\omega)| + 2 \sup_{v \geq 1} |A_v(f(\omega) - f_k(\omega))|.$$

Since $f_k \in G$, the sequence $\{A_n f_k(\omega)\}$ is fundamental a.e. for each k, so the first term on the right in (2.3) goes to 0 as $m, n \to \infty$. By Theorem 2.3, then,

$$(2.4) \quad \limsup_{m,n \to \infty} |A_m f(\omega) - A_n f(\omega)| = \lim_{k \to \infty} \sup_{m,n \geq k} |A_m f(\omega) - A_n f(\omega)|$$

exceeds λ with probability at most $2 \|f - f_k\|_1 / \lambda$; letting $k \to \infty$ and then $\lambda \to 0$, we see that the quantity (2.4) is positive with probability 0: $\{A_n f(\omega)\}$ is fundamental a.e. Thus $A_n f(\omega)$ has a.e. a limit, which must be, by Theorem 2.2, an invariant element of L^1.

This completes our first proof of the ergodic theorem. Note that in the proof that G is closed, Theorem 2.3 plays the same role as the elementary inequality (2.1) does in the proofs that the analogous manifolds E^2 and E^1 (in Theorems 2.1 and 2.2) are closed. Since we are dealing with convergence a.e. in the pointwise ergodic theorem, we cannot get by with an inequality essentially weaker than that given by Theorem 2.3. Theorem 2.3 follows from Theorem 2.4 (replace f there by $|f|$).

The Maximal Ergodic Theorem

Everything hinges on the following result, known as the maximal ergodic theorem.

THEOREM 2.4   *Let*

$$(2.5) \qquad N = \left\{ \omega : \sup_{n \geq 1} \frac{1}{n} \sum_{k=0}^{n-1} f(T^k \omega) > \lambda \right\}.$$

If f is integrable then

$$(2.6) \qquad \lambda P(N) \leq \int_N f \, dP.$$

Note that λ need not be positive.

Proof.   Let

$$G = \left\{ \omega : \sup_{n \geq 1} \sum_{k=0}^{n-1} f(T^k \omega) > 0 \right\}.$$

It is enough to prove

$$\int_G f \, dP \geq 0,$$

since (2.6) then follows upon replacement of f by $f - \lambda$.

If

$$G_k = \left\{ \omega : \max_{1 \leq u \leq k} \sum_{i=0}^{u-1} f(T^i \omega) > 0 \right\},$$

then $\int_{G_k} f \, dP \to \int_G f \, dP$ and hence, by the theorem on arithmetic means, $n^{-1} \sum_{k=1}^{n} \int_{G_k} f \, dP \to \int_G f \, dP$. It suffices therefore to prove

$$(2.7) \qquad \sum_{k=1}^{n} \int_{G_k} f \, dP \geq 0, \quad n = 1, 2, \ldots .$$

For $n = 1$, this inequality is trivial—it does not even involve T. It is instructive to consider the case $n = 2$ in detail. In this case (2.7) becomes

$$(2.8) \qquad \int_{G_1} f(\omega) \, dP + \int_{G_2} f(\omega) \, dP \geq 0,$$

where $G_1 = \{ f(\omega) > 0 \}$ and $G_2 = \{ f(\omega) > 0 \text{ or } f(\omega) + f(T\omega) > 0 \}$. If $G_1' = \{ f(T\omega) > 0 \}$ then, by the change-of-variable formula (we here use the fact that T preserves measure), $\int_{G_1} f(\omega) \, dP = \int_{G_1'} f(T\omega) \, dP$, so that (2.8) is equivalent to

$$(2.9) \qquad \int_{G_2} f(\omega) \, dP + \int_{G_1'} f(T\omega) \, dP \geq 0,$$

and hence to

$$\int_{G_2 \cap G_1'} [f(\omega) + f(T\omega)] \, dP + \int_{G_2 - G_1'} f(\omega) \, dP + \int_{G_1' - G_2} f(T\omega) \, dP \geq 0.$$

But this inequality holds because each of the three integrals involved is nonnegative, the integrand in each case being positive over the domain of integration. A slightly different version of this argument consists in noting first that (2.9) is equivalent to

$$\int [f(\omega)I_{G_2}(\omega) + f(T\omega)I_{G_1'}(\omega)] \, dP \geq 0,$$

and then noting that the integrand is nonnegative for each ω. This second version extends to higher n.

Fix n and let $H_u = T^{-u}G_{n-u}$. Changing variables, we see that

$$\sum_{k=1}^{n} \int_{G_k} f(\omega) \, dP = \sum_{u=0}^{n-1} \int_{G_{n-u}} f(\omega) \, dP$$

$$= \sum_{u=0}^{n-1} \int_{H_u} f(T^u\omega) \, dP = \int \left\{ \sum_{u=0}^{n-1} f(T^u\omega)I_{H_u}(\omega) \right\} \, dP.$$

(This step corresponds to the passage from G_1 to G_1' above; it is the place in which we use the assumption that T preserves measure.) We prove (2.7) by showing that the integrand

(2.10) $$\sum_{u=0}^{n-1} f(T^u\omega)I_{H_u}(\omega)$$

is nonnegative for each ω. Now a point ω' lies in G_k if and only if one of the sums

$$f(\omega'), \, f(\omega') + f(T\omega'), \ldots, f(\omega') + \cdots + f(T^{k-1}\omega')$$

is positive; thus ω' lies in G_{n-u} if and only if one of the sums

$$f(\omega'), \, f(\omega') + f(T\omega'), \ldots, f(\omega') + \cdots + f(T^{n-u-1}\omega')$$

is positive. Therefore $\omega \in H_u = T^{-u}G_{n-u}$, or $T^u\omega \in G_{n-u}$, if and only if one of the sums

(2.11) $f(T^u\omega), \, f(T^u\omega) + f(T^{u+1}\omega), \ldots, f(T^u\omega) + \cdots + f(T^{n-1}\omega)$

is positive. The sum (2.10) is thus $f(T^u\omega)$ summed over these u for which one of the quantities (2.11) is positive.

Fix ω and put $c_u = f(T^u\omega)$. The proof of the maximal ergodic theorem will be complete if we establish the following combinatorial lemma.

LEMMA   *Call the term c_u a leader in the finite sequence $c_0, c_1, \ldots, c_{n-1}$ if one of the sums*

$$c_u, c_u + c_{u+1}, \ldots, c_u + \cdots + c_{n-1}$$

is positive. Then the sum* of the leaders is nonnegative.

Proof. The proof goes by induction on the number n of elements in the sequence. For $n = 1$ the result is trivial. Assume it is true for integers smaller than n. If c_0 is not among the leaders, then all the leaders are leaders also in the shorter sequence $c_1, \ldots, c_{n-1}$, and hence, by induction hypothesis, their sum is nonnegative. Suppose, on the other hand, that c_0 is a leader. If k is the smallest integer for which $c_0 + \cdots + c_k$ is positive, then $c_1, \ldots, c_k$ are also leaders because if one of them, say c_i, were not, then $c_i + \cdots + c_k$ would be nonpositive and hence $c_0 + \cdots + c_{i-1}$ positive, contrary to the choice of k. The leaders $c_0, c_1, \ldots, c_k$ thus have positive sum; the remaining leaders (if there are any) have nonnegative sum because they lead in a sequence shorter than n. This completes the proof.

Second Proof

To deduce the ergodic theorem directly from the maximal ergodic theorem, note first that if A is invariant then (with N defined by (2.5) and f integrable)

$$(2.12) \qquad \lambda P(A \cap N) \leq \int_{A \cap N} f \, dP,$$

as follows easily upon replacement of f by $f \cdot I_A$. Using this fact, we shall show that except on a set of measure 0, the sequence

$$\left\{ \frac{1}{n} \sum_{k=0}^{n-1} f(T^k \omega) \right\}$$

of averages converges (possibly to $+\infty$ or $-\infty$).

For $a < b$ put

$$A_{a,b} = \left\{ \liminf_{n \to \infty} \frac{1}{n} \sum_{k=0}^{n-1} f(T^k \omega) < a < b < \limsup_{n \to \infty} \frac{1}{n} \sum_{k=0}^{n-1} f(T^k \omega) \right\}.$$

---

* An empty sum is by convention 0.

Clearly $A_{a,b}$ is invariant and

$$A_{a,b} = A_{a,b} \cap \left\{ \sup_{n \geq 1} \frac{1}{n} \sum_{k=0}^{n-1} f(T^k \omega) > b \right\}.$$

By (2.12) with $\lambda = b$, therefore, we have

$$bP(A_{a,b}) \leq \int_{A_{a,b}} f \, dP.$$

This same result with $-f, -b, -a$ in place of f, a, b is just

$$\int_{A_{a,b}} f \, dP \leq aP(A_{a,b}).$$

Thus $bP(A_{a,b}) \leq aP(A_{a,b})$, which, since $a < b$, is possible only if $P(A_{a,b}) = 0$. If A is the union of the $A_{a,b}$ over all pairs of rationals a and b with $a < b$, then $P(A) = 0$.

Outside A the limits superior and inferior of the sequence of averages have a common value; thus

$$\lim_{n \to \infty} \frac{1}{n} \sum_{k=0}^{n-1} f(T^k \omega) = \hat{f}(\omega) \qquad \text{a.e.,}$$

where $\hat{f}(\omega)$ is finite, $+\infty$, or $-\infty$. By the change-of-variable formula,

$$\int \frac{1}{n} \sum_{k=0}^{n-1} |f(T^k \omega)| \, dP = \int |f| \, dP,$$

and therefore, by an application of Fatou's lemma,

$$\int |\hat{f}| \, dP \leq \liminf_{n \to \infty} \int \left| \frac{1}{n} \sum_{k=0}^{n-1} f(T^k \omega) \right| \, dP \leq \int |f| \, dP.$$

Thus $\hat{f}$ is integrable; in particular, it is finite-valued a.e.

Since the limit function $\hat{f}$ is invariant, it remains only to show that its integral is that of f. Let us write $a_n(\omega) = n^{-1} \sum_{k=0}^{n-1} f(T^k \omega)$. Since $a_n(\omega) \to \hat{f}(\omega)$ a.e. and since $\int a_n \, dP = \int f \, dP$ by change of variable, we see, operating formally, that

$$(2.13) \qquad \int \hat{f} \, dP = \int \lim_{n \to \infty} a_n \, dP = \lim_{n \to \infty} \int a_n \, dP = \int f \, dP.$$

We shall prove that this interchange of limit and integral is all right.*
If $N_\lambda = \{\omega : \sup_{n \geq 1} |a_n(\omega)| > \lambda\}$, then

$$\int |a_n - \hat{f}| \, dP \leq \int_{N_\lambda{}^c} |a_n - \hat{f}| \, dP + \int_{N_\lambda} |a_n| \, dP + \int_{N_\lambda} |\hat{f}| \, dP.$$

For fixed positive λ, the first term on the right goes to 0 as $n \to \infty$, by the dominated convergence theorem. It suffices, therefore, to show that the second and third terms can be made small, uniformly in n, by choosing λ large. For the third term this is easy, since, by the maximal ergodic theorem, $P(N_\lambda) \leq E\{|f|\}/\lambda \to 0$ as $\lambda \to \infty$. As for the second term, we have

$$\int_{N_\lambda} |a_n| \, dP \leq \frac{1}{n} \sum_{k=0}^{n-1} \int_{N_\lambda} |f(T^k\omega)| \, P(d\omega)$$

and

$$\int_{N_\lambda} |f(T^k\omega)| \, P(d\omega) \leq \int_{\{|f(T^k\omega)| > \alpha\}} |f(T^k\omega)| \, P(d\omega) + \alpha P(N_\lambda),$$

so that, by change of variable,

$$\int_{N_\lambda} |a_n| \, dP \leq \int_{\{|f(\omega)| > \alpha\}} |f(\omega)| \, P(d\omega) + \alpha P(N_\lambda).$$

But we can make the right-hand member of this inequality small by choosing α large and then choosing λ large.

Thus $\int |a_n - \hat{f}| \, dP \to 0$, which justifies the interchange in (2.13)† and completes the proof of the ergodic theorem.

Remarks. von Neumann (1932a) first proved the L^2 ergodic theorem, and G. D. Birkhoff (1931) first proved the pointwise ergodic theorem. The proof here for the maximal ergodic theorem is due to Riesz (1945).

3. FURTHER EXAMPLES

We collect together here a number of examples which we shall use later to illustrate various results.

---

* This is clearly so if f is bounded. Thus we can already conclude that if T is ergodic then the orbits replicate Ω in the sense described in Section 1.

† And, incidentally, proves Theorem 2.2 once more. A slight modification of the argument here leads to a second proof of Theorem 2.1.

Other Shifts

Example 3.1. Let us specialize the general shift (Example 1.2). Let $\Pi = (p_{ij})$ be an $r \times r$ stochastic matrix with rows and columns indexed by the elements of the state space ρ. Let $p = (p_i)$ be a (row) probability vector such that $p\Pi = p$. We make no special assumptions about the matrix Π; it may be irreducible or not, aperiodic or not, etc.*
   The functions

$$p_k(i_1, \ldots, i_k) = p_{i_1} p_{i_1 i_2} \cdots p_{i_{k-1} i_k}$$

satisfy the consistency conditions (1.3), the first of them obviously, the second because Π is stochastic, and the third because p is a probability vector. The stationarity condition (1.4) also holds, because $p\Pi = p$. Therefore there exists a unique measure P, preserved by the shift T, such that

$$P\{x_n(\omega) = i_1, \ldots, x_{n+k-1}(\omega) = i_k\} = p_{i_1} p_{i_1 i_2} \cdots p_{i_{k-1} i_k}.$$

With this measure, we shall call T the *Markov shift*. The Bernoulli shift is the special case $p_{ij} = p_j$. It is possible to define Markov shifts of higher order in an analogous fashion.
   By Theorem 1.2, the general shift T is mixing if and only if $\lim_n P(A \cap T^{-n}B) = P(A)P(B)$ holds for all cylinders A and B. Since every cylinder is a finite, disjoint union of thin cylinders, it is enough that this relation hold for thin cylinders A and B: T is mixing if and only if

$$(3.1) \quad \lim_{n \to \infty} P\{x_1 = i_1, \ldots, x_u = i_u; \ x_{n+1} = j_1, \ldots, x_{n+v} = j_v\}$$
$$= P\{x_1 = i_1, \ldots, x_u = i_u\}P\{x_1 = j_1, \ldots, x_v = j_v\}$$

holds for all choices of the i's and j's. The analogous argument based on Theorem 1.4 shows that T is ergodic if and only if

$$(3.2) \quad \lim_{n \to \infty} \frac{1}{n} \sum_{k=0}^{n-1} P\{x_1 = i_1, \ldots, x_u = i_u; x_{k+1} = j_1, \ldots, x_{k+v} = j_v\}$$
$$= P\{x_1 = i_1, \ldots, x_u = i_u\}P\{x_1 = j_1, \ldots, x_v = j_v\}.$$

---

* Our terminology follows Feller (1957).

According to (1.9), the limit

$$(3.3) \quad \lim_{n \to \infty} \frac{1}{n} \sum_{k=0}^{n-1} P\{x_1 = i_1, \ldots, x_u = i_u; x_{k+1} = j_1, \ldots, x_{k+v} = j_v\}$$

exists even if T is not ergodic.

Consider again the Markov shift. From now on, we assume that $p_i > 0$ for all i in ρ (any state i with $p_i = 0$ is irrelevant to the process, since it can never be entered). We enquire first after conditions for the ergodicity of the Markov shift.

Taking $u = v = 1$ in (3.3), we see that the limit

$$q_{ij} = \lim_{n \to \infty} \frac{1}{n} \sum_{k=0}^{n-1} p_{ij}^{(k)}$$

exists in any case.* If T is ergodic, $q_{ij} = p_j$, by (3.2). On the other hand, if $q_{ij} = p_j$, then it follows that T is ergodic, since the probability appearing in (3.2) is

$$p_{i_1} p_{i_1 i_2} \cdots p_{i_{u-1} i_u} p_{i_u j_1}^{(k+1-u)} p_{j_1 j_2} \cdots p_{j_{v-1} j_v}$$

as long as $k \geq u$.

We shall prove the equivalence of the following four statements.

(i) T *is ergodic.*
(ii) q_{ij} *is independent of i.*
(iii) Π *is irreducible.*†
(iv) $q_{ij} > 0$ *for each pair i and j.*

Let Q be the matrix with entries q_{ij}:

$$(3.4) \qquad\qquad Q = \lim_{n \to \infty} \frac{1}{n} \sum_{k=0}^{n-1} \Pi^k.$$

It is easy to show that Q is a stochastic matrix satisfying

$$(3.5) \qquad\qquad Q\Pi = \Pi Q = Q, \quad Q^2 = Q.$$

Since $p\Pi = p$, we have $p\Pi^k = p$ for all k, and hence, by (3.4), $pQ = p$.

---

* Here $p_{ij}^{(k)}$ are the kth order transition probabilities, with $p_{ij}^{(0)} = \delta_{ij}$.

† A set $\rho_0 \subset \rho$ is closed if $\Sigma_{j \epsilon \rho_0} p_{ij} = 1$ for all i in ρ_0; Π is irreducible if ρ contains no proper closed subset. A requirement equivalent to irreducibility is that for each i and j there exist an n such that $p_{ij}^{(n)} > 0$.

It follows that q_{ij} is independent of i if and only if $q_{ij} = p_j$. Hence the equivalence of (i) and (ii).

Suppose Π is not irreducible, and let ρ_0 be a proper closed subset of ρ. If $A = \{\omega : x_0(\omega) \in \rho_0\}$, then $0 < P(A) < 1$ and $P(A - T^{-1}A) = 0$. Since A is invariant (see the remark following the definition of invariance in Section 1), T is not ergodic. Hence (i) implies (iii).

Since, by (3.5), $q_{ij} = \Sigma_u q_{iu}p_{uj} \geq q_{ik}p_{kj}, q_{ik} > 0$ and $p_{kj} > 0$ together imply $q_{ij} > 0$. If, therefore, ρ_i is the set of j such that $q_{ij} > 0$, then ρ_i is closed. If Π is irreducible, then ρ_i, being nonempty, must coincide with ρ. Thus (iii) implies (iv).

Suppose now that all the q_{ij} are positive and that

$$(3.6) \qquad \sum_j q_{ij}\xi_j = \xi_i, \quad i \in \rho.$$

Let m be the maximum of the ξ_i. If $\xi_i < m$ for some i, then $\xi_k = \Sigma_j q_{kj}\xi_j < \Sigma_j q_{kj}m = m$ for all k, which is impossible. Therefore (iv) implies that (3.6) holds if and only if the ξ_i are all equal. Since $Q^2 = Q$, each column of Q solves (3.6), and hence q_{ij} must be independent of i. Therefore (iv) implies (ii).

We have shown that (i) through (iv) are equivalent to one another and also that all are equivalent to the condition that (3.6) have a unique solution (to within a multiplicative constant, of course). It is easy to see that (ii) holds if and only if the system

$$(3.7) \qquad \sum_i \eta_i q_{ij} = \eta_j, \quad j \in \rho$$

has but one solution. It follows by (3.4) that any solution of

$$(3.8) \qquad \sum_j p_{ij}\xi_j = \xi_i, \quad i \in \rho$$

is a solution of (3.6), and that any solution of

$$(3.9) \qquad \sum_j \eta_i p_{ij} = \eta_j, \quad j \in \rho$$

is a solution of (3.7). Therefore the following two conditions are each equivalent to the ergodicity of T.

(v) *The system* (3.8) *has but one solution.*

(vi) *The system* (3.9) *has but one solution.*

Of course the equivalence of (v) and (vi) follows also from the fact that (3.9) is adjoint to (3.8).

We showed that T is ergodic if and only if $q_{ij} = p_j$; the proof hinges on (3.2). Replacing (3.2) by (3.1) in this argument, we see that T is mixing if and only if

$$(3.10) \qquad \lim_{n \to \infty} p_{ij}^{(n)} = p_j, \quad i, j \in \rho.$$

It is known from the theory of Markov chains that (3.10) holds if and only if Π is irreducible and aperiodic.* We take this fact for granted at present; see p. 122 in Section 11 for a proof.

Example 3.2. It is possible to define the shift transformation on the product of a one-sided sequence of copies of the space ρ, rather than a two-sided sequence. The typical element of Ω is now $\omega = (\omega_1, \omega_2, \ldots)$ with $\omega_n \in \rho$; the coordinate variables are defined as before; and $T(\omega_1, \omega_2, \ldots) = (\omega_2, \omega_3, \ldots)$, so that $(T\omega)_n = \omega_{n+1}$. Functions p_k satisfying the conditions (1.3) and (1.4) determine a unique measure P preserved by T. With such a measure, we call the transformatoin T the *one-sided shift*. The one sided Bernoulli and Markov shifts are the obvious specializations. Note that Example 1.2 (which we may now call the two-sided shift) is invertible, whereas the present one is not.

Example 3.3. Let P' [P''] be a measure, on the space $(\Omega, \mathscr{F})$ of the two-sided shift, under which the coordinate variables x_{2n} with even subscripts are independent and take on the value i with probability p_i, and under which $x_{2n} = x_{2n+1}$ [$x_{2n} = x_{2n-1}$] holds for all n, with probability 1. Although neither P' nor P'' is preserved by the shift T, their average $P = (P' + P'')/2$ is, as follows from the relations

$$P'(T^{-k}B) = \begin{cases} P'(B) \text{ for even } k \\ P''(B) \text{ for odd } k, \end{cases}$$

and

$$P''(T^{-k}B) = \begin{cases} P''(B) \text{ for even } k \\ P'(B) \text{ for odd } k. \end{cases}$$

---

* There is no integer $m > 1$ such that $p_{ii}^{(n)} > 0$ only if m divides n. (In the literature on Markov chains, a *state* is sometimes called ergodic if it is persistent, nonnull, and aperiodic; see Feller (1957, p. 353). We shall shun this usage.)

These relations also imply that

$$\lim_{n \to \infty} \frac{1}{n} \sum_{k=0}^{n-1} \frac{1}{2} [P'(A)P'(T^{-k}B) + P''(A)P''(T^{-k}B)] = P(A)P(B).$$

If A and B are cylinders, then A and $T^{-k}B$ are, for all sufficiently large k, independent under P' and under P'', and it follows that (1.8) holds. Therefore, by Theorem 1.4, T is ergodic. On the other hand, T is not mixing (unless one of the p_i equals 1).

Measures on the Interval

Let us generalize the dyadic transformation (Example 1.6) by replacing the base 2 by a general base $r \geq 2$.

Example 3.4.   Let P be Lebesgue measure on the class $\mathcal{F}$ of Borel subsets of $\Omega = [0, 1)$, but define T by $T\omega = r\omega \pmod{1}$. If $f(\omega) = i$ on $[i/r, (i + 1)/r)$, $i = 0, 1, \ldots, r - 1$, then ω has $\sum_{n=1}^{\infty} f(T^{n-1}\omega)/r^n$ as its expansion in the scale of r (the one that terminates if ω is rational). Just as in the case $r = 2$, T is ergodic (even mixing). An application of the ergodic theorem shows that almost every number is normal in the scale of r (contains all digits in the same proportion). If $x_n(\omega)$ is $f(T^{n-1}\omega)$, the nth digit in the base-r expansion of ω, then the sequence $\{x_1, x_2, \ldots\}$ of random variables is independent with $P\{x_n = i\} = 1/r$, $i = 0, 1, \ldots, r - 1$. We may call T the *r-adic transformation*.

Example 3.5.   Let $\Omega, \mathcal{F}$, and T be as in the preceding example, but let P be any measure preserved by T. An r-adic (dyadic, if $r = 2$) interval has the form $[k/r^n, (k + 1)/r^n)$; it contains a point ω if and only if the first n digits $x_1(\omega), \ldots, x_n(\omega)$ (in the scale of r) have certain specified values. Since the finite, disjoint unions of dyadic intervals constitute a field generating $\mathcal{F}$, T preserves P if and only if it preserves the measure of each dyadic interval, or, equivalently, if and only if $\{x_1, x_2, \ldots\}$ is a stationary process under P.

By means of this example, we can convert facts about ergodic theory and probability theory into facts about the unit interval, and vice versa. From the ergodic theorem we derived the normal number theorem, for example. As an instance of the reverse procedure, we deduce a special case of Kolmogorov's existence theorem from the fact that distribution functions on the unit interval determine measures there.

Suppose P is a measure on the unit interval; P is not necessarily preserved by $T(\omega) = r\omega$ (mod 1), which is out of the discussion for the moment. Let p_k be that function of k-long sequences $(i_1, \ldots, i_k)$ of base-r digits that is defined by

$$(3.11) \qquad p_k(i_1, \ldots, i_k) = P\{x_1(\omega) = i_1, \ldots, x_k(\omega) = i_k\}.$$

Then*

$$(3.12) \qquad \begin{cases} p_k(i_1, \ldots, i_k) \geq 0, \\ \sum_i p_{k+1}(i_1, \ldots, i_k, i) = p_k(i_1, \ldots, i_k), \\ \sum_i p_1(i) = 1. \end{cases}$$

Suppose, on the other hand, we are given functions p_k satisfying (3.12). The problem is then to construct on $\mathscr{F}$ a probability measure P that satisfies (3.11).

Define a function F of r-adic rationals u/r^k in $[0, 1]$ by

$$(3.13) \qquad F\left(\frac{u}{r^k}\right) = \sum \left\{ p_k(i_1, \ldots, i_k) : .i_1 \cdots i_k = \sum_{l=1}^{k} \frac{i_l}{r^l} < \frac{u}{r^k} \right\}.$$

The functional values assigned to u/r^k and to ru/r^{k+1} agree because of the middle constraint in (3.12). By the first and third of these constraints, F is nondecreasing and $F(1) = 1$; since the sum corresponding to the point 0 is empty, $F(0) = 0$. Now make the further assumption that, for any sequence $i_1, \ldots, i_k$ of base-r digits, we have

$$(3.14) \qquad \lim_{v \to \infty} p_{k+v}(i_1, \ldots, i_k, \underbrace{1, \ldots, 1}_{v\ 1's}) = 0.$$

(If (3.11) is to hold, this condition must be satisfied, since there is no ω whose expansion ends in 1's.) It follows from (3.14) that F is a left-continuous function of r-adic rationals and hence can be extended to a distribution function on $[0, 1]$—that is, to a left-continuous,† nondecreasing function with $F(0) = 0$ and $F(1) = 1$. It is a standard fact

---

* These constraints are formally identical with (1.3).

† Left continuity is the proper convention here, as we are working with left-closed intervals, which are the ones naturally associated with expansions that terminate in the rational case.

of real-variable theory that to any distribution function F on $[0, 1]$ there corresponds a unique probability measure P on $\mathscr{F}$ such that

$$(3.15) \qquad P[0, x) = F(x), \qquad 0 \leq x \leq 1.$$

From (3.15) and the definition of F, (3.11) follows immediately.

If P and the p_k are related by (3.11), then T preserves P if and only if

$$(3.16) \qquad p_k(i_1, \ldots, i_k) = \sum_i p_{k+1}(i, i_1, \ldots, i_k).$$

If $p_0, \ldots, p_{r-1}$ are nonnegative numbers less than 1 and summing to 1, and if

$$(3.17) \qquad p_k(i_1, \ldots, i_k) = p_{i_1} p_{i_2} \cdots p_{i_k},$$

then (3.12), (3.14), and (3.16) hold, so that there exists a measure P on $\mathscr{F}$ that satisfies (3.11) and is preserved by T. By the ergodic theorem, the asymptotic relative frequency of occurrence of the digit i in the expansion of ω is p_i, except on a set of P-measure 0. If $p_i \equiv 1/r$, then $F(x) = x$ and P is Lebesgue measure, and we have returned to Example 3.4.

Suppose $r = 3$ and $p_0 = \frac{1}{2}$, $p_1 = 0$, $p_2 = \frac{1}{2}$. Referring to the definition (3.13), we see that F is just the Cantor function; we may call the corresponding measure P *Cantor measure*. The set of ω containing, in their expansions in the scale of 3, the digits 0, 1, and 2 in respective limiting proportions $\frac{1}{2}$, 0, and $\frac{1}{2}$ has Cantor measure 1 and Lebesgue measure 0. The Cantor function is thus singular.*

The very same argument shows that if F arises from functions (3.17) then it is singular, unless the p_i are identically $1/r$. If no p_i equals 0, then F is strictly increasing. The figure shows the graph of F for the case $r = 2$, $p_0 = 0.7$, $p_1 = 0.3$. If this function looks less pernicious than the Cantor function, it is only because the graph is accurate but to within the width of the printed line. That part of the graph lying over $[0, \frac{1}{2}]$ is identical, except for a change of vertical scale, with the part

---

* A support of a probability measure P is any set A such that $P(A) = 1$. Two probability measures are singular with respect to one another, or mutually singular, if there exist disjoint supports for them. A distribution function is singular if the corresponding measure is singular with respect to Lebesgue measure.

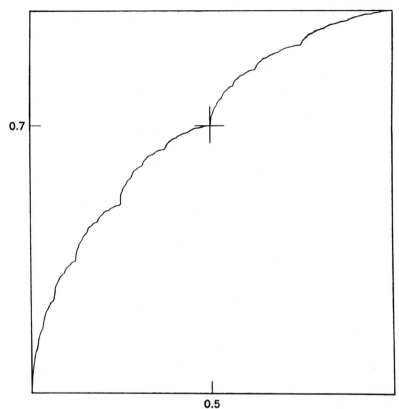

0.7

0.5

lying over $[\frac{1}{2}, 1]$, and each of these parts is identical, except for changes of scale, with the whole graph. It is just this reproductive property* that F must have in order for the digits $x_1(\omega), x_2(\omega), \ldots$ of the base-2 expansion to form a Bernoulli process under the corresponding measure P.

An Existence Theorem

The special case of Kolmogorov's existence theorem needed for the one-sided shift (Example 3.2) follows from the one just given, since any

---

* Shared with the magazine-cover boy who, looking at the magazine cover, sees his picture's picture, and so on in an infinite regress; except here he sees himself on each of two opposing interior pages.

measure P on the interval can be carried over to the space of sequences of elements of $\rho = \{0, 1, \ldots, r - 1\}$ via the mapping $\omega \rightarrow (x_1(\omega), x_2(\omega), \ldots)$. After constructing the measure on $\rho \times \rho \times \cdots$, we may of course substitute for ρ any set of r objects—the state space need not consist of the base-r digits. A violation of (3.14) corresponds in $\rho \times \rho \times \cdots$ to a point of positive probability. Since there is no difficulty in constructing point masses in this space, the condition (3.14) may be suppressed.

This argument shows that if functions p_k of k-long sequences of elements of ρ satisfy the constraints (1.3), then there exists a probability measure P on $\rho \times \rho \times \cdots$ such that

$$p_k(i_1, \ldots, i_k) = P\{x_1(\omega) = i_1, \ldots, x_k(\omega) = i_k\},$$

where the x_l are now the coordinate variables. If (1.4) holds, then P is preserved by the one-sided shift.

The result can be carried over to the two-sided shift in the following way. Consider the mapping ψ from $\rho \times \rho \times \cdots$ to $\cdots \times \rho \times \rho \times \rho \times \cdots$ defined by

$$\psi(\omega_1, \omega_2, \ldots) = (\ldots, \omega_4, \omega_2, \omega_1, \omega_3, \omega_5, \ldots),$$

where ω_1 occupies the 0th position in the image sequence. Given functions p_k satisfying the constraints (1.3) and (1.4), define new functions p_k^+ by

$$p_k^+(i_1, \ldots, i_k) = \begin{cases} p_k(i_{k-1}, \ldots, i_4, i_2, i_1, i_3, \ldots, i_k) & k \text{ odd} \\ p_k(i_k, \ldots, i_4, i_2, i_1, i_3, \ldots, i_{k-1}) & k \text{ even.} \end{cases}$$

Then the p_k^+ satisfy (1.3)—they do not necessarily satisfy (1.4)—and hence there exists a measure P^+ on $\rho \times \rho \times \cdots$ such that

$$p_k^+(i_1, \ldots, i_k) = P^+\{x_1(\omega) = i_1, \ldots, x_k(\omega) = i_k\}.$$

The measure $P^+\psi^{-1}$ on $\cdots \times \rho \times \rho \times \rho \times \cdots$ satisfies (1.2) and is preserved by the two-sided shift. Thus we have the form of the Kolmogorov existence theorem that is needed for Example 1.2.

Ergodicity and Extreme Points

Consider probability measures preserved by some fixed measurable transformation T on some fixed measurable space $(\Omega, \mathscr{F})$. Call P

ergodic if T is ergodic under P. We shall show that if P_1 and P_2 are both ergodic, then they either coincide or are mutually singular. (We used a special case of this to prove the Cantor function singular.) Indeed, if P_1 and P_2 do not coincide, then $P_1(A) \neq P_2(A)$ for some A in $\mathscr{F}$; if A_i is the ω-set where

$$\lim_{n \to \infty} \frac{1}{n} \sum_{k=0}^{n-1} I_A(T^k \omega) = P_i(A),$$

then A_1 and A_2 are disjoint and $P_1(A_1) = P_2(A_2) = 1$, so that P_1 and P_2 are mutually singular.

It follows from this that if P is ergodic, and if P_1 is absolutely continuous with respect to P, and hence is ergodic, then, since P and P_1 cannot be mutually singular, P and P_1 are identical. On the other hand, if P is not ergodic, define P_1 by $P_1(B) = P(B \mid A)$, where A is an invariant set with $0 < P(A) < 1$. Then T preserves P_1 and P_1 is distinct from P and absolutely continuous with respect to it. Thus P is ergodic if and only if there exists no P_1 (preserved by T) that is distinct from P and absolutely continuous with respect to P.

Now suppose that P is a nontrivial average of some P_1 and P_2. Suppose, that is, that $P = \alpha_1 P_1 + \alpha_2 P_2$ (which means that $P(B) = \alpha_1 P_1(B) + \alpha_2 P_2(B)$ for all B in $\mathscr{F}$), where $\alpha_1, \alpha_2 > 0$, $\alpha_1 + \alpha_2 = 1$, and $P_1 \neq P_2$. Since P_1 is then distinct from P and absolutely continuous with respect to it, P is not ergodic. And if P is not ergodic, so that there exists a nontrivial invariant set A, then $P(B) = P(A)P(B \mid A) + P(A^c)P(B \mid A^c)$ gives such a representation $P = \alpha_1 P_1 + \alpha_2 P_2$. Thus P is ergodic if and only if it admits no representation as a nontrivial average of probability measures preserved by T. (Of course an ergodic P may be a nontrivial average of two probability measures *not* preserved by T; see Example 3.3.)

The finite signed measures on $\mathscr{F}$ form a linear space; the probability measures preserved by T form a convex set in this space. We have shown that the ergodic measures are exactly the extreme points of this convex set.

Remarks. Functions of Markov chains provide examples of shifts that are mixing without being Markov shifts; see Rosenblatt (1962), for example. See Harris (1955) for more information about Example 3.5.

4.   APPLICATION TO CONTINUED FRACTIONS*

The Transformation

Any number ω in the unit interval has a simple continued-fraction expansion†

(4.1)
$$\omega = \frac{1\,|}{|a_1} + \frac{1\,|}{|a_2} + \cdots,$$

where the partial quotients a_n are positive integers. The expansion terminates after finitely many steps if and only if ω is rational.

The r-adic transformation $T\omega = r\omega$ (mod 1) on the unit interval (Example 3.4) is useful for studying the ergodic properties of the digits of ω expanded in the scale of r. This is because the digits of $T\omega$ are just those of ω shifted over one place. There is a transformation which shifts the partial quotients the same way, and can be used to study their ergodic properties.

Suppose that ω has the expansion (4.1), and that a second point ω' of the unit interval has the expansion

$$\omega' = \frac{1\,|}{|a_2} + \frac{1\,|}{|a_3} + \cdots.$$

Then

$$\omega = \frac{1}{a_1 + \omega'},$$

so that a_1 is the integer part $[1/\omega]$ of $1/\omega$, and ω' is its fractional part $\{1/\omega\}$. We are thus led to study the transformation that carries ω to $\{1/\omega\}$.

Let $\Omega = [0, 1)$, let $\mathscr{F}$ consist of the Borel subsets of $[0, 1)$, and define T by

$$T\omega = \begin{cases} \{1/\omega\} & \text{if} \quad \omega \neq 0 \\ 0 & \text{if} \quad \omega = 0. \end{cases}$$

---

* This section may be omitted.

† For the elementary properties of continued fractions presupposed here, see, for example, Hardy and Wright (1959), or the opening pages of Khinchine (1964).

If

$$a(\omega) = \begin{cases} [1/\omega] & \text{if } \omega \neq 0 \\ \infty & \text{if } \omega = 0 \end{cases}$$

and

$$a_n(\omega) = a(T^{n-1}\omega), \qquad n = 1, 2, \ldots,$$

then $a_1(\omega), a_2(\omega), \ldots$ are just the partial quotients in the continued-fraction expansion of ω.*

We shall need some of the standard facts about continued fractions. Define integer-valued functions $p_n(\omega)$, $q_n(\omega)$ by the recursions

(4.2)

$$\begin{cases} p_{-1}(\omega) = 1, p_0(\omega) = 0, p_n(\omega) = a_n(\omega)p_{n-1}(\omega) + p_{n-2}(\omega), & n \geq 1, \\ q_{-1}(\omega) = 0, q_0(\omega) = 1, q_n(\omega) = a_n(\omega)q_{n-1}(\omega) + q_{n-2}(\omega), & n \geq 1. \end{cases}$$

(In the rational case, $p_n(\omega)$ and $q_n(\omega)$ are defined only as long as $a_n(\omega)$ is finite.) Standard induction arguments show that

(4.3) $$\omega = \frac{1}{|a_1(\omega)|} + \cdots + \frac{1}{|a_{n-1}(\omega)|} + \frac{1}{|a_n(\omega) + T^n\omega|},$$

(4.4) $$p_{n-1}(\omega)q_n(\omega) - p_n(\omega)q_{n-1}(\omega) = (-1)^n, \qquad n \geq 0,$$

and

(4.5) $$\frac{1}{|a_1(\omega)|} + \cdots + \frac{1}{|a_{n-1}(\omega)|} + \frac{1}{|a_n(\omega) + t|}$$

$$= \frac{p_n(\omega) + tp_{n-1}(\omega)}{q_n(\omega) + tq_{n-1}(\omega)}, \qquad n \geq 1, \qquad 0 \leq t \leq 1.$$

Taking $t = 0$ in (4.5) yields the formula for the nth approximant:

$$\frac{1}{|a_1(\omega)|} + \cdots + \frac{1}{|a_n(\omega)|} = \frac{p_n(\omega)}{q_n(\omega)}.$$

The relations (4.3) and (4.5) imply

$$\omega = \frac{p_n(\omega) + (T^n\omega)p_{n-1}(\omega)}{q_n(\omega) + (T^n\omega)q_{n-1}(\omega)},$$

---

* We have $T^n\omega = 0$ for some n if and only if ω is rational. The partial quotients $a_n(\omega)$ are infinite for $n \geq k$ if the expansion terminates in the kth place; this is the usual convention.

which, together with (4.4), implies

$$\left| \omega - \frac{p_n(\omega)}{q_n(\omega)} \right| = \frac{1}{q_n(\omega)((T^n\omega)^{-1}q_n(\omega) + q_{n-1}(\omega))}.$$

Since

$$a_{n+1}(\omega) \le (T^n\omega)^{-1} \le a_{n+1}(\omega) + 1,$$

we obtain

(4.6)

$$\frac{1}{q_n(\omega)(q_n(\omega) + q_{n+1}(\omega))} \le \left| \omega - \frac{p_n(\omega)}{q_n(\omega)} \right| \le \frac{1}{q_n(\omega)q_{n+1}(\omega)}, \qquad n \ge 1.$$

Finally, we shall need the inequality

(4.7)

$$\left| \log \frac{\omega}{p_n(\omega)/q_n(\omega)} \right| \le \frac{1}{2^{n-2}}, \qquad n \ge 1.$$

For $n = 1$, this can be verified directly. Since

(4.8) $$p_n(\omega) \ge 2^{(n-2)/2}, \qquad q_n(\omega) \ge 2^{(n-1)/2}, \qquad n \ge 2,$$

as follows by induction, we have

$$\left| \frac{\omega}{p_n(\omega)/q_n(\omega)} - 1 \right| \le \frac{1}{2^{n-1}}, \qquad n \ge 2,$$

For $n \ge 2$, (4.7) follows from this and (4.6).

Suppose $a_k, k = 1, \ldots, n$, are positive integers.[*] Let $\Delta_{a_1 \ldots a_n}$ be the set of ω such that $a_1(\omega) = a_1, \ldots, a_n(\omega) = a_n$. The set $\Delta_{a_1 \ldots a_n}$, which we shall call a fundamental interval of rank n, plays here the role than an r-adic interval does in the study of base-r expansions. Now $\Delta_{a_1 \ldots a_n}$ is the image of $[0, 1)$ under the function $\psi_{a_1 \ldots a_n}$ defined by

$$\psi_{a_1 \ldots a_n}(t) = \frac{1}{|a_1|} + \cdots + \frac{1}{|a_{n-1}|} + \frac{1}{|a_n + t|}, \qquad 0 \le t < 1.$$

From the form of the function, it follows that $\psi_{a_1 \ldots a_n}$ is decreasing for odd n and increasing for even n. By (4.5), we have

(4.9)

$$\psi_{a_1 \ldots a_n}(t) = \frac{p_n + tp_{n-1}}{q_n + tq_{n-1}},$$

---

[*] Not to be confused with the functions $a_k(\omega)$; to avoid misunderstanding, we shall never suppress the argument ω in these functions (nor in the $p_k(\omega)$ and $q_k(\omega)$).

where p_n and q_n are defined in terms of the a_k by recursions like (4.2). Therefore

$$\Delta_{a_1 \cdots a_n} = \begin{cases} \left[\dfrac{p_n}{q_n}, \dfrac{p_n + p_{n-1}}{q_n + q_{n-1}}\right) & \text{if } n \text{ is even} \\[3mm] \left[\dfrac{p_n + p_{n-1}}{q_n + q_{n-1}}, \dfrac{p_n}{q_n}\right) & \text{if } n \text{ is odd.} \end{cases}$$

It follows by (4.4) that

$$(4.10) \qquad \lambda(\Delta_{a_1 \cdots a_n}) = \frac{1}{q_n(q_n + q_{n-1})},$$

where λ denotes Lebesque measure. Thus the fundamental intervals of rank n decompose Ω into intervals of length at most 2^{-n+1}. In particular, the class of all fundamental intervals generates the σ-field $\mathscr{F}$ of Borel sets.

Gauss's Measure

It is easy to check that the transformation T does not preserve Lebesgue measure λ. But there is a useful measure on $\mathscr{F}$ which is, as we shall see, preserved by T, namely Gauss's measure

$$(4.11) \qquad P(A) = \frac{1}{\log 2} \int_A \frac{dx}{1 + x}, \qquad A \in \mathscr{F}.$$

Since P and λ are absolutely continuous with respect to each other, they have the same sets of measure 0. Thus if the sequence $a_1(\omega), a_2(\omega), \ldots$ of partial quotients has a certain property a.e. with respect to P, it also has the property a.e. with respect to λ.

To prove that T preserves P, it is enough to show that it preserves the measures of intervals $[0, \alpha]$. Since

$$T^{-1}[0, \alpha] = \bigcup_{k=1}^{\infty} \left[\frac{1}{k + \alpha}, \frac{1}{k}\right],$$

we need only verify the equation

$$\int_0^\alpha \frac{dx}{1 + x} = \sum_{k=1}^{\infty} \int_{1/(k+\alpha)}^{1/k} \frac{dx}{1 + x}.$$

The kth term on the right, however, is

$$\log\left(1 + \frac{1}{k}\right) - \log\left(1 + \frac{1}{k + \alpha}\right)$$

$$= \log\left(1 + \frac{\alpha}{k}\right) - \log\left(1 + \frac{\alpha}{k + 1}\right) = \int_{\alpha/(k+1)}^{\alpha/k} \frac{dx}{1 + x}.$$

We now prove that T is ergodic under P. Fix $a_1 \cdots a_n$ and write ψ for $\psi_{a_1 \cdots a_n}$ and Δ_n for $\Delta_{a_1 \cdots a_n}$. The interval Δ_n has length $\pm(\psi(1) - \psi(0))$, and, if $0 \leq x < y \leq 1$, the interval

$$\{\omega : x \leq T^n\omega < y\} \cap \Delta_n$$

has length $\pm(\psi(y) - \psi(x))$, the signs being $+$ or $-$ according as n is even or odd. Therefore

$$\lambda(T^{-n}[x, y] \,|\, \Delta_n) = \frac{\psi(y) - \psi(x)}{\psi(1) - \psi(0)}.$$

By (4.9) and (4.4),

$$(4.12) \quad \lambda(T^{-n}[x, y] \,|\, \Delta_n) = (y - x)\frac{q_n(q_n + q_{n-1})}{(q_n + xq_{n-1})(q_n + yq_{n-1})}.$$

Since the second factor on the right lies always between $\frac{1}{2}$ and 2,

$$(4.13) \qquad \tfrac{1}{2}\lambda(A) \leq \lambda(T^{-n}A \,|\, \Delta_n) \leq 2\lambda(A),$$

where we have written A for $[x, y]$. But then (4.13) holds also if A is a disjoint union of intervals, and hence holds for any A in $\mathscr{F}$.

Since the density in the definition (4.11) of Gauss's measure is everywhere between $1/2 \log 2$ and $1/\log 2$, we have

$$(4.14) \qquad \frac{\lambda(M)}{2 \log 2} \leq P(M) \leq \frac{\lambda(M)}{\log 2}, \qquad M \in \mathscr{F}.$$

It follows by (4.13) that

$$(4.15) \qquad \frac{1}{C} P(A) \leq P(T^{-n}A \,|\, \Delta_n) \leq CP(A)$$

for all A in $\mathscr{F}$, where C is an absolute constant ($C = 4/\log 2$ will do).

Suppose A is invariant. Then $C^{-1}P(A) \leq P(A \,|\, \Delta_n)$, and hence, if $P(A) > 0$, $C^{-1}P(\Delta_n) \leq P(\Delta_n \,|\, A)$. Therefore

$$(4.16) \qquad \frac{1}{C} P(E) \leq P(E \,|\, A)$$

holds for finite disjoint unions E of fundamental intervals; since these sets form a field generating $\mathscr{F}$, (4.16) holds for any E in $\mathscr{F}$. Taking $E = A^c$, we see that $P(A)$ must be 1. Therefore T is ergodic under P.

It follows by the ergodic theorem that if f is an integrable function on the unit interval, then

$$(4.17) \qquad \lim_{n \to \infty} \frac{1}{n} \sum_{k=0}^{n-1} f(T^k \omega) = \frac{1}{\log 2} \int_0^1 \frac{f(x)}{1 + x}\, dx \quad \text{a.e.}$$

Here "integrable" and "a.e." refer to P or to λ indifferently.

Taking f to be the indicator of the set $\{\omega : a_1(\omega) = k\}$, we see that the asymptotic relative frequency of k among the partial quotients $a_1(\omega), a_2(\omega), \ldots$ is a.e. equal to

$$\frac{1}{\log 2} \int_{1/(k+1)}^{1/k} \frac{dx}{1 + x} = \frac{1}{\log 2} \log \frac{(k + 1)^2}{k(k + 2)}.$$

In particular, the partial quotients are a.e. unbounded.

Taking $f(\omega) = \log a_1(\omega)$, we see that

$$\lim_{n \to \infty} \sqrt[n]{(a_1(\omega) \cdots a_n(\omega))} = \prod_{k=1}^{\infty} \left(1 + \frac{1}{k^2 + 2k}\right)^{\log k/\log 2} \quad \text{a.e.}$$

If $f(\omega) = a_1(\omega)$, then the integral of f diverges to $+\infty$. Operating formally, we arrive at

$$\lim_{n \to \infty} \frac{a_1(\omega) + \cdots + a_n(\omega)}{n} = \infty \quad \text{a.e.}$$

It is not hard to prove this rigorously by a truncation argument.

For applications to Diophantine approximation, the magnitude of $q_n(\omega)$ is more important than that of $a_n(\omega)$. We shall prove that

$$(4.18) \qquad \lim_{n \to \infty} \frac{1}{n} \log q_n(\omega) = \frac{\pi^2}{12 \log 2} \quad \text{a.e.}$$

Let us first show that

$$(4.19) \qquad \frac{1}{q_n(\omega)} = \prod_{k=1}^{n} \left(\frac{1}{|a_k(\omega)|} + \cdots + \frac{1}{|a_n(\omega)|}\right).$$

It follows inductively by the recursions (4.2) that $p_{j+1}(\omega) = q_j(T\omega)$, and therefore

$$(4.20) \qquad \frac{1}{q_n(\omega)} = \prod_{k=1}^{n} \frac{p_{n+1-k}(T^{k-1}\omega)}{q_{n+1-k}(T^{k-1}\omega)},$$

since the numerator of the kth factor on the right cancels the denominator of the $(k + 1)$st. But (4.20) is just (4.19).

Now, by (4.7),

$$\left| \log T^{k-1}\omega - \log \left(\frac{1}{|a_k(\omega)|} + \cdots + \frac{1}{|a_n(\omega)|} \right) \right| \le \frac{1}{2^{n-k-1}}, \qquad 1 \le k \le n,$$

and hence, by (4.19),

$$\log \frac{1}{q_n(\omega)} = \sum_{k=1}^{n} \log T^{k-1}\omega + \sum_{k=1}^{n} \frac{\theta}{2^{n-k-1}} .^*$$

Therefore,

$$(4.21) \qquad \frac{1}{n} \log q_n(\omega) = -\frac{1}{n} \sum_{k=0}^{n-1} \log T^k\omega + 4\frac{\theta}{n}.$$

By the ergodic theorem,

$$\lim_{n \to \infty} \left\{ -\frac{1}{n} \sum_{k=0}^{n-1} \log T^k\omega \right\} = -\frac{1}{\log 2} \int_0^1 \frac{1}{1 + x} \log x \, dx \quad \text{a.e.}$$

Since integration by parts reduces the integral here to

$$\frac{1}{\log 2} \int_0^1 \log (1 + x) \frac{dx}{x} = \frac{1}{\log 2} \sum_{k=0}^{\infty} (-1)^k \int_0^1 \frac{x^k}{k + 1} \, dx$$

$$= \frac{1}{\log 2} \sum_{k=0}^{\infty} \frac{(-1)^k}{(k + 1)^2} = \frac{\pi^2}{12 \log 2},$$

(4.18) follows by (4.21).

The relation (4.18) has several simple but interesting consequences. By (4.6), it implies that

$$\lim_{n \to \infty} \frac{1}{n} \log \left| \omega - \frac{p_n(\omega)}{q_n(\omega)} \right| = -\frac{\pi^2}{6 \log 2} \quad \text{a.e.}$$

Thus the discrepancy between ω and its nth approximant is a.e. of the order $e^{-n\pi^2/6\log 2}$. It follows further, by (4.10), that if $\Delta_n(\omega)$ is the fundamental interval of rank n that contains ω, then

$$\lim_{n \to \infty} \frac{1}{n} \log \lambda(\Delta_n(\omega)) = -\frac{\pi^2}{6 \log 2} \quad \text{a.e.}$$

---

* Here and in what follows, θ is a number, not the same at each occurrence, satisfying $|\theta| \le 1$.

Finally, by (4.14), we have

$$(4.22) \qquad \lim_{n \to \infty} \frac{1}{n} \log P(\Delta_n(\omega)) = -\frac{\pi^2}{6 \log 2} \quad \text{a.e.}$$

Application to Diophantine Approximation

Let $\{\alpha_n\}$ be a sequence of positive numbers, and let E_n be the event $\{a_n(\omega) > \alpha_n\}$. Since $P(E_n) = P\{a_1(\omega) > \alpha_n\}$ is of the order $1/\alpha_n$, it follows by the Borel-Cantelli lemma that if $\Sigma \, 1/\alpha_n$ converges then $a_n(\omega) > \alpha_n$ occurs at most finitely often, except on a set of measure (P or λ) 0.

Suppose on the other hand that $\Sigma \, 1/\alpha_n$ diverges. By (4.15),

$$P(E_{n+1} \mid \Delta_n) \geq \frac{1}{C'(\alpha_{n+1} + 1)}$$

for any fundamental interval of rank n, where C' is an absolute constant. Therefore

$$P(E_m^c \cap \cdots \cap E_{m+k}^c) \leq \prod_{i=0}^{k} \left(1 - \frac{1}{C'(\alpha_{m+i} + 1)}\right).$$

If $\Sigma \, 1/\alpha_n$ diverges, the infinite product diverges to 0, and hence

$$P(E_m^c \cap E_{m+1}^c \cap \cdots) = 0.$$

Since this is true for each m, $a_n(\omega) > \alpha_n$ occurs infinitely often, except on a set of measure 0. Therefore we may state the following result.

THEOREM 4.1 *The event $a_n(\omega) > \alpha_n$ occurs infinitely often with probability 0 or 1, according as $\Sigma \, 1/\alpha_n$ converges or diverges.*

This result and (4.18) lead to the fundamental theorem of the measure theory of approximation.

THEOREM 4.2 *Let $f(q)$ be a positive function of the integer argument q. (i) If $q f(q)$ is nonincreasing and $\Sigma_q \, f(q) = \infty$, then, for almost all ω, the inequality*

$$(4.23) \qquad \left| \omega - \frac{p}{q} \right| < \frac{f(q)}{q}$$

has infinitely many solutions in integers p and q. (ii) *If* $\Sigma_q f(q) < \infty$, *then, for almost all* ω, (4.23) *has at most finitely many solutions.*

Proof. To prove (i), first choose and fix an integer N (say $N = 4$) such that $\log N > \pi^2/12 \log 2$. It follows by (4.18) that

$$(4.24) \qquad \frac{1}{n} \log q_n(\omega) < \log N$$

holds for all but finitely many values of n, except on a set of measure 0. If $\phi(n) = N^n f(N^n)$, then, since $qf(q)$ is nonincreasing,

$$\sum_{q=N^n}^{N^{n+1}-1} f(q) \le 2 \log N \cdot \phi(n),$$

so that $\Sigma_n \phi(n)$ diverges if $\Sigma_q f(q)$ does. It follows by Theorem 4.1 that

$$(4.25) \qquad a_{n+1}(\omega) > \frac{1}{\phi(n)}$$

holds for infinitely many values of n, except on a set of measure 0.

If (4.25) holds, then, by (4.6) and (4.2),

$$\left| \omega - \frac{p_n(\omega)}{q_n(\omega)} \right| < \frac{1}{q_n(\omega)q_{n+1}(\omega)} \le \frac{1}{a_{n+1}(\omega)q_n(\omega)^2} \le \frac{\phi(n)}{q_n(\omega)^2}.$$

But if (4.24) also holds, so that $q_n(\omega) < N^n$, then it follows further, since $qf(q)$ is nonincreasing, that

$$\phi(n) = N^n f(N^n) \le q_n(\omega)f(q_n(\omega)),$$

so that

$$\left| \omega - \frac{p_n(\omega)}{q_n(\omega)} \right| < \frac{f(q_n(\omega))}{q_n(\omega)}.$$

Since (4.24) and (4.25) hold simultaneously for infinitely many values of n, except for ω in a set of measure 0, part (i) of Theorem 4.2 follows.

Part (ii) is a consequence of simple properties of Lebesgue measure. If H_q is the set of ω such that (4.23) holds for some integer p, then H_q is the union of intervals of length $2f(q)/q$ with midpoints of the form p/q. Since there are only q of these in the unit interval,

$$\lambda(H_q) \le 2f(q).$$

Thus part (ii) follows by the Borel-Cantelli lemma.

Mixing and Gauss's Problem

A strengthening of our proof of the ergodicity of T yields further information.

Let $\mathscr{G}_n$ be the σ-field generated by the sets of the form $\{\omega: a_k(\omega) = a\}$ with $k \geq n$, and let $\mathscr{G}_\infty$ be the σ-field $\cap_{n=1}^\infty \mathscr{G}_n$. The sets in $\mathscr{G}_\infty$, which we call the *tail σ-field*, depend only on the "infinitely distant future." We first show that any invariant set is "almost" in the tail σ-field: if A is invariant then $P(A + B) = 0$ for some $B \in \mathscr{G}_\infty$. Since $A \in \mathscr{F}$, we have $T^{-n}A \in \mathscr{G}_n$ even if A is not invariant. But if A is strictly invariant, $A = T^{-n}A \in \mathscr{G}_n$ for all n, and hence $A \in \mathscr{G}_\infty$. And if A is only invariant, then $P(A + B) = 0$ for some strictly invariant set B.

Since there are sets in $\mathscr{G}_\infty$ that are not strictly invariant,[*] conceivably $\mathscr{G}_\infty$ contains a set A with $0 < P(A) < 1$, even though T is ergodic. (If T were not ergodic, certainly $\mathscr{G}_\infty$ would contains such a set A, since invariant sets are "almost" in $\mathscr{G}_\infty$.) Suppose, however, that $A \in \mathscr{G}_\infty$ and $P(A) > 0$. For any n, then, A has the form $A = T^{-n}B$ with $B \in \mathscr{F}$. But, by (4.15),

$$\frac{1}{C} P(A) = \frac{1}{C} P(T^{-n}B) = \frac{1}{C} P(B) \leq P(T^{-n}B \mid \Delta_n) = P(A \mid \Delta_n)$$

for any fundamental interval Δ_n of rank n. Since $P(A) > 0$, $C^{-1}P(\Delta_n) \leq P(\Delta_n \mid A)$. As before (see (4.16)), it follows that $P(A) = 1$.

Thus the tail σ-field $\mathscr{G}_\infty$ is trivial in the sense of containing only sets of measure 0 and 1, a condition at least as strong as ergodicity. We shall in fact see later (at the end of Section 11) that this condition implies that T is mixing.

Gauss stated in a letter to Laplace[†] that

$$(4.26) \qquad \lim_{n \to \infty} \lambda\{\omega: T^n\omega < x\} = \frac{\log(1 + x)}{\log 2} = P[0, x)$$

for each x in the unit interval, and asked for an estimate of the error.

---

[*] For example, the ω-set where $a_n(\omega) = 1$ for infinitely many even values of n.
[†] The letter is quoted by Uspenski (1937, p. 396). It is unclear what proof Gauss had for his assertion.

Now (4.26) is just

$$(4.27) \qquad \lim_{n \to \infty} \int_{T^{-n}A} (\log 2)(1 + \omega)P(d\omega) = P(A),$$

where $A = [0, x)$. The fact that T is mixing under P implies that

$$\lim_{n \to \infty} \int_{T^{-n}A} f(\omega)P(d\omega) = P(A)\int_0^1 f(\omega)P(d\omega)$$

for any indicator f and any Borel set A. Since $(\log 2)(1 + \omega)$ is uniformly approximable by step functions, (4.27) follows (for any Borel set A). Thus Gauss's assertion follows from the fact that T is mixing.

Other methods show that the mixing holds uniformly and exponentially; namely,

$$(4.28) \qquad P(T^{-(n+k)}A \mid \Delta_k) = P(A)(1 + \theta\rho^n)$$

with $|\theta| \leq K$, where K and ρ are positive constants, $\rho < 1$, independent of A, n, k, and Δ_k. From this it follows that the convergence in (4.26) is uniform and exponential.

Remarks. Khinchine (1935, 1936) proved many measure-theoretic results about continued fractions, including Theorem 4.2. His proofs are complicated by the fact that he made no use of the ergodic theorem. Doeblin (1940) seems to have been the first to prove (4.17) in full generality by applying the ergodic theorem (see p. 336 of his paper). For a different proof of the ergodicity of T, see Ryll-Nardzewski (1951).

Kuz'min (1928) first proved (4.26); he gave an error estimate of the order $\rho^{\sqrt{n}}$. Lévy (1929, 1937), improved this to ρ^n, proving (4.28). Doeblin (1940) has a different proof of (4.28), as well as a host of other probabilistic results on continued fractions.

There is a class of number-theoretic transformations on the unit interval containing as special cases the continued-fraction transformation and the transformation $\omega \to r\omega$ (mod 1); see Rényi (1957) and Rohlin (1961a).

Kac (1959) treats a variety of connections between probability theory and other parts of mathematics.

CHAPTER 2

Entropy

5. THE PROBLEM OF ISOMORPHISM

There are pairs of measure-preserving transformations that are formally distinct but really the same. The Bernoulli shift is not altered in any essential respect if the elements of the state space ρ are given new labels. Equally clearly, the rotation $T\omega = c\omega$ of the unit circle (Example 1.5) does not really differ from the transformation $T\omega = \omega + (\arg c)/2\pi$ (mod 1) on the unit interval with Lebesgue measure, and the dyadic transformation $T\omega = 2\omega$ (mod 1) on the unit interval (Example 1.6) should not be distinguished from $T\omega = \omega^2$ on the unit circle with circular Lebesgue measure.

For a slightly deeper example, compare $T\omega = 2\omega$ (mod 1) on the unit interval with the one-sided Bernoulli shift with $\rho = \{0, 1\}$ and $p_0 = p_1 = \frac{1}{2}$. If we match the points of the unit interval with the elements of $\rho \times \rho \times \cdots$ by the correspondence

$$.\omega_1\omega_2 \cdots \leftrightarrow (\omega_1, \omega_2, \ldots)$$

(let us ignore for the moment the ambiguity about base-2 expansions), then sets of matching points (the left half-interval and the cylinder $\{\omega : x_1(\omega) = 0\}$, for instance) have the same measure, and the two transformations act in essentially the same way, since the one sends $.\omega_1\omega_2 \cdots$ to $.\omega_2\omega_3 \cdots$ and the other sends $(\omega_1, \omega_2, \ldots)$ to $(\omega_2, \omega_3, \ldots)$.

Isomorphism

What we need is a notion of isomorphism for measure-preserving transformations—like that for groups, say. Let T be a measure-preserving transformation on $(\Omega, \mathscr{F}, P)$ and let $\tilde{T}$ be a measure-preserving transformation on $(\tilde{\Omega}, \tilde{\mathscr{F}}, \tilde{P})$.* As a first definition—to be modified in a moment—we take T and $\tilde{T}$ to be *isomorphic* if there exists a mapping ϕ from Ω *onto* $\tilde{\Omega}$ such that (i) ϕ is one-to-one; (ii) if $\tilde{A} = \phi A$, then $A \in \mathscr{F}$ if and only if $\tilde{A} \in \tilde{\mathscr{F}}$, in which case $P(A) = \tilde{P}(\tilde{A})$; (iii) $\phi T\omega = \tilde{T}\phi\omega$ holds for all ω. Conditions (i) and (ii) require ϕ to preserve the structure of the measure spaces $(\Omega, \mathscr{F}, P)$ and $(\tilde{\Omega}, \tilde{\mathscr{F}}, \tilde{P})$. Condition (iii) requires ϕ to carry T onto $\tilde{T}$: one gets the same result no matter which of the two routes he takes from the upper-left Ω to the lower-right $\tilde{\Omega}$ in the diagram.

$$
\begin{array}{ccc}
\Omega & \xrightarrow{T} & \Omega \\
\phi \downarrow & & \downarrow \phi \\
\tilde{\Omega} & \xrightarrow{\tilde{T}} & \tilde{\Omega}
\end{array}
$$

Although the pairs of transformations given in the initial paragraph of this section are isomorphic in this sense, the definition is unsatisfactory. Suppose that T is the identity mapping on a space Ω of one point and that $\tilde{T}$ is the identity on a space $\tilde{\Omega}$ of two points ($\tilde{\mathscr{F}}$ consisting of all four subsets) of which one has mass 0 and the other mass 1. Although no mapping of the above sort exists, if only because Ω and $\tilde{\Omega}$ have different cardinality, T and $\tilde{T}$ are essentially the same—the point of $\tilde{\Omega}$ with mass 0 should not be allowed to count. Because of the ambiguity about base-2 expansions, the same difficulty arises with the correspondence ϕ (discussed earlier) defined by

$$.\omega_1\omega_2 \cdots \leftrightarrow (\omega_1, \omega_2, \ldots).$$

We need a definition that is insensitive to sets of measure 0, in the sense that if T and $\tilde{T}$ become isomorphic when a set of measure 0 is cast out from one or both of Ω and $\tilde{\Omega}$, then T and $\tilde{T}$ were isomorphic

---

* From here on, all transformations T, $\tilde{T}$, etc., are assumed to be measure preserving unless the contrary is explicitly stated.

in the first place. Now if Ω_0 is what remains when some set of measure 0 is removed from Ω—if Ω_0 is a set in $\mathscr{F}$ with measure 1—then T can be regarded as a transformation on Ω_0 alone if and only if it carries Ω_0 into itself: $T\omega$ lies in Ω_0 whenever ω lies in Ω_0, or, equivalently, $\Omega_0 \supset T\Omega_0$, or, equivalently again, $\Omega_0 \subset T^{-1}\Omega_0$. The stratagem is now to take T and $\tilde{T}$ to be isomorphic if they become isomorphic in the sense of the preliminary definition when restricted to subsets Ω_0 and $\tilde{\Omega}_0$ satisfying $\Omega_0 \subset T^{-1}\Omega_0$ and $\tilde{\Omega}_0 \subset \tilde{T}^{-1}\tilde{\Omega}_0$, which leads us to the following definition.

Suppose there exist sets Ω_0 *in* $\mathscr{F}$ *and* $\tilde{\Omega}_0$ *in* $\tilde{\mathscr{F}}$, *each of measure* 1, *and a mapping* ϕ *of* Ω_0 *onto* $\tilde{\Omega}_0$, *with the following properties.*

(I_i) *The mapping* ϕ *is one-to-one.*

(I_{ii}) *If* $A \subset \Omega_0$ *and* $\tilde{A} = \phi A$, *then* $A \in \mathscr{F}$ *if and only if* $\tilde{A} \in \tilde{\mathscr{F}}$, *in which case* $P(A) = \tilde{P}(\tilde{A})$.

(I_{iii}) *We have*

$$(5.1) \qquad \Omega_0 \subset T^{-1}\Omega_0 \qquad (i.e., \ \Omega_0 \supset T\Omega_0)$$

and

$$(5.2) \qquad \tilde{\Omega}_0 \subset \tilde{T}^{-1}\tilde{\Omega}_0 \qquad (i.e., \ \tilde{\Omega}_0 \supset \tilde{T}\tilde{\Omega}_0);$$

finally,

$$(5.3) \qquad \phi T\omega = \tilde{T}\phi\omega$$

holds for any ω *in* Ω_0.

We say that T *is isomorphic to* $\tilde{T}$ *(more accurately, that* $(\Omega, \mathscr{F}, P, T)$ *is isomorphic to* $(\tilde{\Omega}, \tilde{\mathscr{F}}, \tilde{P}, \tilde{T})$*) in case such* Ω_0, $\tilde{\Omega}_0$, *and* ϕ *exist.* * To stress the role of the sets Ω_0 and $\tilde{\Omega}_0$ and the mapping ϕ, we may say that T is isomorphic to $\tilde{T}$ *under the triple* $(\Omega_0, \tilde{\Omega}_0, \phi)$.

(Conditions (I_i) and (I_{ii}) constitute a definition of sameness of the measure spaces $(\Omega, \mathscr{F}, P)$ and $(\tilde{\Omega}, \tilde{\mathscr{F}}, \tilde{P})$ themselves. Condition (I_{iii})— it alone involves T and $\tilde{T}$—stipulates that the two transformations be abstractly identical.)

The following remarks contain some of the measure-theoretic details

---

* This concept is sometimes called isomorphism modulo 0, or isomorphism modulo sets of measure 0, or almost-isomorphism; having rejected the preliminary definition, we may safely omit such qualifying phrases.

about sets of measure 0 that an accurate treatment of isomorphism entails.

Remark 1. The preliminary definition above corresponds to the special case in which it is possible to choose the triple $(\Omega_0, \tilde{\Omega}_0, \phi)$ in such a way that $\Omega_0 = \Omega$ and $\tilde{\Omega}_0 = \tilde{\Omega}$. In this special case,

$$(5.4) \qquad\qquad T^{-n}\phi^{-1}\tilde{A} = \phi^{-1}\tilde{T}^{-n}\tilde{A}$$

holds for any subset $\tilde{A}$ of $\tilde{\Omega}$ and any $n \geq 0$.

Remark 2. In connection with (5.3), note that if $\omega \in \Omega_0$, then $\phi\omega \in \tilde{\Omega}_0$, so that, by (5.1) and (5.2), $T\omega$ and $\tilde{T}\phi\omega$ lie respectively in Ω_0 and $\tilde{\Omega}_0$; (5.3) requires $T\omega$ and $\tilde{T}\phi\omega$ to correspond under ϕ in this case. Suppose we weaken condition (I_{iii}) by dropping the requirements (5.1) and (5.2), assuming only that (5.3) holds whenever the points ω and $T\omega$ happen both to lie in Ω_0. If $(\Omega_0, \tilde{\Omega}_0, \phi)$ satisfies the conditions of the definition, but with (I_{iii}) weakened in this way, then, although T and $\tilde{T}$ need not be isomorphic under $(\Omega_0, \tilde{\Omega}_0, \phi)$, it is not hard to see that they are isomorphic under a related triple, namely $(\Omega_1, \tilde{\Omega}_1, \phi_1)$, where $\Omega_1 = \bigcap_{n=0}^{\infty} T^{-n}\Omega_0$ and $\tilde{\Omega}_1 = \phi\Omega_1$, and where ϕ_1 is the restriction of ϕ to Ω_1. (As a matter of fact, T and $\tilde{T}$ are even isomorphic if in place of (I_{iii}) we only require that (5.3) hold whenever all three conditions $\omega \in \Omega_0$, $T\omega \in \Omega_0$, and $\tilde{T}\phi\omega \in \tilde{\Omega}_0$ are satisfied.)

Remark 3. We must show that isomorphism is an equivalence relation. Clearly T is isomorphic to itself; isomorphism is reflexive. If T is isomorphic to $\tilde{T}$ under $(\Omega_0, \tilde{\Omega}_0, \phi)$, then $\tilde{T}$ is isomorphic to T under $(\tilde{\Omega}_0, \Omega_0, \phi^{-1})$; hence isomorphism is symmetric. To prove transitivity, we must show that if T is isomorphic to $\tilde{T}$, and if $\tilde{T}$ is isomorphic to a third transformation T' (defined on $(\Omega', \mathscr{F}', P')$), then T is isomorphic to T'. Suppose that T is isomorphic to $\tilde{T}$ under $(\Omega_0, \tilde{\Omega}_0, \phi)$, and that $\tilde{T}$ is isomorphic to T' under $(\tilde{\Omega}_1, \Omega_1', \psi)$. Let $\tilde{\Omega}_2 = \tilde{\Omega}_0 \cap \tilde{\Omega}_1$, $\Omega_2 = \phi^{-1}\tilde{\Omega}_2$, and $\Omega_2' = \psi\tilde{\Omega}_2$, and take ϕ_2 and ψ_2 to be the restrictions of ϕ and ψ to Ω_2 and $\tilde{\Omega}_2$, respectively. It is not hard to show that T is isomorphic to $\tilde{T}$ under $(\Omega_2, \tilde{\Omega}_2, \phi_2)$, and that $\tilde{T}$ is isomorphic to T' under $(\tilde{\Omega}_2, \Omega_2', \psi_2)$. Since the range of ϕ_2 coincides with the domain of ψ_2, we may compose ϕ_2 and ψ_2 to obtain a one-to-one mapping ξ from Ω_2 onto Ω_2': $\xi(\omega) = \psi_2(\phi_2(\omega))$. It is now easy to check that T is isomorphic to T' under $(\Omega_2, \Omega_2', \xi)$.

Remark 4. If T is isomorphic to $\tilde{T}$ under $(\Omega_0, \tilde{\Omega}_0, \phi)$, then, as follows from (5.1) and (5.2), we have

(5.5) $\Omega_0 \subset T^{-1}\Omega_0 \subset T^{-2}\Omega_0 \subset \cdots$ (i.e., $\Omega_0 \supset T\Omega_0 \supset T^2\Omega_0 \supset \cdots$)

and

(5.6) $\tilde{\Omega}_0 \subset \tilde{T}^{-1}\tilde{\Omega}_0 \subset \tilde{T}^{-2}\tilde{\Omega}_0 \subset \cdots$ (i.e., $\tilde{\Omega}_0 \supset \tilde{T}\tilde{\Omega}_0 \supset \tilde{T}^2\tilde{\Omega}_0 \supset \cdots$).

It follows further, by induction from (5.3), that if $\omega \in \Omega_0$ then

(5.7) $$\phi T^n \omega = \tilde{T}^n \phi \omega$$

holds for all $n \geq 0$. (In particular, T^n and $\tilde{T}^n$ are isomorphic for all n.) Finally, it follows from (5.5), (5.6), and (5.7) that if $\tilde{A}$ and $\tilde{B}$ are sets in $\tilde{\mathscr{F}}$, and if

(5.8) $$A = \phi^{-1}(\tilde{\Omega}_0 \cap \tilde{A}), \qquad B = \phi^{-1}(\tilde{\Omega}_0 \cap \tilde{B}),$$

then

(5.9) $$A \cap T^{-n}B = \phi^{-1}(\tilde{\Omega}_0 \cap \tilde{A} \cap \tilde{T}^{-n}\tilde{B}), \qquad n \geq 0,$$

(ϕ maps only from Ω_0 to $\tilde{\Omega}_0$; hence the intersection with $\tilde{\Omega}_0$), from which it follows, since Ω_0 and $\tilde{\Omega}_0$ have measure 1, that

(5.10) $$P(A \cap T^{-n}B) = \tilde{P}(\tilde{A} \cap \tilde{T}^{-n}\tilde{B}).$$

Remark 5. Invertible transformations T and $\tilde{T}$ that are isomorphic are in fact isomorphic under a triple $(\Omega_0, \tilde{\Omega}_0, \phi)$ with the special property that Ω_0 and $\tilde{\Omega}_0$ are strictly invariant: $\Omega_0 = T^{-1}\Omega_0$ and $\tilde{\Omega}_0 = \tilde{T}^{-1}\tilde{\Omega}_0$ (replace Ω_0 by $\cap_{n=-\infty}^{\infty} T^n\Omega_0$ and $\tilde{\Omega}_0$ by $\cap_{n=-\infty}^{\infty} \tilde{T}^n\tilde{\Omega}_0$, if necessary). This is not true in general, however: take $\tilde{\Omega}$ to be a one-point space, and take $\tilde{T}$ to be the one-sided shift with all the mass concentrated in some one point of the form $(i, i, i, \ldots)$.

The various pairs of transformations discussed at the beginning of this section are isomorphic in the sense of our definition. Here are several more such pairs.

Example 5.1. Transform the unit square Ω by doubling each x-coordinate and halving each y-coordinate. The transformed square

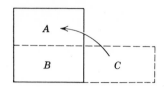

consists of the rectangles B and C in the diagram. Now send C onto A by translation. This defines a transformation T, called the baker's transformation, of Ω into itself which preserves Lebesgue measure; T is isomorphic to the Bernoulli shift $(\frac{1}{2}, \frac{1}{2})$* via the correspondence

$$(x, y) = (.x_1 x_2 \ldots, .y_1 y_2 \cdots) \leftrightarrow (\ldots, y_2, y_1, x_1, x_2, \ldots),$$

where $.x_1 x_2 \cdots$ and $.y_1 y_2 \cdots$ are the dyadic expansions of x and y.

Example 5.2. Let T be the Markov shift having state space ρ, stationary probabilities p_i, and transition probabilities p_{ij}. Then T^2 is isomorphic to the Markov shift $\tilde{T}$ having state space $\tilde{\rho} = \rho^2$, stationary probabilities $p_{(i,j)} = p_i p_{ij}$, and transition probabilities $p_{(i,j)(k,l)} = p_{jk} p_{kl}$. If $\Omega[\tilde{\Omega}]$ is the space of doubly infinite sequences of elements of $\rho[\tilde{\rho}]$, and if $x_n[\tilde{x}_n]$ are the coordinate variables, we need only take $\Omega_0 = \Omega$ and $\tilde{\Omega}_0 = \tilde{\Omega}$, and define ϕ by $\tilde{x}_n(\phi\omega) = (x_{2n}(\omega), x_{2n+1}(\omega))$.

Example 5.3. If we take the stationary and transition probabilities corresponding to $\tilde{T}$ in the preceding example to be $p_{(i,j)} = p_i p_{ij}$ and $p_{(i,j)(k,l)} = \delta_{jk} p_{kl}$, respectively, then $\tilde{T}$ is isomorphic to T itself. We take Ω_0 to be Ω again, but this time define $\tilde{\Omega}_0$ as the set of $\tilde{\omega}$ for which, for all n, the second component of $\tilde{x}_n(\tilde{\omega})$ coincides with the first component of $\tilde{x}_{n+1}(\tilde{\omega})$, and we define ϕ by $\tilde{x}_n(\phi\omega) = (x_{n-1}(\omega), x_n(\omega))$.

Example 5.4. Let T be the two-sided shift with state space $\rho = \{0, 1\}$, where we assume the measure P has no point-masses. Let $\tilde{\Omega}$ be the space of doubly infinite sequences of reals, as in Example 1.7. For ω in Ω, let $\phi\omega$ be the point in $\tilde{\Omega}$ whose nth coordinate is

$$\sum_{k=0}^{\infty} x_{n-k}(\omega)/2^{k+1} = .x_n(\omega) x_{n-1}(\omega) \cdots \quad \text{(dyadic expansion).}$$

---

* By the Bernoulli shift $(p_1, \ldots, p_r)$, we mean the one with probabilities p_i on the state space ρ. The exact nature of the elements of ρ is entirely irrelevant; we write $(p_1, \ldots, p_r)$ for the vector of probabilities even though ρ may not consist of the first r integers. In all that follows, all shifts are two-sided, unless the contrary is stated.

Then T is isomorphic to the shift $\tilde{T}$ on $\tilde{\Omega}$ with the measure $\tilde{P} = P\phi^{-1}$. It can be shown that, under $\tilde{P}$, the coordinate variables $\{\tilde{x}_n\}$ in $\tilde{\Omega}$ form a Markov process with the unit interval for state space.

A final example shows that our definition of isomorphism is still in a sense inadequate.

Example 5.5. Compare the identity transformation T on a space Ω of just one point with the identity $\tilde{T}$ on a space $\tilde{\Omega}$ of two points, where $\tilde{\mathscr{F}}$ contains only the empty set and $\tilde{\Omega}$ itself. Even though T and $\tilde{T}$ are not isomorphic, they have essentially the same structure because $\tilde{\mathscr{F}}$, by being so small, prevents us from distinguishing between the two points of $\tilde{\Omega}$.

This example represents a difficulty which can be got around by replacing isomorphism with the notion of conjugacy. Roughly speaking, one largely ignores points and point transformations and works instead with sets and set transformations, and formulates appropriate notions of sameness for these. Two transformations that are the same in the sense of this theory are called conjugate.

It is a question of what notion of sameness one chooses to adopt. The transformations T and $\tilde{T}$ of Example 5.5 turn out to satisfy the definition of conjugacy. That they fail to be isomorphic may be ascribed to a defect of the space $(\tilde{\Omega}, \tilde{\mathscr{F}}, \tilde{P})$ on which $\tilde{T}$ is defined. The notions of isomorphism and conjugacy coincide for most natural spaces; since they coincide for all the specific spaces encountered in this book in connection with examples (except, of course, the one just mentioned), we take isomorphism as our notion of sameness for measure-preserving transformations. Later in this section (p. 66), however, we define conjugacy and prove that it does indeed coincide with isomorphism for transformations on a class of spaces sufficiently broad to include all those concrete spaces to which we here apply our general results.

Invariants

Just as one can ask whether the alternating group on five letters and the group of symmetries of the icosahedron are different concrete representations of the same algebraic structure—that is, whether they are isomorphic in the sense of group theory (they are)—one can ask whether two concretely presented measure-preserving transformations are abstractly the same in the sense of the definition of isomorphism we have adopted. For example, is the Bernoulli shift $(\frac{1}{2}, \frac{1}{2})$ isomorphic to the Bernoulli shift $(\frac{1}{3}, \frac{1}{3}, \frac{1}{3})$?

To prove that two transformations are isomorphic requires constructing the relevant triple $(\Omega_0, \tilde{\Omega}_0, \phi)$. To prove that two transformations are not isomorphic requires the rejection—preferably simultaneous—of all possible choices of $(\Omega_0, \tilde{\Omega}_0, \phi)$. Just as two groups cannot be isomorphic if one is commutative while the other is not, two measure-preserving transformations cannot be isomorphic, as the following argument shows, if one has the mixing property while the other has not.

Suppose that T is isomorphic to $\tilde{T}$ under $(\Omega_0, \tilde{\Omega}_0, \phi)$ and that T has the mixing property; we must prove that $\tilde{T}$ necessarily has the mixing property too. To see the essential point of the argument, suppose at first that $\Omega_0 = \Omega$ and $\tilde{\Omega}_0 = \tilde{\Omega}$ (so that T and $\tilde{T}$ are isomorphic in the sense of the preliminary—rejected—definition). For any sets $\tilde{A}$ and $\tilde{B}$ in $\tilde{\mathscr{F}}$ we then have (see (5.4))

$$\tilde{P}(\tilde{A} \cap \tilde{T}^{-n}\tilde{B}) = P(\phi^{-1}\tilde{A} \cap \phi^{-1}\tilde{T}^{-n}\tilde{B}) = P(\phi^{-1}\tilde{A} \cap T^{-n}\phi^{-1}\tilde{B})$$

$$\to P(\phi^{-1}\tilde{A})P(\phi^{-1}\tilde{B}) = \tilde{P}(\tilde{A})\tilde{P}(\tilde{B}),$$

where we have used the mixing property for T. Thus $\tilde{T}$ is mixing.

A modification of this proof covers the general case, in which we do not assume $\Omega_0 = \Omega$ and $\tilde{\Omega}_0 = \tilde{\Omega}$. Given $\tilde{A}$ and $\tilde{B}$ in $\tilde{\mathscr{F}}$, put $A = \phi^{-1}(\tilde{\Omega}_0 \cap \tilde{A})$ and $B = \phi^{-1}(\tilde{\Omega}_0 \cap \tilde{B})$; by (5.10),

$$\tilde{P}(\tilde{A} \cap \tilde{T}^{-n}\tilde{B}) = P(A \cap T^{-n}B) \to P(A)P(B) = \tilde{P}(\tilde{A})\tilde{P}(\tilde{B}).$$

Thus the mixing property is an *invariant*: if one member of a pair of measure-preserving transformations has the property, so has the other. Using this invariant, we see that no Bernoulli shift can be isomorphic to a rotation of the circle, or to a Markov shift with a periodic transition matrix.

Ergodicity is another invariant (replace the ordinary limits in the preceding proof by Cesàro limits and apply Theorem 1.4). Therefore, for example, no Markov Shift with a reducible transition matrix can be isomorphic to any Markov shift with an irreducible one.*

Invertibility is not quite invariant: modify an appropriate invertible transformation by sending all the points in some set of measure 0 onto the same point. If, however, T is isomorphic to an invertible $\tilde{T}$, then T is one-to-one on some subset Ω_0 of measure 1. It follows that a two-sided shift cannot be isomorphic to a one-sided shift, unless the latter concentrates all its mass at points of the form $(i, i, i, \ldots)$. Although it is possible to formulate an invariant definition of invertibility, we forbear.

The more structures an invariant distinguishes between, the more useful it is; it is best of all if it is complete. Dimension is a complete invariant among vector spaces (over the reals, say), in the sense that two vector spaces of the same dimension are necessarily isomorphic. Ergodicity is by no means a complete invariant among measure-preserving transformations: there exist obviously nonisomorphic pairs of transformations that are both ergodic (or both nonergodic). The mixing property likewise fails to be complete.

Again, are the Bernoulli shift $(\frac{1}{2}, \frac{1}{2})$ and the Bernoulli shift $(\frac{1}{3}, \frac{1}{3}, \frac{1}{3})$ isomorphic? Ergodicity and mixing are certainly not invariants of sufficient strength to distinguish between them, since both of them are mixing and hence ergodic. The problem of whether these two Bernoulli shifts are isomorphic resisted solution for many years. Kolmogorov finally resolved it in the negative by inventing a new numerical invariant—the *entropy* of a measure-preserving transformation. It turns out that the Bernoulli shifts $(\frac{1}{2}, \frac{1}{2})$ and $(\frac{1}{3}, \frac{1}{3}, \frac{1}{3})$ have different entropies and hence are nonisomorphic.

Kolmogorov's invariant is the notion of entropy which Shannon earlier introduced into information theory—modified in an essential respect. Here we shall invert the historical order. In this chapter we study Kolmogorov's invariant in detail, and apply the results to information theory later on.

---

* Another invariant, more powerful than mixing and ergodicity, is the spectral structure of the isometry induced by T. It is discussed at the end of this section.

Entropy

We need a number of definitions. Postponing the motivation, we first set them out formally. Throughout what follows, $\mathscr{A}$, $\mathscr{B}$, and $\mathscr{C}$ denote finite subfields of $\mathscr{F}$. (A finite subfield is automatically a σ-field.) If $\{A_1, \ldots, A_n\}$ is an $\mathscr{F}$-decomposition of Ω, that is, a finite, disjoint collection of nonempty elements of $\mathscr{F}$ whose union is Ω, then the class of all finite unions of elements of the decomposition is a finite subfield of $\mathscr{F}$. It is not hard to see that, conversely, any finite subfield arises in this way from some one $\mathscr{F}$-decomposition. The elements of the decomposition will be called the *atoms* of the corresponding finite field. There is a complete duality between $\mathscr{F}$-decompositions and finite subfields of $\mathscr{F}$. For instance, $\mathscr{A} \subset \mathscr{B}$ if and only if the decomposition corresponding to $\mathscr{B}$ refines that corresponding to $\mathscr{A}$, in the sense that each atom of $\mathscr{A}$ is a union of atoms of $\mathscr{B}$.

For any collection $\mathscr{E}$ of sets, $T^{-n}\mathscr{E} = \{T^{-n}E\colon E \in \mathscr{E}\}$; if $\mathscr{E}$ is a field (or σ-field, or finite field, or $\mathscr{F}$-decomposition) then the same is true of $T^{-n}\mathscr{E}$. If T is invertible, the same statement holds for $T^{n}\mathscr{E} = \{T^{n}E\colon E \in \mathscr{E}\}$. If $\mathscr{E}_{\alpha}$, $\alpha \in A$, are arbitrary collections of sets, $\bigvee_{\alpha \in A}\mathscr{E}_{\alpha}$ denotes the σ-field generated by $\bigcup_{\alpha \in A}\mathscr{E}_{\alpha}$ (we also write $\bigvee_{i=1}^{n}\mathscr{E}_{i} = \mathscr{E}_1 \vee \cdots \vee \mathscr{E}_n$ in the finite case). If $\mathscr{A}$ and $\mathscr{B}$ are finite fields then $\mathscr{A} \vee \mathscr{B}$ is finite as well; indeed, the atoms of $\mathscr{A} \vee \mathscr{B}$ are precisely the (nonempty sets among the) intersections $A \cap B$ of an atom A of $\mathscr{A}$ and B an atom of $\mathscr{B}$.

Throughout the book, $\eta(t)$ denotes the function on the unit interval defined by*

$$(5.11) \qquad \eta(t) = \begin{cases} -t \log t & \text{if } 0 < t \leq 1 \\ 0 = 0 \log 0 & \text{if } t = 0. \end{cases}$$

We continually use the basic properties of η: it is nonnegative, continuous, strictly concave, and satisfies $\eta(0) = \eta(1) = 0$.

The entropy of T is defined in three steps. The entropy of a finite field $\mathscr{A}$ is defined by

$$(5.12) \qquad H(\mathscr{A}) = \sum_{A} \eta(P(A)) = -\sum_{A} P(A) \log P(A),$$

---

* All logarithms are natural ones.

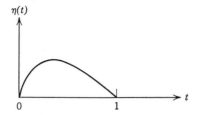

where the summation extends over the atoms A of $\mathscr{A}$. The entropy of a finite field $\mathscr{A}$ relative to T is

(5.13) $$h(\mathscr{A}, T) = \limsup_{n \to \infty} \frac{1}{n} H\left(\bigvee_{k=0}^{n-1} T^{-k}\mathscr{A}\right).$$

(It turns out that the limit superior here is really an ordinary limit.) Finally, the entropy of T is

(5.14) $$h(T) = \sup h(\mathscr{A}, T),$$

where the supremum extends over all finite subfields $\mathscr{A}$ of $\mathscr{F}$.

To understand the intuitive ideas lying back of these definitions, consider first a die with r faces. We regard the nonnegative quantity

(5.15) $$\sum_{i=1}^{r} \eta(p_i) = -\sum_{i=1}^{r} p_i \log p_i,$$

in which $p_1, \ldots, p_r$ represent the probabilities of the different faces, as a measure of the amount of *randomness* in a single roll of the die. Although we do not go into the matter here, it is possible to derive (5.15) from a set of axioms one feels a measure of randomness should satisfy. Observe, though, that (5.15) is a maximum (namely $\log r$) if and only if* each $p_i = 1/r$; this die, one feels, is "the most random." At the other extreme, (5.15) vanishes if and only if one of the p_i is 1, the others being 0; such a die is "least random."

In any case, we regard (5.15) as measuring the amount of randomness in the experiment consisting of one roll of the die, and we call it the

---

* The function $\sum_{r=1}^{i} \eta(p_i + t\epsilon_i)$ has a negative second derivative with respect to the real variable t; hence (5.15) is a strictly concave function of probability vectors $(p_1, \ldots, p_r)$. Its maximum can be found by differentiation.

entropy of the experiment. It also measures the amount of *uncertainty* in the experiment—that is, the amount of uncertainty, before the roll, about how it will turn out. Finally, it measures the *information* in the experiment, or the amount one learns from the outcome of the roll. That randomness and uncertainty have a natural common measure causes no surprise. That uncertainty and information should be measured by the same function is reasonable because of the "formula"

information gained = uncertainty removed.

(In all this we assume the experimenter knows the probabilities p_i—no statistical inference is involved—but he does not know in advance which face will come up on a particular roll.)

A finite field $\mathscr{A}$ plays the role of an experiment with finitely many outcomes. Tyche draws a point ω from the space Ω, according to the probability measure P, but she reveals to the experimenter only which atom of $\mathscr{A}$ it is that contains ω. The atoms of $\mathscr{A}$ act as the outcomes of the experiment, and (5.12) measures the information in it (and the uncertainty about it).

For example, to draw an ω from the twelve-point space

$$\Omega: \begin{array}{cccccc} (H,1) & (H,2) & (H,3) & (H,4) & (H,5) & (H,6) \\ (T,1) & (T,2) & (T,3) & (T,4) & (T,5) & (T,6), \end{array}$$

Tyche tosses a coin with sides H and T and rolls a die with faces $1, 2, \ldots, 6$. To know the outcome of the coin-toss alone is to know which row of the array ω came from; the two rows are the atoms of the finite field that formally represents the coin-tossing experiment. The entropy of this finite field depends not on the probabilities of the twelve individual points, but only on the probabilities of the two atoms.

Since $\mathscr{A} \vee \mathscr{B}$ has as its atoms those of $\mathscr{A}$ intersected with those of $\mathscr{B}$, to know which atom of $\mathscr{A} \vee \mathscr{B}$ contains ω is to know which atom of $\mathscr{A}$ contains ω and, at the same time, which atom of $\mathscr{B}$ contains ω. Thus $\mathscr{A} \vee \mathscr{B}$, regarded as an experiment, is the conjunction of the experiments corresponding to $\mathscr{A}$ and $\mathscr{B}$.

If T is measure-preserving, then $T^{-1}\mathscr{A}$ is a finite field with the same number of atoms as $\mathscr{A}$, and corresponding atoms have equal probabilities. Since $\mathscr{A}$ and $T^{-1}\mathscr{A}$ have the same probabilistic structure, they may be regarded as replicates of the same experiment. Notice, however, that these replicates are not necessarily independent of one another; knowledge that ω lies in some particular atom of $\mathscr{A}$ may help the experimenter in guessing which atom of $T^{-1}\mathscr{A}$ it is that contains ω (that is, which atom of $\mathscr{A}$ it is that contains $T\omega$). We shall regard $\mathscr{A}$ and $T^{-1}\mathscr{A}$ as replicates carried out at successive times (on successive days, say), and we shall do this even if T is not actually a shift.

In this interpretation, the finite field $\mathsf{V}_{k=0}^{n-1} T^{-k}\mathscr{A}$ corresponds to the compound experiment consisting of n replications $\mathscr{A}$, $T^{-1}\mathscr{A}$, ..., $T^{-(n-1)}\mathscr{A}$ of the experiment corresponding to $\mathscr{A}$. Divide $H(\mathsf{V}_{k=0}^{n-1} T^{-k} \mathscr{A})$, the amount of information in this experiment, by n, in order to prorate the information among the n replications. As $n \to \infty$, the information $n^{-1}H(\mathsf{V}_{k=0}^{n-1} T^{-k}\mathscr{A})$ per replication approaches (as we shall see) a limit $h(\mathscr{A}, T)$, which we view as the long-run rate at which replications of $\mathscr{A}$ produce information. And $h(T)$ is the supremum of this rate over all experiments $\mathscr{A}$.

An illuminating special case is the shift. Regard the state space ρ as an alphabet and the variables x_n—the coordinate variables—as the letters produced successively by an *information source*. In English, E occurs more frequently than Q, as is known to all, including the inventor of Morse code, who assigned $\cdot$ to E and $--\cdot-$ to Q. Carrying this idea further, one arrives at the profitable point of view that English text is produced by a probability mechanism. The shift provides the appropriate mathematical model, with the measure P describing the structure of the language.

Now let $\mathscr{A}$ be the finite field with atoms $\{\omega: x_0(\omega) = i\}$, where i ranges over the alphabet ρ. This field, which we may conveniently call the "time-0 field," since it specifies the letter produced at time 0, has entropy $\Sigma_{i\in\rho} \eta(P\{x_0 = i\})$, a quantity which measures the amount of information the source generates in producing a single, isolated letter. Since $T^{-k}\{x_0 = i\} = \{x_k = i\}$, the atoms of $\mathsf{V}_{k=0}^{n-1} T^{-k}\mathscr{A}$ are the r^n sets $\{x_0 = i_0, \ldots, x_{n-1} = i_{n-1}\}$. Thus

$$(5.16) \quad \frac{1}{n} H\left(\bigvee_{k=0}^{n-1} T^{-k}\mathscr{A}\right) = \frac{1}{n} \sum_{i_0 \cdots i_{n-1}} \eta(P\{x_0 = i_0, \ldots, x_{n-1} = i_{n-1}\})$$

is the information per letter in a message of length n. The limit $h(\mathscr{A}, T)$ is the information rate of the source.*

If T is the Bernoulli shift $(p_1, \ldots, p_r)$, then (5.16) becomes

$$\frac{1}{n} \sum_{i_0 \cdots i_{n-1}} \eta(p_{i_0} p_{i_1} \cdots p_{i_{n-1}}) = -\sum_i p_i \log p_i,$$

as an easy computation shows, so that a source producing successive letters independently has information rate

$$h(\mathscr{A}, T) = -\sum_i p_i \log p_i.$$

Notice that this last rate is greatest if the probabilities p_i of the various letters are all $1/r$, the "purely random" case, which seems paradoxical at first. But the closer a source is to being purely random, the less stereotyped, and hence more informative, it is. e. e. cummings demands closer attention than Edgar Guest.† It is not, however, a matter of the worth of what the source produces—all that is in question is the extent to which the output is predictable.

Returning to the mathematics, let us show that entropy is invariant under isomorphism. Let T be isomorphic to $\tilde{T}$ under the triple $(\Omega_0, \tilde{\Omega}_0, \phi)$, where we assume at first, for simplicity, that $\Omega_0 = \Omega$ and $\tilde{\Omega}_0 = \tilde{\Omega}$. Then to each finite subfield $\mathscr{A}$ of $\mathscr{F}$ there corresponds a finite subfield $\tilde{\mathscr{A}} = \phi\mathscr{A} = \{\phi A : A \in \mathscr{A}\}$ of $\tilde{\mathscr{F}}$, and conversely. Since ϕ carries P into $\tilde{P}$, $H(\mathscr{A}) = H(\tilde{\mathscr{A}})$. If $\mathscr{A}$ and $\tilde{\mathscr{A}}$ correspond in this way, then, by (5.4), so do $\mathsf{V}_{k=0}^{n-1} T^{-k}\mathscr{A}$ and $\mathsf{V}_{k=0}^{n-1} T^{-k}\tilde{\mathscr{A}}$, and hence, by (5.13), $h(\mathscr{A}, T) = h(\tilde{\mathscr{A}}, \tilde{T})$. Thus there is, for each $\mathscr{A}$, an $\tilde{\mathscr{A}}$ with $h(\mathscr{A}, T) = h(\tilde{\mathscr{A}}, \tilde{T})$, and vice versa. Taking the suprema, we see that $h(T) = h(\tilde{T})$.

If we do not make the special assumption that $\Omega_0 = \Omega$ and $\tilde{\Omega}_0 = \tilde{\Omega}$, a slightly more involved argument is required. Since isomorphism is a symmetric relation, it suffices to prove $h(\tilde{T}) \leq h(T)$. Let $\tilde{\mathscr{A}}$ be a finite subfield of $\tilde{\mathscr{F}}$ with atoms $\tilde{A}_1, \ldots, \tilde{A}_r$. Put $A_i = \phi^{-1}(\tilde{\Omega}_0 \cap \tilde{A}_i)$,

---

* This is Shannon's definition. Kolmogorov's idea was to study $h(T)$, which is defined for any T (not just for shifts), and has implications for ergodic theory.
† Compare cummings (1958) with Guest (1917).

$i = 1, \ldots, r$, and let $\mathscr{A}$ be the finite subfield of $\mathscr{F}$ having the $r + 1$ sets $A_1, \ldots, A_r, \Omega_0{}^c$ as its atoms. By an easy extension of (5.10), we have

$$H\left(\bigvee_{k=0}^{n-1} \tilde{T}^{-k}\tilde{\mathscr{A}}\right) = \sum_{i_0 \cdots i_{n-1}} \eta\left(\tilde{P}\left(\bigcap_{k=0}^{n-1} \tilde{T}^{-k}\tilde{A}_{i_k}\right)\right)$$

$$= \sum_{i_0 \cdots i_{n-1}} \eta\left(P\left(\bigcap_{k=0}^{n-1} T^{-k}A_{i_k}\right)\right).$$

This last sum extends over all the atoms of $\bigvee_{k=0}^{n-1} T^{-k}\mathscr{A}$ except those involving a factor $T^{-k}\Omega_0{}^c$, all of which have measure 0. Therefore $H(\bigvee_{k=0}^{n-1} \tilde{T}^{-k}\tilde{\mathscr{A}}) = H(\bigvee_{k=0}^{n-1} T^{-k}\mathscr{A})$, so that $h(\tilde{\mathscr{A}}, \tilde{T}) = h(\mathscr{A}, T)$. Since $h(\tilde{\mathscr{A}}, \tilde{T}) \leq h(T)$ now holds for any $\mathscr{A}$, $h(\tilde{T}) \leq h(T)$ follows.

Thus isomorphism preserves entropy. We may note at this point, however, that entropy is not a complete invariant. If T_k is a cyclic permutation of k points of equal mass (the σ-field consisting of all subsets of the space), then $h(T_k) = 0$ for all k, although the T_k for different k are clearly nonisomorphic.

It is essential to understand the difference between $h(\mathscr{A}, T)$ and $h(T)$ and why the latter is introduced. If the entropy of T were taken to be $h(\mathscr{A}, T)$ for some "naturally" selected $\mathscr{A}$—for example, the time-0 field in the case of a shift—then it would be useless for the isomorphism problem because not invariantly defined. We define $h(T)$ as the supremum of the $h(\mathscr{A}, T)$ exactly in order to make it invariant. But now arises the problem of how to compute it. We have computed $h(\mathscr{A}, T)$ for the Bernoulli shift and the time-0 field, for instance, but conceivably some $h(\mathscr{B}, T)$ exceeds $h(\mathscr{A}, T)$. Something further is required if we are to compute the entropy of the Bernoulli shift itself.

Kolmogorov and Sinai proved the essential result needed here, namely that *if T is invertible and if $\mathscr{A}$ is a finite field such that* [*] $\bigvee_{n=-\infty}^{\infty} T^n\mathscr{A} = \mathscr{F}$, *then $h(T) = h(\mathscr{A}, T)$*. Assuming the truth of this theorem, which we prove, together with variants of it, in Section 7, we can compute the entropy of the Bernoulli shift. Indeed, if $\mathscr{A}$ is the time-0 field then $\bigvee_{n=-\infty}^{\infty} T^n\mathscr{A}$ contains all sets of the form $T^{-n}\{x_0 = i\} = \{x_n = i\}$, hence all cylinders, and so must coincide

---

[*] Recall that $\bigvee_{n=-\infty}^{\infty} T^n\mathscr{A}$ is the σ-field generated by $\bigcup_{n=-\infty}^{\infty} T^n\mathscr{A}$.

with the σ-field generated by the cylinders. It follows that $h(T) = h(\mathscr{A}, T) = -\Sigma_i p_i \log p_i$—an intended consequence of the theory, but not a definition. In particular, the Bernoulli shift $(\tfrac{1}{2}, \tfrac{1}{2})$ and the Bernoulli shift $(\tfrac{1}{3}, \tfrac{1}{3}, \tfrac{1}{3})$ have respective entropies $\log 2$ and $\log 3$, and hence are nonisomorphic.

Entropy is thus a strong enough invariant to solve the old problem posed earlier. It is now clear what the program should be. We must derive enough properties of $H(\mathscr{A})$, $h(\mathscr{A}, T)$, and $h(T)$ to prove the Kolmogorov-Sinai result, which is central to the whole theory.

Coding theory, treated in Chapter 5, has close connections with the problem of isomorphism. Many of the results of this chapter find further application there.

Isomorphism vs. Conjugacy*

Suppose that T is isomorphic to $\tilde{T}$ under the triple $(\Omega_0, \tilde{\Omega}_0, \phi)$. We can use the isomorphism to match sets in $\mathscr{F}$ with sets in $\tilde{\mathscr{F}}$ in the following way.

We call sets A and B in $\mathscr{F}$ equivalent, and we write $A \sim B$, whenever $P(A + B) = 0$; the analogous definition applies to sets in $\tilde{\mathscr{F}}$. This notion of equivalence is indeed reflexive, symmetric, and transitive. If A is a set in $\mathscr{F}$ and $\tilde{A}$ is a set in $\tilde{\mathscr{F}}$, let us match them whenever there exist a set A_0 in $\mathscr{F}$ and a set $\tilde{A}_0$ in $\tilde{\mathscr{F}}$ such that $A_0 \subset \Omega_0$, $\tilde{A}_0 \subset \tilde{\Omega}_0$, $A \sim A_0$, $\tilde{A} \sim \tilde{A}_0$, and $\tilde{A}_0 = \phi A_0$. We shall indicate that A and $\tilde{A}$ are thus matched (that is, that there exist such A_0 and $\tilde{A}_0$) by writing $A \leftrightarrow \tilde{A}$.

This matching is a many-to-many correspondence between $\mathscr{F}$ and $\tilde{\mathscr{F}}$. It is not hard to verify that it has the following properties. (All the sets mentioned are assumed to lie in $\mathscr{F}$ or $\tilde{\mathscr{F}}$, as appropriate.)

(C_i) *To any A there is at least one $\tilde{A}$ such that $A \leftrightarrow \tilde{A}$; to any $\tilde{A}$ there is at least one A such that $A \leftrightarrow \tilde{A}$.*

(C_{ii}) *If $A \leftrightarrow \tilde{A}$, then $A \leftrightarrow \tilde{B}$ if and only if $\tilde{A} \sim \tilde{B}$; if $A \leftrightarrow \tilde{A}$, then $B \leftrightarrow \tilde{A}$ if and only if $A \sim B$.*

---

* The remainder of this section may be omitted.

(C_{iii}) *If* $A \leftrightarrow \tilde{A}$, *then* $\Omega - A \leftrightarrow \tilde{\Omega} - \tilde{A}$; *if* $A_n \leftrightarrow \tilde{A}_n$, *the range of the index being finite or countable, then* $\bigcup_n A_n \leftrightarrow \bigcup_n \tilde{A}_n$.

(C_{iv}) *If* $A \leftrightarrow \tilde{A}$, *then* $P(A) = \tilde{P}(\tilde{A})$.

(C_v) *If* $A \leftrightarrow \tilde{A}$, *then* $T^{-1}A \leftrightarrow \tilde{T}^{-1}\tilde{A}$.

This correspondence is effectively a one-to-one correspondence between equivalence classes of sets (see (C_i) and (C_{ii})). It preserves complements and finite or countable unions (see (C_{iii})), it preserves measure (see (C_{iv})), and it persists under the inverse mapping operation (see (C_v)).

Suppose now that between $\mathcal{F}$ and $\tilde{\mathcal{F}}$ we are given *a priori* a many-to-many correspondence satisfying these five conditions. In this case we say that T and $\tilde{T}$ are *conjugate*.* Clearly conjugacy is an equivalence relation.

The correspondence defining a conjugacy automatically has certain properties beyond (C_i) through (C_v). It follows from (C_{iii}) that the correspondence preserves all finite and countable set-theoretic operations (differences, symmetric differences, and finite or countable intersections, for example). Furthermore, if $T^{-1}A \leftrightarrow \tilde{T}^{-1}\tilde{A}$, then, by ($C_i$), there is a $\tilde{B}$ such that $A \leftrightarrow \tilde{B}$; it follows by ($C_v$) that $T^{-1}A \leftrightarrow \tilde{T}^{-1}\tilde{B}$, so that, by ($C_{ii}$), $\tilde{T}^{-1}\tilde{A} \sim \tilde{T}^{-1}\tilde{B}$ and hence† $\tilde{A} \sim \tilde{B}$, which implies $A \leftrightarrow \tilde{A}$. Thus the following additional property holds.

(C_{vi}) *If* $T^{-1}A \leftrightarrow \tilde{T}^{-1}\tilde{A}$, *then* $A \leftrightarrow \tilde{A}$.

If T and $\tilde{T}$ are invertible, it follows from (C_v) and (C_{vi}) that $A \leftrightarrow \tilde{A}$ if and only if $TA \leftrightarrow \tilde{T}\tilde{A}$.

We have seen that if T and $\tilde{T}$ are isomorphic then they are conjugate as well. Example 5.5 shows that the converse proposition is not in general true. We are going to prove that this converse does hold if we make the additional assumption that Ω and $\tilde{\Omega}$ are separable, complete metric

---

* This formulation eliminates the need of introducing measure algebras. In measure-algebra terms, though, $A \sim B$ if and only if $A + B$ lies in the ideal $\mathcal{N}$ of sets of measure 0, and a correspondence of the above kind exists if and only if the quotient algebras $\mathcal{F}/\mathcal{N}$ and $\tilde{\mathcal{F}}/\tilde{\mathcal{N}}$ and the transformations on them are abstractly identical.
† Notice that $A \sim B$ if and only if $T^{-1}A \sim T^{-1}B$, and similarly for sets in $\tilde{\Omega}$.

spaces, and that $\mathscr{F}$ and $\tilde{\mathscr{F}}$ are the σ-fields of Borel sets in these spaces (that is, that $\mathscr{F}$ and $\tilde{\mathscr{F}}$ are the σ-fields generated by the open sets, or, what is the same thing, in view of the assumption of separability, that $\mathscr{F}$ and $\tilde{\mathscr{F}}$ are the σ-fields generated by the spheres).

The concrete spaces $(\Omega, \mathscr{F})$ we have encountered in the various examples can all be defined in topological terms, although they have not been presented that way. If Ω is the circle, the space on which the rotations (Example 1.5) are defined, Ω has a natural metric—the distance between two points is the length of the shortest arc connecting them— under which it is a separable, complete metric space; since the spheres are arcs, the relevant σ-field $\mathscr{F}$ consists of the Borel sets for the metric.

Several transformations (the continued-fraction transformation and the various transformations $T\omega = r\omega$ (mod 1)) have been defined on the half-open unit interval $\Omega = [0, 1)$. The σ-field involved here consists of the ordinary linear Borel subsets of $[0, 1)$; it is the σ-field generated by the open subsets of $[0, 1)$ with the Euclidean metric. Under this metric, Ω is separable but not complete; since $[0, 1)$ is homeomorphic to $[0, \infty)$ with the Euclidean metric, it can be remetrized so as to be complete as well as separable.

We have also considered transformations on finite spaces Ω with the class of all subsets of Ω in the role of $\mathscr{F}$. Here we need only consider the discrete metric in Ω, the distance between distinct points being 1, say. (Compare the space $\tilde{\Omega}$ of Example 5.5, where $\tilde{\mathscr{F}}$ is too small.)

In the space $\Omega = \cdots \times \rho \times \rho \times \rho \times \cdots$ of the two-sided shift, the relevant σ-field $\mathscr{F}$ is generated by the thin cylinders

$$(5.17) \qquad \{\omega : x_l(\omega) = i_l, u \leq l \leq v\}.$$

If the distance between two points ω and ω' is defined to be

$$\sum_{n=-\infty}^{\infty} \delta(x_n(\omega), x_n(\omega'))/2^{|n|},$$

where $\delta(i, j)$ is 1 or 0 according as i and j are the same element of ρ or not, then Ω becomes a separable, complete metric space. If ω_0 lies in the cylinder (5.17), and if $0 < \epsilon < (\frac{1}{2})^{|u|+|v|}$, then the open sphere of radius ϵ about ω_0 is contained in (5.17). On the other hand, if $-u = v > 0$, if $(\frac{1}{2})^{v-2} < \epsilon$, and if $i_l = x_l(\omega_0)$ for $|l| \leq v$, then ω_0 lies in (5.17), which is in turn contained in the open sphere of radius ϵ about ω_0. Thus the thin cylinders form a base for the topology, and it follows that $\mathscr{F}$ coincides with the class of Borel sets for this topology. The one-sided product space $\rho \times \rho \times \cdots$ can be treated in the same way.

More generally, it can also be shown* that the topological product of a doubly infinite sequence of copies of any separable, complete metric space can be metrized as a separable, complete space, which takes care of Example 1.7.

The following theorem therefore shows that we are justified in contenting ourselves here with isomorphism as our notion of sameness for measure-preserving transformations.

THEOREM 5.1 *Let T and $\tilde{T}$ be measure-preserving transformations on $(\Omega, \mathscr{F}, P)$ and $(\tilde{\Omega}, \tilde{\mathscr{F}}, \tilde{P})$ respectively, where Ω and $\tilde{\Omega}$ are separable, complete metric spaces and $\mathscr{F}$ and $\tilde{\mathscr{F}}$ are the σ-fields of Borel sets in these two spaces. If T and $\tilde{T}$ are conjugate, then they are isomorphic.*

For the proof we need three lemmas which relate the measures to the topologies.

LEMMA 1 *For any A in $\mathscr{F}$ and any $\epsilon > 0$, there exist a closed set F and an open set G such that $F \subset A \subset G$ and $P(G - F) < \epsilon$.*
Proof.   Let $\mathscr{G}$ be the class of sets in $\mathscr{F}$ with the asserted property; it is enough to show that $\mathscr{G}$ is a σ-field containing the open sets. Clearly $\mathscr{G}$ is closed under complementation. Given sets A_n in $\mathscr{G}$, choose closed sets F_n and open sets G_n such that $F_n \subset A_n \subset G_n$ and $P(G_n - F_n) < \epsilon/2^{n+1}$. If $F = \cup_n F_n$ and $G = \cup_n G_n$, then $F \subset A = \cup_n A_n \subset G$ and $P(G - F) < \epsilon/2$. Now G is open; although F is not necessarily closed, it can be replaced by a finite, hence closed, subunion $F_0 = \cup_{n \le n_0} F_n$ such that $P(F - F_0) < \epsilon/2$, which shows that $A \in \mathscr{G}$. Thus $\mathscr{G}$ is a σ-field. Since $\mathscr{G}$ is closed under complementation, the proof will be complete if we show that it contains all closed sets A. For such an A, however, the sets G_k of points within distance $1/k$ of some point of A are open and decrease to A; hence we may take F to be A and G to be one of the G_k.

---

* See Dunford and Schwartz (1958, p. 32), for example.

LEMMA 2   *If $A \in \mathscr{F}$ and if $\epsilon > 0$, then there exist finitely or countably many pairwise disjoint sets, $F_1, F_2, \ldots$, such that each F_n is a closed set with diameter less than ϵ, and such that $\bigcup_n F_n \subset A$ and*

$$P(A - \bigcup_n F_n) = 0.$$

Proof.   By Lemma 1, A contains a closed set F_1 such that $P(A - F_1) < 1$, $A - F_1$ contains a closed set F_2 such that $P((A - F_1) - F_2) < \frac{1}{2}$, $A - F_1 - F_2$ contains a closed set F_3 such that

$$P((A - F_1 - F_2) - F_3) < \tfrac{1}{3},$$

and so on. The disjoint closed sets so constructed satisfy $\bigcup_n F_n \subset A$ and $P(A - \bigcup_n F_n) = 0$.

Now, since Ω is assumed separable, A is a countable, disjoint union of measurable sets A_k of diameter less than ϵ. For each A_k, construct a sequence $\{F_{kn}\}$ as above. All these sets together satisfy the requirements of the lemma.

If $\mathscr{G}$ and $\mathscr{H}$ are two pairwise disjoint families of sets, we say that $\mathscr{H}$ refines $\mathscr{G}$ if each element of $\mathscr{H}$ is a subset of some element of $\mathscr{G}$. It follows in this case that each element of $\mathscr{H}$ is contained in exactly one element of $\mathscr{G}$, that if $H \in \mathscr{H}$ and $G \in \mathscr{G}$ and $H \cap G \neq 0$ then $H \subset G$, and that the union of all the sets in $\mathscr{H}$ is contained in the union of all the sets in $\mathscr{G}$. Such families are partitions of the unions of their elements.

LEMMA 3   *Suppose that $\mathscr{C}_1, \mathscr{C}_2, \ldots$ are partitions of Ω into finitely or countably many sets of $\mathscr{F}$, such that each element of $\mathscr{C}_n$ has diameter less than ϵ_n, where $\epsilon_n \to 0$. Then $\bigcup_n \mathscr{C}_n$ generates $\mathscr{F}$. Let $\mathscr{D}_n$ consist of the finite and countable unions of elements of $\mathscr{C}_n$; if $\mathscr{C}_{n+1}$ refines $\mathscr{C}_n$ for each n, then $\mathscr{D}_1 \subset \mathscr{D}_2 \subset \cdots$ and $\bigcup_n \mathscr{D}_n$ is a field generating $\mathscr{F}$.*
Proof.   Given any closed set F, let A_n be the union of those elements of $\mathscr{C}_n$ that intersect F. Then $F \subset A_n$, and any point in A_n is within distance ϵ_n of some point of F; since F is closed, it follows that $F = \bigcap_n A_n$. The σ-field generated by $\bigcup_n \mathscr{C}_n$ therefore contains all the closed sets, and so coincides with $\mathscr{F}$. The rest of the lemma is easy to prove.

These three lemmas are also true in $(\tilde{\Omega}, \tilde{\mathscr{F}}, \tilde{P})$, of course.

Suppose now that T and $\tilde{T}$ are conjugate under a correspondence satisfying the requirements (C_i) through (C_v). To prove that T and $\tilde{T}$ are actually isomorphic, we first construct two sequences

$$\mathscr{C}_1, \mathscr{C}_2, \dots$$

$$\tilde{\mathscr{C}}_1, \tilde{\mathscr{C}}_2, \dots$$

of classes with the following properties.

(π_1) The class $\mathscr{C}_n[\tilde{\mathscr{C}}_n]$ is a (nonempty) finite or countable, pairwise disjoint family of sets in $\mathscr{F}[\tilde{\mathscr{F}}]$. The elements of $\mathscr{C}_n[\tilde{\mathscr{C}}_n]$ all have positive P-measure $[\tilde{P}$-measure$]$, and hence are nonempty.

(π_2) The family $\mathscr{C}_{n+1}[\tilde{\mathscr{C}}_{n+1}]$ refines both $\mathscr{C}_n[\tilde{\mathscr{C}}_n]$ and $T^{-1}\mathscr{C}_n[T^{-1}\tilde{\mathscr{C}}_n]$.

(π_3) For n odd [for n even], the sets in $\mathscr{C}_n[\tilde{\mathscr{C}}_n]$ are closed and have diameters less than $1/n$.

(π_4) There is a one-to-one mapping from $\mathscr{C}_n$ onto $\tilde{\mathscr{C}}_n$ with the property that if C is any element of $\mathscr{C}_n$ and if $\tilde{C}$ is its image in $\tilde{\mathscr{C}}_n$ under this mapping, then $C \leftrightarrow \tilde{C}$.

(π_5) If $\Omega_n[\tilde{\Omega}_n]$ is the union of all the elements of $\mathscr{C}_n[\tilde{\mathscr{C}}_n]$, then $P(\Omega_n) = 1[\tilde{P}(\tilde{\Omega}_n) = 1]$.

We first construct $\mathscr{C}_1$ and $\tilde{\mathscr{C}}_1$. By Lemma 2, there exists a finite or countable, disjoint family of closed sets whose union Ω_1 satisfies $P(\Omega_1) = 1$ and whose elements have diameter less than 1. Let $\mathscr{C}_1$ consist of those elements in the family that have positive measure.

If $C_1, C_2, \dots$ are the elements of $\mathscr{C}_1$, then, according to (C_i), there are sets $\tilde{C}_1, \tilde{C}_2, \dots$ in $\tilde{\mathscr{F}}$ such that $C_u \leftrightarrow \tilde{C}_u$. The family of sets $\tilde{C}_u - \bigcup_{u' \neq u} \tilde{C}_{u'}$ satisfies all the requirements for $\tilde{C}_1$.

Suppose now that the partial sequences

$$\mathscr{C}_1, \mathscr{C}_2, \dots, \mathscr{C}_n$$

$$\tilde{\mathscr{C}}_1, \tilde{\mathscr{C}}_2, \dots, \tilde{\mathscr{C}}_n$$

have been constructed. We shall show how to construct $\mathscr{C}_{n+1}$ and $\tilde{\mathscr{C}}_{n+1}$. Suppose first that n is even (so that $n + 1$ is odd).

Let $C_1, C_2, \dots$ be the elements of $\mathscr{C}_n$, and let $\tilde{C}_1, \tilde{C}_2, \dots$ be the elements of $\tilde{\mathscr{C}}_n$, with the ordering so chosen that $C_u \leftrightarrow \tilde{C}_u$. By Lemma 2, each set $C_{uv} = C_u \cap T^{-1}C_v$ contains pairwise disjoint sets C_{uv1},

$C_{uv2}, \ldots$ which are closed, have diameters less than $1/(n+1)$, and satisfy $P(C_{uv} - \bigcup_w C_{uvw}) = 0$. Let $\tilde{D}_{uvw}$ be sets in $\tilde{\mathscr{F}}$ such that $C_{uvw} \leftrightarrow \tilde{D}_{uvw}$, define $\tilde{E}_{uvw} = \tilde{D}_{uvw} \cap \tilde{C}_u \cap T^{-1}\tilde{C}_v$, and let $\tilde{C}_{uvw} = \tilde{E}_{uvw} - \bigcup_{w' \neq w} \tilde{E}_{uvw'}$. It follows from the properties (C_i) through (C_v) of the correspondence defining the conjugacy that the family $\mathscr{C}_{n+1}$ consisting of the C_{uvw} and the family $\tilde{\mathscr{C}}_{n+1}$ consisting of the $\tilde{C}_{uvw}$ have all the properties required of them, except that some of the sets in them may have measure 0. Remove any such sets.

If n is odd (so that $n+1$ is even), we simply reverse the order of the construction, first constructing $\tilde{\mathscr{C}}_{n+1}$ by applying Lemma 2 in $\tilde{\Omega}$, and then constructing $\mathscr{C}_{n+1}$ by means of the conjugacy correspondence.

This completes the construction of the sequences $\mathscr{C}_1, \mathscr{C}_2, \ldots$ and $\tilde{\mathscr{C}}_1, \tilde{\mathscr{C}}_2, \ldots$. If $\Omega_0 = \bigcap_{n=1}^{\infty} \Omega_n$ and $\tilde{\Omega}_0 = \bigcap_{n=1}^{\infty} \tilde{\Omega}_n$, then $P(\Omega_0) = 1$ and $P(\tilde{\Omega}_0) = 1$. We shall define a mapping ϕ from Ω_0 onto $\tilde{\Omega}_0$ that will give rise to an isomorphism between T and $\tilde{T}$.

A *chain* in Ω is a sequence $\{C_n\}$ of sets such that $C_1 \supset C_2 \supset \cdots$ and $C_n \in \mathscr{C}_n$. It follows by (π_3) and the fact that the C_n are nonempty that the intersection of the chain consists of a single point in Ω_0. Conversely, any point in Ω_0 arises in this way from exactly one chain. The same thing is true in $\tilde{\Omega}$.

Let us replace $\mathscr{C}_n$ by the family $\{C \cap \Omega_0 : C \in \mathscr{C}_n\}$ and $\tilde{\mathscr{C}}_n$ by the family $\{\tilde{C} \cap \tilde{\Omega}_0 : \tilde{C} \in \tilde{\mathscr{C}}_n\}$. Then chains still have intersections consisting of a single point in Ω_0 or in $\tilde{\Omega}_0$, and the conditions (π_1) through (π_5) still obtain, except that $\mathscr{C}_n$ for n odd and $\tilde{\mathscr{C}}_n$ for n even need no longer consist of closed sets (which no longer matters). The family $\mathscr{C}_n[\tilde{\mathscr{C}}_n]$ is now a partition of $\Omega_0[\tilde{\Omega}_0]$.

We now define the mapping ϕ. Any ω in Ω_0 gives rise to a unique chain $\{C_n\}$ in Ω, which corresponds by (π_4) to a unique chain $\{\tilde{C}_n\}$ in $\tilde{\Omega}$ ($C_n \leftrightarrow \tilde{C}_n$ for all n), and this second chain determines a unique point $\phi\omega$ in $\tilde{\Omega}_0$. Since all these steps can be reversed, ϕ is one-to-one and its range is all of $\tilde{\Omega}_0$. Condition (I_i) of the definition of isomorphism is thus satisfied.

We turn to condition (I_{ii}). Now Ω_0 is a metric space with the metric it inherits from Ω, and the σ-field $\mathscr{F}_0$ of Borel sets in Ω_0 consists exactly of the subsets of Ω_0 that lie in $\mathscr{F}$. Let $\mathscr{G}_0$ be the class of sets A in $\mathscr{F}_0$

for which $\phi A \in \tilde{\mathscr{F}}$ and $P(A) = \tilde{P}(\phi A)$. If $C \in \mathscr{C}_n$, then ϕC is the set in $\tilde{\mathscr{C}}_n$ to which it corresponds according to (π_4). Therefore $\mathscr{G}_0$ contains $\mathscr{C}_n$ and hence also the finite and countable unions of elements of $\mathscr{C}_n$. Since $\mathscr{G}_0$ is clearly a monotone class, it follows by Lemma 3 that $\mathscr{G}_0 = \mathscr{F}_0$. This and the analogous result with the roles of Ω and $\tilde{\Omega}$ interchanged show that if $A \subset \Omega_0$, then $A \in \mathscr{F}$ if and only if $\phi A \in \tilde{\mathscr{F}}$, and that $P(A) = P(\phi A)$ in this case. Therefore condition $(\mathrm{I}_{\mathrm{ii}})$ is satisfied.

As a preliminary to proving that ϕ commutes properly with T and $\tilde{T}$, let us show that if $\{C_n\}$ and $\{D_n\}$ are respectively the chains determined by points ω and ω' of Ω_0 then $\omega' = T\omega$ if and only if $C_n \subset T^{-1}D_{n-1}$ for all $n > 1$. (The analogous proposition holds in $\tilde{\Omega}_0$). If $C_n \subset T^{-1}D_{n-1}$ for $n > 1$, then $T\omega$ and ω' both lie in D_{n-1} for $n > 1$ and so must coincide. If, on the other hand, $\omega' = T\omega$, then the element C_n of the partition $\mathscr{C}_n$ and the element $T^{-1}D_{n-1}$ of the partition $T^{-1}\mathscr{C}_{n-1}$ share the point ω; since the first partition refines the second, $C_n \subset T^{-1}D_{n-1}$.

Suppose now that $\omega \in \Omega_0$ and $T\omega \in \Omega_0$, so that $\phi\omega \in \tilde{\Omega}_0$ and $\phi T\omega \in \tilde{\Omega}_0$. Let $\{C_n\}$, $\{D_n\}$, $\{\tilde{C}_n\}$, and $\{\tilde{D}_n\}$ be the chains arising from the points ω, $T\omega$, $\phi\omega$, $\phi T\omega$, respectively. To prove $\tilde{T}\phi\omega = \phi T\omega$, it is enough to show that $\tilde{C}_n \subset \tilde{T}^{-1}\tilde{D}_{n-1}$. But, since ω goes into $T\omega$, $C_n \subset T^{-1}D_{n-1}$. Also, $C_n \leftrightarrow \tilde{C}_n$ and $D_{n-1} \leftrightarrow \tilde{D}_{n-1}$, so that $C_n = C_n \cap T^{-1}D_{n-1} \leftrightarrow \tilde{C}_n \cap \tilde{T}^{-1}\tilde{D}_{n-1}$. Therefore $\tilde{C}_n \cap \tilde{T}^{-1}\tilde{D}_{n-1}$ has positive measure and so is nonempty; $\tilde{C}_n \subset \tilde{T}^{-1}\tilde{D}_{n-1}$ follows.

We have shown that the triple $(\Omega_0, \tilde{\Omega}_0, \phi)$ satisfies conditions $(\mathrm{I}_{\mathrm{i}})$ and $(\mathrm{I}_{\mathrm{ii}})$ of the definition of isomorphism, and we have shown that it satisfies condition $(\mathrm{I}_{\mathrm{iii}})$ weakened in accordance with Remark 2 following that definition. Therefore T and $\tilde{T}$ are isomorphic.

Isomorphism vs. Spectral Equivalence*

Although this book hardly touches on the isometries induced by measure-preserving transformations, we should point out the difference between isomorphism and spectral equivalence.

---

* This topic may be omitted.

If T is a measure-preserving transformation on $(\Omega, \mathscr{F}, P)$, the equation $(Uf)(\omega) = f(T\omega)$ defines a transformation on the Hilbert space $L^2(\Omega)$ of square-integrable functions on $(\Omega, \mathscr{F}, P)$. As was pointed out in Section 2 (where U was denoted $\hat{T}$), U is an isometry. Let us show that if T is isomorphic to a second transformation $\tilde{T}$ (on $(\tilde{\Omega}, \tilde{\mathscr{F}}, \tilde{P})$), then the isometry U is abstractly the same as the isometry $\tilde{U}$ induced on $L^2(\tilde{\Omega})$ by $\tilde{T}$.

Suppose that T and $\tilde{T}$ are isomorphic under $(\Omega_0, \tilde{\Omega}_0, \phi)$. For $\tilde{f}$ in $L^2(\tilde{\Omega})$, let $V\tilde{f}$ be the function on Ω with value $f(\phi\omega)$ at ω. (This defines $V\tilde{f}$ only on Ω_0; extend it in any manner to Ω—elements of $L^2(\Omega)$ are determined only to within sets of measure 0.) Clearly V is a linear mapping from $L^2(\tilde{\Omega})$ to $L^2(\Omega)$. It follows from properties (I_i) and (I_{ii}) of the isomorphism that V is one-to-one, that its range is all of $L^2(\Omega)$, and that it preserves lengths and inner products. Finally, (I_{iii}) implies that $V\tilde{U} = UV$, or $\tilde{U} = V^{-1}UV$.

Hilbert-space operators connected by such a V are said to have identical spectral structure, or to be spectrally equivalent—this is the notion of sameness appropriate to operators. We have shown that the spectral structure of the induced isometry is invariant under isomorphism. (It is invariant under conjugacy too.) If U and $\tilde{U}$ are spectrally equivalent, we may say that T and $\tilde{T}$ themselves are spectrally equivalent.

If f lies in $L^2(\Omega)$, then f is invariant $(f(T\omega) = f(\omega)$ a.e.) if and only if $Uf = f$. Now T is ergodic if and only if the invariant functions are all a.e. constant. Since the functions that are a.e. constant are, as elements of $L^2(\Omega)$, scalar multiples of one another, T is ergodic if and only if the subspace of solutions to $Uf = f$ has dimension 1.

If the subspace of solutions of $Uf = f$ has dimension 1, then the same thing is true of any spectrally equivalent copy of U. Therefore, to know the spectral structure of U is to know in particular whether or not T is ergodic. The spectral structure of the induced isometry is thus a finer invariant than ergodicity: if T and $\tilde{T}$ are spectrally equivalent, then they both ergodic or neither is. It can also be shown* that the spectral structure is a finer invariant than mixing.

We are going to show that the Bernoulli shifts induce isometries

---

* See Halmos (1956).

which all have the very same spectral structure. As pointed out in the discussion of entropy, it follows by the Kolmogorov-Sinai theorem (proved in Section 7) that there exist Bernoulli shifts that have different entropies and hence are nonisomorphic. Entropy is thus an invariant capable of distinguishing some transformations that cannot be distinguished by spectral structure—it is of course, hopeless to try to distinguish these transformations by invariants such as mixing and ergodicity, since these invariants are not as fine as the spectral structure. (On the other hand, there are spectrally distinct transformations with the same entropy. Consider again, for various k, the cyclic permutations of k points of equal mass.)

Let T be a Bernoulli shift. We may take $\rho = \{1, 2, \ldots, r\}$ as the state space and $p_1, p_2, \ldots, p_r$ as the probabilities, and we assume that the p_i are all positive. Let $\xi_i = (\xi_i(1), \ldots, \xi_i(r))$, $i = 1, 2, \ldots, r$, be vectors such that

$$(5.18) \qquad \sum_k p_k \xi_i(k) \xi_j(k) = \delta_{ij}, \qquad i, j = 1, 2, \ldots, r,$$

and such that

$$(5.19) \qquad \xi_1 = (1, 1, \ldots, 1).$$

In other words, the vectors $(\xi_i(1)/\sqrt{p_1}, \ldots, \xi_r(r)/\sqrt{p_r})$ form an orthonormal basis for r-space, with the first such vector prescribed.

Consider doubly infinite sequences $u = (\ldots, u_{-1}, u_0, u_1, \ldots)$ of elements of $\{1, 2, \ldots, r\}$. Let $\mathscr{U}$ be the collection of such sequences having only finitely many coordinates u_n distinct from 1. For u in $\mathscr{U}$, define a function g_u on Ω by

$$(5.20) \qquad g_u(\omega) = \prod_{n=-\infty}^{\infty} \xi_{u_n}(x_n(\omega)),$$

where x_n are the coordinate variables. Since only finitely many of the u_n differ from 1, the product (5.20) is really a finite one (see (5.19)).

The functions g_u are elements of $L^2(\Omega)$. Since the variables x_n are independent under P, we have, by (5.18),

$$(g_u, g_v) = \prod_{n=-\infty}^{\infty} \int \xi_{u_n}(x_n(\omega)) \xi_{v_n}(x_n(\omega)) P\,(d\omega)$$

$$= \prod_{n=-\infty}^{\infty} \delta_{u_n v_n}, \qquad u, v \in \mathscr{U}.$$

Thus the g_u are orthonormal.

Any function in $L^2(\Omega)$ can be approximated in the L^2-sense by simple functions $\Sigma_{i=1}^{k}\alpha_i I_{A_i}$. Since the A_i can be approximated by sets depending only on finitely many coordinates (cylinders), the functions depending only on finitely many coordinates span $L^2(\Omega)$. But a function depending only on (say) n coordinates can be identified with a point in nr-space; since the ξ_i span r-space, such a function is a finite linear combination of the g_u. Therefore $\{g_u: u \in \mathcal{U}\}$ is an orthonormal basis for $L^2(\Omega)$.

Define $\theta: \mathcal{U} \to \mathcal{U}$ by $(\theta u)_n = u_{n-1}$. Since

$$(Ug_u)(\omega) = g_u(T\omega) = \prod_{n=-\infty}^{\infty} \xi_{u_{n-1}}(x_n(\omega)),$$

we have

$$Ug_u = g_{\theta u}.$$

Now let $u^{(0)}, u^{(1)}, \dots$ be a sequence of elements of $\mathcal{U}$ such that $u^{(0)}$ consists entirely of 1's, such that if $i \neq j$ then $u^{(i)} = \theta^n u^{(j)}$ holds for no $n = 0, \pm 1, \dots$ (the $u^{(i)}$ are not slides of one another), and such that any u in $\mathcal{U}$ has the form $u = \theta^n u^{(i)}$ for some $i = 0, 1, \dots$ and some $n = 0, \pm 1, \dots$ (any u is a slide of some $u^{(i)}$). Let $f_0 = g_{u^{(0)}}$, and, for $i = 1, 2, \dots$ and $n = 0, \pm 1, \dots$, let $f_{i,n} = g_{\theta^n u^{(i)}}$. The system $\{g_u: u \in \mathcal{U}\}$ now takes the following form.

$$f_0$$
$$\dots, f_{1,-1}, f_{1,0}, f_{1,1}, \dots$$
$$\dots, f_{2,-1}, f_{2,0}, f_{2,1}, \dots$$
$$\dots \dots \dots \dots \dots \dots \dots \dots$$
$$\dots \dots \dots \dots \dots \dots \dots \dots$$

The elements of this array form an orthonormal basis for $L^2(\Omega)$, $Uf_0 = f_0$, and, for $i \geq 1$, $Uf_{i,n} = f_{i,n+1}$, $n = 0, \pm 1, \dots$. This specification of the spectral structure of U is independent of r and of the probabilities $p_1, p_2, \dots, p_r$.

We have seen that isomorphic measure-preserving transformations are spectrally equivalent. The result just proved, together with the fact that there exist nonisomorphic Bernoulli shifts, shows that spectrally equivalent transformations need by no means be isomorphic (or conjugate either). In other words, the spectral structure of the induced isometry is not a complete invariant.

Remarks. See Harris (1955) for Example 5.4.

Entropy was introduced into communication theory by Shannon (1948). Komogorov (1958) defined the entropy of the general measure-preserving transformation; a basic contribution was made by Sinai (1959a).

Theorem 5.1 is due to von Neumann (1932b). See Jacobs (1960 and 1962–1963) for further information and references.

Halmos (1956) has an extensive discussion of induced isometries.

6. PROPERTIES OF $H(\mathscr{A})$ AND $h(\mathscr{A}, T)$

A useful auxiliary concept is the entropy (or conditional entropy) of $\mathscr{A}$ given $\mathscr{B}$, defined* by

(6.1)

$$H(\mathscr{A} \mid \mathscr{B}) = \sum_B P(B) \sum_A \eta(P(A \mid B)) = - \sum_{A,B} P(A \cap B) \log P(A \mid B),$$

where the sums extend over the atoms of $\mathscr{A}$ and $\mathscr{B}$, and where we suppress any term involving an atom B of measure 0.

Tyche, having drawn a point ω from Ω according to the measure P, reports to the experimenter which atom of $\mathscr{B}$ it lies in. He is in general still uncertain which atom of $\mathscr{A}$ the point ω is in, the amount of his uncertainty being measured by $\Sigma_A \, \eta(P(A \mid B))$ if B is the particular atom of $\mathscr{B}$ that contains ω. Thus (6.1) measures the average amount of uncertainty about the outcome of the experiment $\mathscr{A}$, given knowledge of the outcome of the experiment $\mathscr{B}$. Alternatively, $H(\mathscr{A} \mid \mathscr{B})$ measures the amount of additional information the experimenter gains on learning the outcome of $\mathscr{A}$, assuming he already knows the outcome of $\mathscr{B}$.

If 2 denotes the field consisting of Ω and the empty set, then clearly $H(\mathscr{A} \mid 2) = H(\mathscr{A})$.

---

* The endpaper at the back of the book and the page following the index each summarize the definitions and properties of the different kinds of entropy.

Properties of $H(\mathscr{A})$ and $H(\mathscr{A} \mid \mathscr{B})$

We are going to prove the following five pairs of relations concerning entropy and conditional entropy for finite fields. The first formula is basic:

(A_1) $\quad H(\mathscr{A} \vee \mathscr{B} \mid \mathscr{C}) = H(\mathscr{A} \mid \mathscr{C}) + H(\mathscr{B} \mid \mathscr{A} \vee \mathscr{C}),$

(A_1') $\quad\quad H(\mathscr{A} \vee \mathscr{B}) = H(\mathscr{A}) + H(\mathscr{B} \mid \mathscr{A}).$

Formula (A_1') in effect says that the information in the experiments $\mathscr{A}$ and $\mathscr{B}$ together equals the information in $\mathscr{A}$ plus the amount of information remaining in $\mathscr{B}$ when the result of $\mathscr{A}$ is known. There is the analogous interpretation for (A_1).

Conditional entropy is nondecreasing in its first argument:

(A_2) $\quad H(\mathscr{A} \mid \mathscr{C}) \leq H(\mathscr{B} \mid \mathscr{C})$ if $\mathscr{A} \subset \mathscr{B},$

(A_2') $\quad\quad H(\mathscr{A}) \leq H(\mathscr{B})$ if $\mathscr{A} \subset \mathscr{B}.$

This makes sense: if $\mathscr{A} \subset \mathscr{B}$, then $\mathscr{B}$ refines $\mathscr{A}$; to know the outcome of $\mathscr{B}$ is also to know the outcome of $\mathscr{A}$; hence $\mathscr{B}$ is more informative.

Conditional entropy is nonincreasing in its second argument:

(A_3) $\quad H(\mathscr{A} \mid \mathscr{C}) \leq H(\mathscr{A} \mid \mathscr{B})$ if $\mathscr{C} \supset \mathscr{B}$

(A_3') $\quad\quad H(\mathscr{A} \mid \mathscr{C}) \leq H(\mathscr{A}).$

If knowledge of the outcome of $\mathscr{C}$ implies knowledge of the outcome of $\mathscr{B}$, then the experimenter's remaining uncertainty about the outcome of $\mathscr{A}$ should be less if he knows the outcome of $\mathscr{C}$ than if he only knows the outcome of $\mathscr{B}$.

Conditional entropy is subadditive in its first argument:

(A_4) $\quad H(\mathscr{A} \vee \mathscr{B} \mid \mathscr{C}) \leq H(\mathscr{A} \mid \mathscr{C}) + H(\mathscr{B} \mid \mathscr{C})$

(A_4') $\quad\quad H(\mathscr{A} \vee \mathscr{B}) \leq H(\mathscr{A}) + H(\mathscr{B}).$

Finally,

(A_5) $\quad\quad H(T^{-1}\mathscr{A} \mid T^{-1}\mathscr{B}) = H(\mathscr{A} \mid \mathscr{B}).$

(A_5') $\quad\quad\quad H(T^{-1}\mathscr{A}) = H(\mathscr{A}).$

Note that for each i, (A_i') follows immediately from (A_i) if we set an appropriate field equal to 2.

The relation (A_1) is analogous to the conditional probability formula

$$P(A \cap B \mid C) = P(A \mid C)P(B \mid A \cap C).$$

In fact (A_1) follows from this formula and the fact that the atoms of $\mathscr{A} \vee \mathscr{B}$ and $\mathscr{A} \vee \mathscr{C}$ are respectively the sets of the form $A \cap B$ and $A \cap C$, where A, B, and C are atoms of $\mathscr{A}$, $\mathscr{B}$, and $\mathscr{C}$:

$$
\begin{aligned}
H(\mathscr{A} \vee \mathscr{B} \mid \mathscr{C}) &= - \sum_{A,B,C} P(A \cap B \cap C) \log P(A \cap B \mid C) \\
&= - \sum_{A,B,C} P(A \cap B \cap C) \log P(A \mid C) \\
&\quad - \sum_{A,B,C} P(A \cap B \cap C) \log P(B \mid A \cap C) \\
&= - \sum_{A,C} P(A \cap C) \log P(A \mid C) \\
&\quad - \sum_{A,B,C} P(B \cap (A \cap C)) \log P(B \mid A \cap C) \\
&= H(\mathscr{A} \mid \mathscr{C}) + H(\mathscr{B} \mid \mathscr{A} \vee \mathscr{C}).
\end{aligned}
$$

If $\mathscr{A} \subset \mathscr{B}$ then $\mathscr{A} \vee \mathscr{B} = \mathscr{B}$; hence ($A_2$) follows from ($A_1$) and the obvious nonnegativity of conditional entropy.

To prove (A_3), note that, since the function $\eta(t) = -t \log t$ is concave,

$$\sum_C \eta(P(A \mid C))P(C \mid B) \leq \eta\left(\sum_C P(A \mid C)P(C \mid B)\right).$$

Since $\mathscr{B} \subset \mathscr{C}$, B is a union of atoms of $\mathscr{C}$; hence

$$\sum_C P(A \mid C)P(C \mid B) = \sum_{C \subset B} \frac{P(A \cap C)}{P(C)} \frac{P(C)}{P(B)} = P(A \mid B).$$

Therefore

$$\sum_C \eta(P(A \mid C))P(C \mid B) \leq \eta(P(A \mid B)).$$

Multiplying this inequality by $P(B)$ and adding over A and B yields (A_3).

Finally, (A_4) follows immediately from (A_1) and (A_3). And (A_5) is obvious.

If $\mathscr{A} = \mathscr{B}$ then, by (A_1'), $H(\mathscr{A} \mid \mathscr{B}) = 0$. It is intuitively clear that if $\mathscr{A}$ and $\mathscr{B}$ are very nearly equal, in the sense that each atom of one differs by set of small measure from some atom of the other, then $H(\mathscr{A} \mid \mathscr{B})$ should be small. This idea lies behind the proof of the following result.

THEOREM 6.1   *Suppose the finite field $\mathscr{A}$ is contained in the σ-field generated by the field $\mathscr{F}_0$ (or, more generally, that each atom of $\mathscr{A}$ differs by a set of measure 0 from some element of the σ-field generated by $\mathscr{F}_0$). Then for any positive ϵ there is a finite subfield $\mathscr{B}$ of $\mathscr{F}_0$ such that $H(\mathscr{A} \mid \mathscr{B}) < \epsilon$.*

Proof. We may without loss of generality assume that the atoms $A_1, \ldots, A_r$ of $\mathscr{A}$ all have positive measure. Since $\eta(t)$ is continuous and $\eta(0) = \eta(1) = 0$, there exists a δ_0 $(0 < \delta_0 < 1)$ such that $\eta(t) < \epsilon/r$ if either $0 \leq t \leq \delta_0$ or $1 - \delta_0 \leq t \leq 1$.

If we can find in $\mathscr{F}_0$ a finite subfield $\mathscr{B}$ whose atoms $B_1, \ldots, B_r$ satisfy

$$P(A_i \mid B_i) > 1 - \delta_0, \, i = 1, \ldots, r,$$

we shall then also have $P(A_j \mid B_i) < \delta_0$ for $j \neq i$, and hence

$$H(\mathscr{A} \mid \mathscr{B}) = \sum_{ij} P(B_j)\eta(P(A_i \mid B_j)) < \sum_{ij} P(B_j)\frac{\epsilon}{r} = \epsilon.$$

If the atoms B_i satisfy

$$(6.2) \qquad P(A_i + B_i) < \delta = \min_{1 \leq i \leq r} \delta_0 \frac{P(A_i)}{2},$$

then, since $P(A_i) \leq P(B_i) + \delta < P(B_i) + P(A_i)/2$, we shall have $P(A_i)/2 < P(B_i)$ and hence $P(B_i) - P(A_i \cap B_i) < \delta < \delta_0 P(B_i)$, or $P(A_i \mid B_i) > 1 - \delta_0$. It therefore suffices to produce a $\mathscr{B}$ with atoms satisfying (6.2).

By the hypothesis of the theorem, there exists, for each i, a set B_i' in $\mathscr{F}_0$ with $P(A_i + B_i') < \lambda$, where λ will be chosen in a moment. If $i \neq j$ then $P(B_i' \cap B_j') \leq P(B_i' + A_i) + P(A_j + B_j') < 2\lambda$, so that $P(N) < r(r-1)\lambda$, where $N = \bigcup_{i \neq j}(B_i' \cap B_j')$. Define $B_i = B_i' - N$ for $1 \leq i < r$ and $B_r = \Omega - \bigcup_{i < r} B_i$; then the B_i lie in $\mathscr{F}_0$ and $P(A_i + B_i) < \lambda + r(r-1)\lambda$ if $i < r$, and hence $P(A_r + B_r) < (r-1)(\lambda + r(r-1)\lambda)$. If λ is small enough then (6.2) holds.

The following theorem, which makes precise in another way the idea that if the atoms of $\mathscr{A}$ are close to those of $\mathscr{B}$ then $H(\mathscr{A} \mid \mathscr{B})$ is small, will be used only in Chapter 5, for coding theory.

THEOREM 6.2   *Suppose the atoms* $A_1, \ldots, A_r$ *of* $\mathscr{A}$ *are equal in number to the atoms* $B_1, \ldots, B_r$ *of* $\mathscr{B}$. *Then*

$$H(\mathscr{A} \mid \mathscr{B}) \leq \eta(d) + \eta(1 - d) + d \log (r - 1),$$

where

$$d = \sum_j P(B_j)P(A_j{}^c \mid B_j) = \sum_{i \neq j} P(A_i \cap B_j) = \sum_i P(A_i)P(B_i{}^c \mid A_i).$$

Proof.   First,

$$H(\mathscr{A} \mid \mathscr{B}) = \sum_j P(B_j)\left[\eta(P(A_j \mid B_j)) + \sum_{i \neq j}\eta(P(A_i \mid B_j))\right].$$

For fixed j, we have*

$$\sum_{i \neq j}\eta(P(A_i \mid B_j)) = P(A_j{}^c \mid B_j)\sum_{i \neq j}\eta\left(\frac{P(A_i \mid B_j)}{P(A_j{}^c \mid B_j)}\right) + \eta(P(A_j{}^c \mid B_j))$$

$$\leq P(A_j{}^c \mid B_j) \log (r - 1) + \eta(P(A_j{}^c \mid B_j)).$$

Hence

$$H(\mathscr{A} \mid \mathscr{B}) \leq \sum_j P(B_j)[\eta(P(A_j \mid B_j)) + \eta(P(A_j{}^c \mid B_j))]$$
$$+ \sum_j P(B_j)P(A_j{}^c \mid B_j) \log (r - 1).$$

The second sum equals $d \log (r - 1)$. If $\mathscr{E}$ is the field with atoms $E = \bigcup_{i \neq j}(A_i \cap B_j)$ and E^c, then the first sum is $H(\mathscr{E} \mid \mathscr{B})$. Since

$$H(\mathscr{E} \mid \mathscr{B}) \leq H(\mathscr{E}) = \eta(P(E)) + \eta(P(E^c)) = \eta(d) + \eta(1 - d),$$

the proof is complete.

If $P(B_j{}^c \mid A_j) \leq \epsilon$ for all j, then $d \leq \epsilon$, a fact which leads to a slightly more efficient proof of Theorem 6.1.

Properties of $h(\mathscr{A}, T)$

We prove first that the limit superior in the definition (5.13) of $h(\mathscr{A}, T)$ can be replaced by an ordinary limit. In fact, (A$_1'$) and (A$_5'$) imply

$$H\left(\mathscr{A} \mid \bigvee_{i=1}^{k} T^{-i}\mathscr{A}\right) = H\left(\bigvee_{i=0}^{k} T^{-i}\mathscr{A}\right) - H\left(\bigvee_{i=1}^{k} T^{-i}\mathscr{A}\right)$$

$$= H\left(\bigvee_{i=1}^{k} T^{-i}\mathscr{A}\right) - H\left(\bigvee_{i=0}^{k-1} T^{-i}\mathscr{A}\right).$$

---

* Nonnegative $t_1 \ldots, t_k$ adding to 1 satisfy $\sum_{i=1}^{k} \eta(t_i) \leq \log k$.

Adding over k, we have

$$H\left(\bigvee_{i=0}^{n-1} T^{-i}\mathscr{A}\right) = H(\mathscr{A}) + \sum_{k=1}^{n-1} H\left(\mathscr{A} \,\middle|\, \bigvee_{i=1}^{k} T^{-i}\mathscr{A}\right).$$

By (A_3), $H(\mathscr{A} \mid \bigvee_{i=1}^{k} T^{-i}\mathscr{A})$ is nonincreasing in k and hence has a finite limit. By taking Cesàro means and applying the preceding equation, we obtain

$$(B_1) \quad h(\mathscr{A}, T) = \lim_{n \to \infty} \frac{1}{n} H\left(\bigvee_{i=0}^{n-1} T^{-i}\mathscr{A}\right) = \lim_{n \to \infty} H\left(\mathscr{A} \,\middle|\, \bigvee_{i=1}^{n} T^{-i}\mathscr{A}\right).$$

Furthermore, both of the sequences whose limits appear in (B_1) are nonincreasing. A similar argument shows that

$$(B_1') \qquad h(\mathscr{A}, T) = \lim_{n \to \infty} H\left(T^{-n}\mathscr{A} \,\middle|\, \bigvee_{i=0}^{n-1} T^{-i}\mathscr{A}\right).$$

where again the limit is approached monotonically from above. If T is invertible, then

$$(B_1'') \qquad h(\mathscr{A}, T) = \lim_{n \to \infty} H\left(\mathscr{A} \,\middle|\, \bigvee_{i=1}^{n} T^{i}\mathscr{A}\right),$$

as we can see by applying T^n to the right side of (B_1').

The relation (B_1') provides another interpretation of $h(\mathscr{A}, T)$. The amount of uncertainty about what will be the outcome of the $(n + 1)$st replication $T^{-n}\mathscr{A}$ of $\mathscr{A}$, given the outcomes of the first n replications $\mathscr{A}, T^{-1}\mathscr{A}, \ldots, T^{-(n-1)}\mathscr{A}$, is $H(T^{-n}\mathscr{A} \mid \bigvee_{i=0}^{n-1} T^{-i}\mathscr{A})$. As n tends to infinity, this quantity, which is also the amount of information the $(n + 1)$st replication gives, over and above that provided by the first n replications, settles down to $h(\mathscr{A}, T)$.

From (B_1) and (A_2'),

$$(B_2) \qquad h(\mathscr{A}, T) \le h(\mathscr{B}, T) \quad \text{if } \mathscr{A} \subset \mathscr{B}$$

follows immediately.

If $u \le v$, where we assume that $u \ge 0$ if T is noninvertible, then

$$\bigvee_{i=0}^{n-1} T^{-i}\left\{\bigvee_{j=u}^{v} T^{-j}\mathscr{A}\right\} = T^{-u}\left\{\bigvee_{k=0}^{n+v-u-1} T^{-k}\mathscr{A}\right\},$$

so that, by (A_5'),

$$\frac{1}{n} H\left(\bigvee_{i=0}^{n-1} T^{-i}\left\{\bigvee_{j=u}^{v} T^{-j}\mathscr{A}\right\}\right) = \frac{n+v-u}{n} \frac{1}{n+v-u} H\left(\bigvee_{k=0}^{n+v-u-1} T^{-k}\mathscr{A}\right).$$

It follows by (B$_1$) that

(B$_3$)
$$h\left(\bigvee_{j=u}^{v} T^{-j}\mathscr{A},\, T\right) = h(\mathscr{A}, T).$$

If $u = v = 1$, this becomes

$$h(T^{-1}\mathscr{A}, T) = h(\mathscr{A}, T).$$

If $u = 0$, it becomes

$$h\left(\bigvee_{j=0}^{v} T^{-j}\mathscr{A},\, T\right) = h(\mathscr{A}, T),$$

which says that the information per experiment in the sequence

$$\bigvee_{j=0}^{v} T^{-j}\mathscr{A}, \quad \bigvee_{j=1}^{v+1} T^{-j}\mathscr{A}, \quad \bigvee_{j=2}^{v+2} T^{-j}\mathscr{A}, \ldots$$

of experiments is the same as in the sequence

$$\mathscr{A}, T^{-1}\mathscr{A}, T^{-2}\mathscr{A}, \ldots.$$

One naturally expects this, because of the overlap between neighboring experiments of the first of these sequences.

If $k \geq 1$ then

$$\frac{1}{n} H\left(\bigvee_{i=0}^{n-1} (T^{k})^{-i}\left\{\bigvee_{j=0}^{k-1} T^{-j}\mathscr{A}\right\}\right) = k\frac{1}{nk} H\left(\bigvee_{u=0}^{nk-1} T^{-u}\mathscr{A}\right),$$

so that, by (B$_1$) again,

(B$_4$)
$$h\left(\bigvee_{j=0}^{k-1} T^{-j}\mathscr{A},\, T^{k}\right) = kh(\mathscr{A}, T), \qquad k \geq 1.$$

The last property of $h(\mathscr{A}, T)$ we need is a generalization of (B$_2$):

(B$_5$)
$$h(\mathscr{A}, T) \leq h(\mathscr{B}, T) + H(\mathscr{A} \mid \mathscr{B}).$$

To prove this, observe that, by (A$_2'$) and (A$_1'$),

$$H\left(\bigvee_{i=0}^{n-1} T^{-i}\mathscr{A}\right) \leq H\left(\bigvee_{i=0}^{n-1} T^{-i}\mathscr{A} \vee \bigvee_{j=0}^{n-1} T^{-j}\mathscr{B}\right)$$

$$= H\left(\bigvee_{j=0}^{n-1} T^{-j}\mathscr{B}\right) + H\left(\bigvee_{i=0}^{n-1} T^{-i}\mathscr{A} \,\middle|\, \bigvee_{j=0}^{n-1} T^{-j}\mathscr{B}\right).$$

Applying successively (A_4), (A_3), and (A_5), we have

$$H\left(\bigvee_{i=0}^{n-1} T^{-i}\mathscr{A} \;\middle|\; \bigvee_{j=0}^{n-1} T^{-j}\mathscr{B}\right) \leq \sum_{i=0}^{n-1} H\left(T^{-i}\mathscr{A} \;\middle|\; \bigvee_{j=0}^{n-1} T^{-j}\mathscr{B}\right)$$

$$\leq \sum_{i=0}^{n-1} H(T^{-i}\mathscr{A} \mid T^{-i}\mathscr{B}) = nH(\mathscr{A} \mid \mathscr{B}).$$

Combining the preceding inequalities, we obtain

$$\frac{1}{n} H\left(\bigvee_{i=0}^{n-1} T^{-i}\mathscr{A}\right) \leq \frac{1}{n} H\left(\bigvee_{j=0}^{n-1} T^{-j}\mathscr{B}\right) + H(\mathscr{A} \mid \mathscr{B}),$$

from which (B_5) follows via (B_1).

7.   PROPERTIES OF $h(T)$

The Kolmogorov-Sinai Theorem

We are now in a position to prove the Kolmogorov-Sinai theorem, which enables us in many cases to compute the entropy

$$h(T) = \sup h(\mathscr{A}, T).$$

THEOREM 7.1   *If T is invertible and $\bigvee_{n=-\infty}^{\infty} T^n\mathscr{A} = \mathscr{F}$, then $h(T) = h(\mathscr{A}, T)$.*
Proof.   We must show that if $\mathscr{B}$ is any finite subfield of $\mathscr{F}$, then

$$h(\mathscr{B}, T) \leq h(\mathscr{A}, T).$$

Let $\mathscr{A}_n = \bigvee_{k=-n}^{n} T^k\mathscr{A}$; it follows by (B_3) that

$$h(\mathscr{A}_n, T) = h(\mathscr{A}, T),$$

and by (B_5) that

$$h(\mathscr{B}, T) \leq h(\mathscr{A}_n, T) + H(\mathscr{B} \mid \mathscr{A}_n)$$

$$= h(\mathscr{A}, T) + H(\mathscr{B} \mid \mathscr{A}_n).$$

It therefore suffices to show that

$$\lim_{n \to \infty} H(\mathscr{B} \mid \mathscr{A}_n) = 0,$$

which we shall prove by an application of Theorem 6.1.

If $\mathscr{F}_0 = \mathsf{U}_n \mathscr{A}_n$, then $\mathscr{F}_0$ is a (finitely additive) field which generates $\mathscr{F}$. By Theorem 6.1, there is, for any positive ϵ, a finite subfield $\mathscr{C}$ of $\mathscr{F}_0$ such that $H(\mathscr{B} \mid \mathscr{C}) < \epsilon$. Now $\mathscr{C}$ lies in some $\mathscr{A}_{n_0}$; if $n \geq n_0$ then

$$H(\mathscr{B} \mid \mathscr{A}_n) \leq H(\mathscr{B} \mid \mathscr{A}_{n_0}) \leq H(\mathscr{B} \mid \mathscr{C}) < \epsilon,$$

by (A_3). This proves the theorem.

Substituting $\mathsf{V}_{k=0}^n T^{-k} \mathscr{A}$ for $\mathscr{A}_n$ in this proof leads to the following result, in which we do not assume that T is invertible.

COROLLARY. *If* $\mathsf{V}_{n=0}^\infty T^{-n} \mathscr{A} = \mathscr{F}$, *then* $h(T) = h(\mathscr{A}, T)$.

Calculation of Entropy

Theorem 7.1 warrants the entropy calculations of Section 5. Let us carry these through again in a slightly different way. With T the general two-sided shift corresponding to a process $\{x_n\}$ with finite state space ρ (Example 1.2), take $\mathscr{A}$ to be the time-0 field (the field with atoms $\{x_0 = i\}$, $i \in \rho$). Since $\mathsf{V}_{n=-\infty}^\infty T^n \mathscr{A} = \mathscr{F}$, it follows by Theorem 7.1 that $h(T) = h(\mathscr{A}, T)$. Let us compute $h(\mathscr{A}, T)$ by the formula

$$h(\mathscr{A}, T) = \lim_{n \to \infty} H\left(\mathscr{A} \mid \bigvee_{k=1}^n T^k \mathscr{A}\right).$$

The general atom of $\mathsf{V}_{k=1}^n T^k \mathscr{A}$ is $\{x_{-1} = i_{-1}, \ldots, x_{-n} = i_{-n}\}$, and hence

$$H\left(\mathscr{A} \mid \bigvee_{k=1}^n T^k \mathscr{A}\right) = \sum_{i_{-1}, \ldots, i_{-n}} P\{x_{-1} = i_{-1}, \ldots, x_{-n} = i_{-n}\}$$
$$\times \sum_{i_0} \eta(P\{x_0 = i_0 \mid x_{-1} = i_{-1}, \ldots, x_{-n} = i_{-n}\}).$$

It follows from this that the entropy of the shift satisfies

(7.1) $$h(T) \leq \log r,$$

where r is the number of states.

If T is the Bernoulli shift $(p_1, \ldots, p_r)$ then, since

$$P\{x_0 = i_0 \mid x_{-1} = i_{-1}, \ldots, x_{-n} = i_{-n}\} = p_{i_0},$$

the $H(\mathscr{A} \mid \mathsf{V}_{k=1}^n T^k \mathscr{A})$ all coincide with $-\Sigma_i p_i \log p_i$. We conclude that

(7.2) $$h(T) = h(\mathscr{A}, T) = -\sum_i p_i \log p_i.$$

Now take T to be the Markov shift corresponding to the transition matrix $\Pi = (p_{ij})$ and stationary probabilities $p = (p_i)$. This time $P\{x_0 = i_0 \mid x_{-1} = i_{-1}, \ldots, x_{-n} = i_{-n}\} = p_{i_{-1}i_0}$, so that

$$H\left(\mathscr{A} \;\middle|\; \bigvee_{k=1}^{n} T^k \mathscr{A}\right) = -\sum_{i_{-1} \cdots i_{-n}} p_{i_{-n}} p_{i_{-n}i_{-n+1}} \cdots p_{i_{-2}i_{-1}} \sum_{i_0} p_{i_{-1}i_0} \log p_{i_{-1}i_0}$$
$$= -\sum_{ij} p_i p_{ij} \log p_{ij}.$$

Therefore—and this holds without any regularity assumptions on Π—

$$(7.3) \qquad h(T) = h(\mathscr{A}, T) = -\sum_{ij} p_i p_{ij} \log p_{ij}.$$

This result can also be established by proving

$$H\left(\bigvee_{k=0}^{n-1} T^{-k} \mathscr{A}\right) = -(n-1) \sum_{ij} p_i p_{ij} \log p_{ij} - \sum_i p_i \log p_i \qquad (n \geq 1).$$

Of course, a Bernoulli shift is also a Markov shift, and in this case the computations (7.2) and (7.3) agree. Thus two Bernoulli shifts, or, more generally, two Markov shifts, are nonisomorphic if their entropies differ. In particular, the Bernoulli shift $(\frac{1}{2}, \frac{1}{2})$ and the Bernoulli shift $(\frac{1}{3}, \frac{1}{3}, \frac{1}{3})$, having respective entropies $\log 2$ and $\log 3$, are nonisomorphic.

To show that the shift in Example 3.3 has entropy $-(\frac{1}{2}) \sum_i p_i \log p_i$ presents no difficulty.

By the corollary to Theorem 7.1, (7.2) and (7.3) also hold for one-sided Bernoulli and Markov shifts.

It is interesting to note that if T is invertible and $\bigvee_{n=0}^{\infty} T^{-n} \mathscr{A} = \mathscr{F}$, then $h(T) = h(\mathscr{A}, T) = 0$. Intuitively, the past determines the future in such a case—or the future determines the past; it depends on which orientation is chosen—and hence the corresponding conditional entropies should vanish. The proof consists in converting this idea into mathematics. Indeed, it follows that $\mathscr{A} \subset \mathscr{F} = T^{-1}\mathscr{F} = \bigvee_{i=1}^{\infty} T^{-i} \mathscr{A}$, so that, by Theorem 6.1, the field $\bigcup_{n=1}^{\infty} \bigvee_{i=1}^{n} T^{-i} \mathscr{A}$ contains, for each ϵ, a finite subfield $\mathscr{B}$ with $H(\mathscr{A} \mid \mathscr{B}) < \epsilon$. But then $H(\mathscr{A} \mid \bigvee_{i=1}^{n} T^{-i} \mathscr{A}) \leq H(\mathscr{A} \mid \mathscr{B}) < \epsilon$ for large n, so that, by (B_1), $h(T) = h(\mathscr{A}, T) = 0$.

By means of this fact, we can show that an irrational rotation of the circle (Example 1.5) has entropy 0. Let $\mathscr{A}$ have as atoms the upper half-circle A and its complement A^c. If $T\omega = c\omega$, then the half-circle

$T^{-n}A$ starts at the point c^{-n}. If c is not a root of unity, then $\{c^{-1}, c^{-2}, \ldots\}$ is dense, and hence *any* half circle can be approximated by the $T^{-n}A$ and thus lies in $\bigvee_{n=0}^{\infty} T^{-n}\mathscr{A}$. It follows without difficulty that $\bigvee_{n=0}^{\infty} T^{-n}\mathscr{A}$ contains any arc, and hence coincides with $\mathscr{F}$.

The relation (B₄), along with (B₂), implies $h(T^k) = kh(T)$ for $k \geq 1$. If T is invertible then $h(T) = h(T^{-1})$, since

$$H\left(\bigvee_{k=0}^{n-1} T^{-k}\mathscr{A}\right) = H\left(\bigvee_{k=0}^{n-1} (T^{-1})^{-k}\mathscr{A}\right).$$

Thus we can compute the entropy of any meaningful power of T.

THEOREM 7.2 *For* $k \geq 1$, $h(T^k) = kh(T)$. *If* T *is invertible then* $h(T^k) = |k| \cdot h(T)$ *for any integer* k.

If T is a rotation $T\omega = c\omega$ of the circle, with c a root of unity, then $h(T) = 0$. For if c is a kth root of unity then $T^k = I$, so that $h(T) = k \cdot h(I) = 0$.

Some Extensions*

If $\mathscr{G}_1$ and $\mathscr{G}_2$ are σ-subfields of $\mathscr{F}$, let us write $\mathscr{G}_1 \stackrel{*}{=} \mathscr{G}_2$ to indicate that every set in $\mathscr{G}_1$ differs by a set of measure 0 from some set in $\mathscr{G}_2$, and vice versa. The following result contains Theorem 7.1, as well as others.

THEOREM 7.3 *Let* $\{\mathscr{G}_n\}$ *be a nondecreasing sequence of (finitely additive) fields. If*

$$\bigvee_{n=1}^{\infty} \bigvee_{i=0}^{\infty} T^{-i}\mathscr{G}_n \stackrel{*}{=} \mathscr{F},$$

or if T *is invertible and*

$$\bigvee_{n=1}^{\infty} \bigvee_{i=-\infty}^{\infty} T^i\mathscr{G}_n \stackrel{*}{=} \mathscr{F},$$

then

$$h(T) = \lim_{n \to \infty} \sup_{\mathscr{A} \subset \mathscr{G}_n} h(\mathscr{A}, T).$$

Proof. We give the proof for the case $\bigvee_{n=1}^{\infty}\bigvee_{i=0}^{\infty} T^{-i}\mathscr{G}_n \stackrel{*}{=} \mathscr{F}$. If $\mathscr{H}_n$ is the field generated by $\bigcup_{i=0}^{n} T^{-i}\mathscr{G}_n$, and $\mathscr{F}_0$ is the field $\bigcup_{n=1}^{\infty}\mathscr{H}_n$, then

---

* The results of the rest of this section will not be used in the sequel.

every set in $\mathscr{F}$ differs by a set of measure 0 from some set in the σ-field generated by $\mathscr{F}_0$, and it follows by Theorem 6.1 and (B_5) (just as in the central step in the proof of Theorem 7.1) that

$$(7.4) \qquad\qquad h(T) = \sup_{\mathscr{B} \subset \mathscr{F}_0} h(\mathscr{B}, T).$$

If $\mathscr{B} \subset \mathscr{F}_0$, then $\mathscr{B}$ is contained in $\mathscr{H}_n$ for some n, and hence* has atoms $B_1, \ldots, B_k$ of the form

$$B_u = \bigcup_{v=1}^{l} \bigcap_{i=0}^{n} T^{-i} G_{iuv}, \qquad u = 1, \ldots, k,$$

with $G_{iuv} \in \mathscr{G}_n$. If $\mathscr{A}$ is the field generated by the G_{iuv}, then $\mathscr{A}$ is finite, $\mathscr{A} \subset \mathscr{G}_n$, and $\mathscr{B} \subset \bigvee_{i=0}^{\infty} T^{-i} \mathscr{A}$. Therefore, by (B_2) and (B_3),

$$h(\mathscr{B}, T) \le h\left(\bigvee_{i=0}^{n} T^{-i} \mathscr{A}, T \right) = h(\mathscr{A}, T) \le \sup_{\mathscr{A} \subset \mathscr{G}_n} h(\mathscr{A}, T).$$

Since the right-most member of this inequality is nondecreasing in n, the theorem follows via (7.4). The invertible case goes through in like manner.

If the $\mathscr{G}_n$ are σ-fields and if $T^{-1}\mathscr{G}_n \subset \mathscr{G}_n$, then T can also be viewed as a measure-preserving transformation T_n on the space $(\Omega, \mathscr{G}_n, P)$. If this is so, it follows from Theorem 7.3 that if $\{\mathscr{G}_n\}$ is nondecreasing and $\bigvee_{n=1}^{\infty} \mathscr{G}_n \overset{*}{=} \mathscr{F}$, then $h(T) = \lim_n h(T_n)$.

Taking $\mathscr{G}_n$ to be $\mathscr{A}$, we see that Theorem 7.3 contains Theorem 7.1 and its corollary.

COROLLARY 1   *If $\{\mathscr{A}_n\}$ is a nondecreasing sequence of finite fields with $\bigvee_{n=1}^{\infty} \mathscr{A}_n \overset{*}{=} \mathscr{F}$, then*

$$h(T) = \lim_{n \to \infty} h(\mathscr{A}_n, T).$$

COROLLARY 2   *If $\mathscr{B} \subset \bigvee_{i=0}^{\infty} T^{-i} \mathscr{A}$, or if T is invertible and $\mathscr{B} \subset \bigvee_{i=-\infty}^{\infty} T^i \mathscr{A}$, then $h(\mathscr{B}, T) \le h(\mathscr{A}, T)$.*

To prove this corollary, consider T as a transformation on $(\Omega, \mathscr{F}_0, P_0)$, where $\mathscr{F}_0$ is $\bigvee_{i=0}^{\infty} T^{-i} \mathscr{A}$ or $\bigvee_{i=-\infty}^{\infty} T^i \mathscr{A}$, as appropriate, and P_0 is the restriction of P to $\mathscr{F}_0$.

---

* If $\mathscr{M}$ and $\mathscr{N}$ are fields, then the field generated by $\mathscr{M} \cup \mathscr{N}$ consists of the finite unions of sets of the form $M \cap N$ with $M \in \mathscr{M}$ and $N \in \mathscr{N}$.

COROLLARY 3   *If $\mathscr{G}$ is a field, and if either $\bigvee_{i=0}^{\infty} T^i \mathscr{G} \overset{*}{=} \mathscr{F}$ or T is invertible and $\bigvee_{i=-\infty}^{\infty} T^i \mathscr{G} \overset{*}{=} \mathscr{F}$, then*

$$h(T) = \sup_{\mathscr{A} \subset \mathscr{G}} h(\mathscr{A}, T).$$

COROLLARY 4   *If $\mathscr{F}_0$ is a field which generates $\mathscr{F}$, then*

$$h(T) = \sup_{\mathscr{A} \subset \mathscr{F}_0} h(\mathscr{A}, T).$$

The last corollary enables us to compute the entropy of direct products. If, for $i = 1, 2$, T_i is a measure-preserving transformation on the space $(\Omega_i, \mathscr{F}_i, P_i)$, the direct product $T_1 \times T_2$ is the measure-preserving transformation, on the product of these two measure spaces, defined by $(T_1 \times T_2)(\omega_1, \omega_2) = (T_1\omega_1, T_2\omega_2)$.

THEOREM 7.4   *The direct product satisfies*

$$h(T_1 \times T_2) = h(T_1) + h(T_2).$$

Proof. If $\mathscr{A}_i$ is a finite subfield of $\mathscr{F}_i$ $(i = 1, 2)$ then, writing $2_i = \{0, \Omega_i\}$, we have

$$\bigvee_{i=0}^{n-1}(T_1 \times T_2)^{-i}(\mathscr{A}_1 \times \mathscr{A}_2) = \bigvee_{i=0}^{n-1}(T_1^{-i}\mathscr{A}_1 \times 2_2) \vee \bigvee_{i=0}^{n-1}(2_1 \times T_2^{-1}\mathscr{A}_2).$$

(If $\mathscr{A}_1$ and $\mathscr{A}_2$ are σ-fields in Ω_1 and Ω_2, then $\mathscr{A}_1 \times \mathscr{A}_2$ is the σ-field in $\Omega_1 \times \Omega_2$ generated by the sets $A_1 \times A_2$ with A_1 and A_2 in $\mathscr{A}_1$ and $\mathscr{A}_2$, respectively; if $\mathscr{A}_1$ and $\mathscr{A}_2$ are finite, then so is $\mathscr{A}_1 \times \mathscr{A}_2$, and its atoms are the sets $A_1 \times A_2$ with A_1 and A_2 atoms of $\mathscr{A}_1$ and $\mathscr{A}_2$, respectively.) Since the two fields on the right in this equation are independent, in the sense that if M and N lie respectively in these fields then $P(M \cap N) = P(M)P(N)$, where $P = P_1 \times P_2$, it follows that

$$
\begin{aligned}
H\left(\bigvee_{i=0}^{n-1}(T_1 \times T_2)^{-i}(\mathscr{A}_1 \times \mathscr{A}_2)\right) \\
= H\left(\bigvee_{i=0}^{n-1}(T_1^{-i}\mathscr{A}_1 \times 2_2)\right) + H\left(\bigvee_{i=0}^{n-1}(2_1 \times T_2^{-i}\mathscr{A}_2)\right) \\
= H\left(\bigvee_{i=0}^{n-1}T_1^{-i}\mathscr{A}_1\right) + H\left(\bigvee_{i=0}^{n-1}T_2^{-i}\mathscr{A}_2\right).
\end{aligned}
$$

Dividing by n and passing to the limit, we obtain

$$h(\mathscr{A}_1 \times \mathscr{A}_2, T_1 \times T_2) = h(\mathscr{A}_1, T_1) + h(\mathscr{A}_2, T_2).$$

And now the theorem follows from Corollary 4, since the rectangles with bases in $\mathscr{F}_1$ and $\mathscr{F}_2$ generate $\mathscr{F}_1 \times \mathscr{F}_2$.

As a final calculation, let us find the entropy of Example 1.7 with P defined as product measure:

$$(7.5) \qquad P\{\omega: x_l(\omega) \in E_l,\, n \leq l \leq n + k\} = \prod_{l=n}^{n+k} \mu(E_l),$$

where μ is a measure on the Borel sets of the line. It follows from Corollary 3 that

$$h(T) = \sup \sum_{i=1}^{k} \eta(\mu(E_i)),$$

where the supremum extends over decompositions $E_1, \ldots, E_k$ of the line into Borel sets. If μ does not consist exclusively of point masses, then $h(T) = \infty$. If μ does consist of point masses, say $p_1, p_2, \ldots$, then

$$h(T) = -\sum_{j=1}^{\infty} p_j \log p_j.$$

If the series diverges, $h(T)$ is infinite.

Remarks. The layout of this and the preceding section draws on Halmos (1959) and Brown (1963), as well as on the papers of Kolmogorov and Sinai. For further information on the subject, see the excellent review paper by Rohlin (1960). The bibliography at the end of this book lists further papers.

8. THE COMPLETENESS PROBLEM*

Some Open Problems

As we observed in Section 5, if T_k is a cyclic permutation of k points of equal mass, then $h(T_k) = 0$, although the different T_k are not isomorphic. Moreover, any rotation of the circle also has entropy 0, although it is not isomorphic to any of the T_k. Thus entropy fails to be a complete invariant.

---

* The material of this section, which consists mostly of questions, enters only incidentally into what follows.

If T is a Markov shift, then, as we have seen,

$$h(T) = -\sum_{ij} p_i p_{ij} \log p_{ij}.$$

Consider the three transition matrices

$$\begin{bmatrix} \frac{1}{2} & \frac{1}{2} \\ \frac{1}{2} & \frac{1}{2} \end{bmatrix}, \quad \begin{bmatrix} 0 & 0 & \frac{1}{2} & \frac{1}{2} \\ 0 & 0 & \frac{1}{2} & \frac{1}{2} \\ \frac{1}{2} & \frac{1}{2} & 0 & 0 \\ \frac{1}{2} & \frac{1}{2} & 0 & 0 \end{bmatrix}, \quad \begin{bmatrix} \frac{1}{2} & \frac{1}{2} & 0 & 0 \\ \frac{1}{2} & \frac{1}{2} & 0 & 0 \\ 0 & 0 & \frac{1}{2} & \frac{1}{2} \\ 0 & 0 & \frac{1}{2} & \frac{1}{2} \end{bmatrix},$$

and the three corresponding stationary probability distributions

$$(\tfrac{1}{2}, \tfrac{1}{2}), \qquad (\tfrac{1}{4}, \tfrac{1}{4}, \tfrac{1}{4}, \tfrac{1}{4}), \qquad (\tfrac{1}{4}, \tfrac{1}{4}, \tfrac{1}{4}, \tfrac{1}{4});$$

let T_1, T_2, T_3 be the three resulting Markov shifts. Then T_1 is mixing, T_2 is ergodic but not mixing, and T_3 is not even ergodic; in particular, no two of them are isomorphic. Since each has entropy $\log 2$, entropy fails to be complete among the Markov shifts, or even among the ergodic Markov shifts.

The general question of the extent to which entropy is a complete invariant generates several specific unanswered questions.

Question 1. Is entropy complete among the Bernoulli shifts? Let T be the Bernoulli shift $(p_1, \ldots, p_r)$; let $\tilde{T}$ be the Bernoulli shift $(\tilde{p}_1, \ldots, \tilde{p}_{\tilde{r}})$. If T and $\tilde{T}$ are isomorphic, then

(8.1) $$-\sum_i p_i \log p_i = -\sum_i \tilde{p}_i \log \tilde{p}_i.$$

Does (8.1) imply that T and $\tilde{T}$ are isomorphic? The answer is unknown. If $(p_1, \ldots, p_r)$ is just a permutation of $(\tilde{p}_1, \ldots, \tilde{p}_{\tilde{r}})$ $(r = \tilde{r})$, then the answer is yes—trivially. Suppose, however, that the sets of probabilities are $(\tfrac{1}{4}, \tfrac{1}{4}, \tfrac{1}{4}, \tfrac{1}{4})$ and $(\tfrac{1}{2}, \tfrac{1}{8}, \tfrac{1}{8}, \tfrac{1}{8}, \tfrac{1}{8})$. Then (8.1) holds, but there is *a priori* no more reason to expect T and $\tilde{T}$ to be isomorphic than there is to expect the Bernoulli shift $(\tfrac{1}{2}, \tfrac{1}{2})$ to be isomorphic to the Bernoulli shift $(\tfrac{1}{3}, \tfrac{1}{3}, \tfrac{1}{3})$. Meshalkin, however, proved the striking fact that T and $\tilde{T}$ are isomorphic. This may incline one to think the answer to Question 1 is yes.

In this direction, Sinai proved the following remarkable theorem. To say that two measure-preserving transformations T and $\tilde{T}$ are isomorphic is to say (if we neglect details about sets of measure zero) that there exists a one-to-one mapping ϕ of Ω onto $\tilde{\Omega}$ that carries P onto $\tilde{P}$ and satisfies $\tilde{T}\phi = \phi T$. Suppose we require that $\phi(\Omega)$ be all of $\tilde{\Omega}$, and that ϕ carry P onto $\tilde{P}$ and satisfy $\tilde{T}\phi = \phi T$, but drop the requirement that it be one-to-one. If such a ϕ exists, we say that $\tilde{T}$ is a *factor transformation* of T. It is easy to show that $h(\tilde{T}) \leq h(T)$ in this case. If each of T and $\tilde{T}$ is a factor transformation of the other, in which case $h(T) = h(\tilde{T})$, we say they are *weakly isomorphic*. (It can be shown that weak isomorphism preserves not only entropy, but also the properties of being ergodic and mixing.) Sinai showed that two Bernoulli shifts with the same entropy are weakly isomorphic and, moreover, that the mappings $\phi: \Omega \to \tilde{\Omega}$ and $\psi: \tilde{\Omega} \to \Omega$ involved in the definition of weak isomorphism can be selected to depend only on the past. This means that the nth coordinate $(\phi\omega)_n[(\psi\tilde{\omega})_n]$ of $\phi\omega[\psi\tilde{\omega}]$ is a function only of the coordinates $\ldots, \omega_{n-1}, \omega_n[\ldots, \tilde{\omega}_{n-1}, \tilde{\omega}_n]$ of $\omega[\tilde{\omega}]$.

Although the converse is trivial, it is not known whether weak isomorphism implies ordinary isomorphism. To see the difficulty involved here, consider an example. Suppose $T = \tilde{T}$ is the two-sided Bernoulli shift $(\frac{1}{2}, \frac{1}{2})$, with state space $\{0, 1\}$. Then T and $\tilde{T}$ are weakly isomorphic via the mappings ϕ and ψ defined by

$$(\phi\omega)_n = \omega_{n-1} + \omega_n \ (\text{mod } 2)$$
$$(\psi\tilde{\omega})_n = \tilde{\omega}_{n-1} + \tilde{\omega}_n \ (\text{mod } 2).$$

Actually, of course, T and $\tilde{T}$, being identical, are isomorphic. But each of ϕ and ψ is two-to-one, and it is hard to see how they can be used to recover the identity, or any of the other invertible mappings that make T and $\tilde{T}$ isomorphic.

Question 2. Is entropy complete among the mixing Markov shifts? Again the answer is unknown.

Kolmogorov Shifts

Before stating our third question, we introduce a new concept. Let $\mathscr{A}$ be the time-0 field for the general shift with state space ρ (Example 1.2). If $\mathscr{F}_n = \bigvee_{k=n}^{\infty} T^{-k}\mathscr{A}$, then $\mathscr{F}_n$ is the σ-field generated by the sets

$\{x_k = i\}$ with $i \in \rho$ and $k \geq n$. The shift T is said to be a Kolmogorov shift if the sets in the σ-field $\mathscr{F}_\infty = \cap_{n=1}^\infty \mathscr{F}_n$ are all trivial in the sense of having measure either 0 or 1. The sets in $\mathscr{F}_\infty$ depend on the "infinitely distant future" (see the end of Section 4, where a similar class of sets is defined for the continued-fraction transformation).

There is a general concept of a Kolmogorov transformation, defined in an invariant fashion, which reduces to the above notion in the case of a shift.

We shall see in Section 11 that any Kolmogorov shift is mixing. It can be shown by example* that not all shifts with the mixing property are Kolmogorov shifts.

The zero-one law implies that any Bernoulli shift is a Kolmogorov shift. The following argument shows that, more generally, the shift corresponding to an irreducible, aperiodic Markov chain is a Kolmogorov shift. In fact, in this case $\lim_n p_{ij}^{(n)} = p_j$, so that, if $\epsilon_n = \max_{i,j \in \rho} |p_{ij}^{(n)} - p_j|$, then $\lim_n \epsilon_n = 0$. From the theory of Markov chains it follows that if A lies in the σ-field generated by the $\{x_k = i\}$ with $k \leq l$, and if B lies in the σ-field generated by the $\{x_k = i\}$ with $k \geq l + n$ (in $\mathscr{F}_{l+n}$, that is), then

$$(8.2) \qquad |P(A \cap B) - P(A)P(B)| \leq \epsilon_n.$$

If B lies in $\mathscr{F}_\infty$ then it lies in $\mathscr{F}_{l+n}$ for all n, so that

$$(8.3) \qquad P(A \cap B) = P(A)P(B)$$

for any cylinder A. But the collection of sets A for which (8.3) holds forms a σ-field and hence coincides with $\mathscr{F}$. Thus (8.3) holds with $A = B$; so $P(B)$ is 0 or 1.

Question 3. Is entropy complete among the Kolmogorov shifts? Once more the answer is unknown.

As a final question, consider the following isomorphism problem, which entropy alone cannot resolve. Let T and $\tilde{T}$ be two versions of Example 1.7, corresponding to products of two different measures μ and $\tilde{\mu}$ on the line (see (7.5)). If neither μ nor $\tilde{\mu}$ consists exclusively of point masses, then $h(T) = h(\tilde{T}) = \infty$. Under what conditions are T

---

* See Blum and Franck (1965).

and $\tilde{T}$ isomorphic in this case? If neither μ nor $\tilde{\mu}$ has a point mass at all, then it is well known that there exists a mapping of the line into itself that carries μ into $\tilde{\mu}$. This mapping can be extended coordinate-wise to provide an isomorphism between T and $\tilde{T}$. But what about the mixed case?

Remarks. See Meshalkin (1959) for the isomorphism of the Bernoulli shifts $(\frac{1}{4}, \frac{1}{4}, \frac{1}{4}, \frac{1}{4})$ and $(\frac{1}{2}, \frac{1}{8}, \frac{1}{8}, \frac{1}{8}, \frac{1}{8})$. See Sinai (1962a) for the notion of weak isomorphism. Kolmogorov (1958) introduced Kolmogorov transformations, calling them *quasi-regular*.

CHAPTER 3

Conditional Probability and Expectation*

9. CONDITIONAL PROBABILITY

The Finite Case

The concept of conditional probability with respect to a σ-field under-lies much of modern probability theory. Consider, first, the notion of the conditional probability of a set M with respect to another set A. It is defined by $P(M \mid A) = P(M \cap A)/P(A)$ (unless $P(A)$ vanishes, in which case it is not defined at all).

If Tyche draws a point ω from Ω according to the probability measure P (on the σ-field $\mathscr{F}$), $P(M)$ is the chance that ω comes from M. If the point drawn happens to come from the set A, and if Tyche reports this fact (and this fact only) to the experimenter, then, as far as the experi-menter is concerned, $P(M \mid A)$ is the chance that ω lies also in M. We take this heuristic statement as our point of departure.

On the other hand, if the point Tyche draws happens to come from A^c, and the experimenter is told this, then his new probability for the

---

* The reader familiar with the notions of conditional probability and expectation with respect to a σ-field may skip this chapter, making backward references later on, if necessary. The reader unfamiliar with these ideas may skip it too, if he will take a few later theorems without proof, or else restrict their hypotheses by assuming that all shifts occurring are Markov shifts.

event $\omega \in M$ is $P(M \mid A^c)$. It is convenient to link these two conditional probabilities by means of the step function

$$
f(\omega) = \begin{cases} P(M \mid A) = \dfrac{P(M \cap A)}{P(A)} & \text{if } \omega \in A \\[2mm] P(M \mid A^c) = \dfrac{P(M \cap A^c)}{P(A^c)} & \text{if } \omega \in A^c. \end{cases}
$$

Tyche reports to the experimenter whether the point she drew came from A or whether it came from A^c; the experimenter's new probability for the event $\omega \in M$ is then just $f(\omega)$. While the experimenter does not know the argument ω of f, he knows enough from Tyche's report to compute its value $f(\omega)$. Note that the value $f(\omega)$ determines whether $\omega \in A$ or $\omega \in A^c$, unless $P(M \mid A) = P(M \mid A^c)$ (that is, unless M and A are independent), in which case the conditional probability of M coincides with the unconditional one anyway. Therefore, instead of reporting which of A and A^c contains ω, Tyche may just as well hand over the value $f(\omega)$.

The sets A and A^c form an $\mathscr{F}$-decomposition of Ω. The ideas just set out carry over to any $\mathscr{F}$-decomposition or, equivalently, to any finite subfield $\mathscr{A}$ of $\mathscr{F}$. If $A_1, \ldots, A_r$ are the atoms of $\mathscr{A}$, consider, for any M in $\mathscr{F}$, the step function

$$
f(\omega) = P(M \mid A_i) = \frac{P(M \cap A_i)}{P(A_i)} \quad \text{if } \omega \in A_i, \quad i = 1, \ldots, r.
$$

Tyche, having drawn a point ω from Ω according to P, tells the experimenter which atom of $\mathscr{A}$ contains it. The experimenter's new probability for M has the value $f(\omega)$. As before, the experimenter has sufficient knowledge—after Tyche's report—to compute $f(\omega)$, even though he is ignorant of ω itself. And again, for conditional probability purposes, knowing the value $f(\omega)$ is as good as knowing which of the A_i contains ω.

We write $P\{M \parallel \mathscr{A}\}$ for the function (or random variable) f and call it *the conditional probability of M given the finite field $\mathscr{A}$*. Although the argument ω is usually suppressed, whenever it needs to be exhibited, we shall write $P\{M \parallel \mathscr{A}\}_\omega$.

Thus $P\{M \parallel \mathscr{A}\}$ is the step function whose value on A_i is the old-fashioned conditional probability $P(M \mid A_i)$. This definition needs to be completed, since $P(M \mid A_i)$ is not defined if $P(A_i) = 0$. We could leave $P\{M \parallel \mathscr{A}\}$ undefined over such atoms of $\mathscr{A}$, or we could always assign some fixed value, say 0. We shall take a third course: if $P(A_i) = 0$, the value of $P\{M \parallel \mathscr{A}\}$ on A_i is any real number.* Thus, if $\mathscr{A}$ contains any atoms of measure 0, $P\{M \parallel \mathscr{A}\}$ stands for any one of a whole family of functions on Ω. To stress this, we sometimes call $P\{M \parallel \mathscr{A}\}$ a *version* of the conditional probability of M given $\mathscr{A}$. Note that any two versions are equal a.e.

Any version of the random variable $P\{M \parallel \mathscr{A}\}$ has two basic properties: (i) it is integrable and measurable with respect to $\mathscr{A}$† and (ii)

$$(9.1) \qquad \int_A P\{M \parallel \mathscr{A}\}\, dP = P(M \cap A)$$

holds for any set A in the finite field $\mathscr{A}$. And it is easy to show that any random variable having these two properties is a version of $P\{M \parallel \mathscr{A}\}$.

The General Case

Since $\mathscr{A}$ consists of the finite, disjoint unions of its atoms $A_1, \ldots, A_r$, to know which atom of $\mathscr{A}$ it is that contains ω is the same thing as to know which ones among the 2^r sets in $\mathscr{A}$ contain ω and which ones do not. This second way of looking at the matter carries over to the general σ-subfield of $\mathscr{F}$.

If $\mathscr{G}$ is such a σ-subfield, we can in principle imagine Tyche drawing an ω and then reporting to the experimenter which sets G in $\mathscr{G}$ contain ω and which do not.‡ We shall define a function $P\{M \parallel \mathscr{G}\}$ whose

---

* We do demand that the value be the same for all points of A_i, so that $P\{M \parallel \mathscr{A}\}$ is a step function with the atoms of $\mathscr{A}$ for its sets of constancy.

† We require that $P\{M \parallel \mathscr{A}\}$ be constant even over atoms of measure 0 in order to ensure this.

‡ Tyche effectively hands over not ω, but a vector with components indexed by the elements G of $\mathscr{G}$, the Gth component being $I_G(\omega)$.

value $P\{M \parallel \mathcal{G}\}_\omega$ at ω is what we intuitively feel should be the experimenter's new probability for the event $\omega \in M$ after receipt of Tyche's report.

For any M in $\mathcal{F}$, define $P\{M \parallel \mathcal{G}\}$ to be any integrable random variable that (i) is measurable with respect to the σ-subfield $\mathcal{G}$ and (ii) satisfies the functional equation

$$(9.2) \qquad \int_G P\{M \parallel \mathcal{G}\}\, dP = P(M \cap G), \qquad G \in \mathcal{G}.$$

If $\mathcal{G}$ is finite, this definition reduces to the previous one (see (9.1)).

Condition (i) corresponds to the requirement that the value of $P\{M \parallel \mathcal{G}\}$ be computable on the basis of Tyche's report alone. Condition (ii) has a gambling interpretation. Suppose that Tyche, after giving the experimenter her report, offers him the opportunity of betting on the event M (unless M lies in $\mathcal{G}$, he does not know whether it has occurred). She demands an entry fee and will pay 1 dr. if M has occurred and nothing otherwise. If $P\{M \parallel \mathcal{G}\}$ is to be the experimenter's conditional probability for M after he has Tyche's report, then $P\{M \parallel \mathcal{G}\}$ dr. is the fair entry fee. If the experimenter decides to bet and pays this fee, then he gains $1 - P\{M \parallel \mathcal{G}\}$ dr. in case M occurs, and he gains $-P\{M \parallel \mathcal{G}\}$ dr. otherwise, so that his gain is

$$(9.3) \quad (1 - P\{M \parallel \mathcal{G}\})I_M + (-P\{M \parallel \mathcal{G}\})I_{M^c} = I_M - P\{M \parallel \mathcal{G}\}.$$

If he declines to bet, his gain is automatically 0. Suppose he adopts the strategy of betting if G occurs, but not otherwise, where G is some set in $\mathcal{G}$. He can actually carry out this strategy, since, after Tyche's report, he knows whether or not G has occurred. His expected gain with this strategy is the integral of (9.3) over G:

$$(9.4) \qquad \int_G (I_M - P\{M \parallel \mathcal{G}\})\, dP.$$

But (9.2) is exactly the requirement that (9.4) vanish for each G in $\mathcal{G}$. If $P\{M \parallel \mathcal{G}\}$ is to fulfill our heuristic requirements, then the just entry fee should not lead to strategies favorable or unfavorable to the experimenter.

We must, of course, prove the existence of random variables

$P\{M \parallel \mathscr{G}\}$ satisfying conditions (i) and (ii), which we do by applying the Radon-Nikodym theorem. Define a completely additive set function ϕ on the σ-field $\mathscr{G}$ by

$$\phi(G) = P(M \cap G), \qquad G \in \mathscr{G}.$$

Then ϕ is a finite measure on $\mathscr{G}$ and is clearly absolutely continuous with respect to P restricted to $\mathscr{G}$ ($P(G) = 0$ implies $\phi(G) = 0$ for $G \in \mathscr{G}$). By the Radon-Nikodym theorem, therefore, there exists an integrable function f which is measurable with respect to $\mathscr{G}$ and satisfies*

(9.5)
$$\int_G f \, dP = \phi(G). \qquad G \in \mathscr{G}.$$

We rewrite f as the function $P\{M \parallel \mathscr{G}\}$ and call it the conditional probability of M given $\mathscr{G}$; in this notation, (9.5) becomes (9.2). Thus a conditional probability function exists.

There may be more than one such random variable $P\{M \parallel \mathscr{G}\}$. We have seen that this may be so even if $\mathscr{G}$ is finite. As before, then, we speak of a *version* of the conditional probability. Any two such versions f and g are both integrable and measurable $\mathscr{G}$ and satisfy $\int_G f \, dP = \int_G g \, dP$ for all G in $\mathscr{G}$; it follows that $f = g$ a.e. To this extent, conditional probabilities are unique.†

Example 9.1. Suppose that $M \in \mathscr{G}$, which will always hold, for example, if $\mathscr{G}$ coincides with the whole σ-field $\mathscr{F}$. Then $P\{M \parallel \mathscr{G}\} = I_M$ a.e. Intuitively, if $M \in \mathscr{G}$, then to know which elements of $\mathscr{G}$ contain ω is, in particular, to know whether or not M has occurred.

---

* Here we apply the Radon-Nikodym theorem, not in the original measure space $(\Omega, \mathscr{F}, P)$, but in the space $(\Omega, \mathscr{G}, P)$. This ensures the measurability of f with respect to $\mathscr{G}$. Although $\int_G f \, dP$ is then an integral of f in the sense of $(\Omega, \mathscr{G}, P)$, there is no difficulty in showing that it coincides with the integral in the sense of $(\Omega, \mathscr{F}, P)$.
† Our definition differs slightly from that of Doob (1953). He allows as a version any function $P\{M \parallel \mathscr{G}\}$, measurable with respect to $\mathscr{F}$ and integrable, that satisfies the functional equation (9.2) and equals a.e. some function measurable with respect to $\mathscr{G}$. If $\mathscr{G}$ is finite, this amounts to relaxing the requirement that $P\{M \parallel \mathscr{G}\}$ be constant over atoms having measure 0.

Example 9.2.   If $\mathscr{G} = 2 = \{0, \Omega\}$, then $P\{M \parallel \mathscr{G}\}_\omega = P(M)$ for each ω. The experimenter learns, from Tyche's report, nothing he did not already know.

Example 9.3.   Let Ω be the plane R^2 and let $\mathscr{F}$ be the class of planar Borel sets. Any point ω in Ω is a pair $(x(\omega), y(\omega))$—x and y are the coordinate variables. Let the σ-subfield $\mathscr{G}$ consist of the vertical strips; that is, the elements of $\mathscr{G}$ are the Cartesian products $E \times R^1 = \{\omega : x(\omega) \in E\}$, with E a linear Borel set. If the experimenter knows for each vertical strip $E \times R^1$ whether it contains ω or not, then he knows this in particular for each strip $\{\xi\} \times R^1$, with ξ a real number—and conversely. Thus Tyche's report effectively gives the value of $x(\omega)$. Suppose now that P is a probability measure on $\mathscr{F}$ having a density $p(\xi, \eta)$ with respect to planar Lebesgue measure:

$$P(M) = \iint\limits_{M} p(\xi, \eta) \, d\xi \, d\eta.$$

We shall show that if $M = \{\omega : y(\omega) \in F\}$, where F is a linear Borel set, then a version of $P\{M \parallel \mathscr{G}\}$ is given by $\psi(x(\omega))$, where

(9.6)
$$\psi(\xi) = \frac{\displaystyle\int_F p(\xi, \eta) \, d\eta}{\displaystyle\int_{R_1} p(\xi, \eta) \, d\eta}.$$

Since $\psi(x(\omega))$ depends measurably on $x(\omega)$, it is measurable with respect to $\mathscr{G}$. The general element of $\mathscr{G}$ being $\{\omega : x(\omega) \in E\}$, we need therefore only show that

(9.7)
$$\int_{\{x \in E\}} \psi(x(\omega)) P(d\omega) = P\{x \in E, y \in F\}.$$

However, since the random variable x has a distribution on the line with density $p(\xi) = \int_{R^1} p(\xi, \eta) \, d\eta$, the left side of (9.7) is

$$\int_E p(\xi) \psi(\xi) \, d\xi = \int_E \left\{ \int_F p(\xi, \eta) \, d\eta \right\} d\xi$$

$$= \iint\limits_{E \times F} p(\xi, \eta) \, d\xi \, d\eta = P\{x \in E, y \in F\},$$

where the next-to-last equality follows by Fubini's theorem. Thus $\psi(x(\omega))$ is a version of $P\{M \parallel \mathcal{G}\}$.

The right-hand member of (9.6) is the classical formula (not in past times set in any logical framework) for the conditional probability of the event $\{y \in F\}$, given that $x = \xi$. The present discussion can be regarded either as a justification of the classical formula, or as an example supporting our mathematical definition of conditional probability.

If x is a random variable on any probability space $(\Omega, \mathcal{F}, P)$, the σ-field $\mathcal{G}$ generated by x (the smallest σ-field with respect to which x is measurable) consists of the sets $\{\omega: x(\omega) \in E\}$, with E ranging over the linear Borel sets. Since to know which sets of this form contain ω and which do not is to know the value of $x(\omega)$, we call $P\{M \parallel \mathcal{G}\}$ the conditional probability of M given x and rewrite it $P\{M \parallel x\}$. Example 9.3 is a special case. In the same way, we define the conditional probability $P\{M \parallel x_1, x_2, \ldots\}$ of M, given all the variables $x_1, x_2, \ldots$ of a finite or infinite sequence, as $P\{M \parallel \mathcal{G}\}$ with the σ-field generated by these variables for $\mathcal{G}$.

Example 9.4. Consider the Markov shift (Example 3.1). The measure P is determined by the relation

$$P\{x_n = i_n, \ldots, x_{n+l} = i_{n+l}\} = p_{i_n} p_{i_n i_{n+1}} \cdots p_{i_{n+l-1} i_{n+l}}.$$

(This relation is the important thing in the present example—the shift itself is irrelevant.) By the formula for conditional probability with respect to a finite field,

$$(9.8) \qquad P\{x_0 = i \parallel x_{-n}, \ldots, x_{-1}\}_\omega = p_{x_{-1}(\omega), i} \quad \text{a.e.}^*$$

To prove the intuitively obvious formula

$$(9.9) \qquad P\{x_0 = i \parallel \cdots x_{-2}, x_{-1}\}_\omega = p_{x_{-1}(\omega), i} \quad \text{a.e.}$$

---

* The random variables x_n are not numerical-valued, but take their values in the finite set ρ. Conditional probabilities for such variables are still defined in terms of the σ-fields they generate.

requires a further argument, however. It is an easy consequence of the following theorem.

THEOREM 9.1 *Let $\mathscr{G}_0$ be a (finitely additive) field generating the σ-field $\mathscr{G}$. An integrable function f is a version of $P\{M \parallel \mathscr{G}\}$ if it is measurable with respect to $\mathscr{G}$ and if*

$$(9.10) \qquad \int_G f\, dP = P(M \cap G)$$

holds for all G in $\mathscr{G}_0$.

Proof. Each member of (9.10) is, as a function of G, a measure on $\mathscr{G}$. Since they agree on $\mathscr{G}_0$, they must agree on $\mathscr{G}$.

Example 9.5. Let T be the dyadic transformation $T\omega = 2\omega$ (mod 1) on the unit interval with Lebesgue measure $(\Omega, \mathscr{F}, P)$ (see Example 1.6). In Section 1 we showed that if M is invariant and if F lies in the field $\mathscr{F}_0$ of finite, disjoint unions of dyadic intervals, then M and F are independent, so that $\int_F P(M)\, dP = P(M \cap F)$. Since $\mathscr{F}_0$ generates $\mathscr{F}$, Theorem 9.1 implies $P\{M \parallel \mathscr{F}\} = P(M)$. But (see Example 9.1), $P\{M \parallel \mathscr{F}\} = I_M$ a.e. Therefore $P(M)$ is either 0 or 1, and we have another proof that T is ergodic.

The following example shows that out interpretation of conditional probability in terms of Tyche breaks down in certain pathological cases.

Example 9.6. Let $(\Omega, \mathscr{F}, P)$ be the unit interval Ω with Lebesgue measure P on the σ-field $\mathscr{F}$ of Borel sets, and take $\mathscr{G}$ to be the σ-sub-field of sets that are either countable or have countable complements. Then the function identically equal to $P(M)$ is a version of $P\{M \parallel \mathscr{G}\}$:

$$(9.11) \qquad P\{M \parallel \mathscr{G}\}_\omega = P(M) \quad \text{a.e.}$$

But, since $\mathscr{G}$ contains all one-point sets, to know which elements of $\mathscr{G}$ contain ω, and which do not, is to know ω itself. On receipt of Tyche's report, then, the experimenter knows whether the event $\omega \in M$ occurred or not, and we should have

$$(9.12) \qquad P\{M \parallel \mathscr{G}\}_\omega = \begin{cases} 1 & \text{if} \quad \omega \in M \\ 0 & \text{if} \quad \omega \notin M. \end{cases}$$

The mathematical definition leads to (9.11); the heuristics lead to (9.12). Of course (9.11) is right and (9.12) is wrong.*

Despite the fact that our interpretation breaks down in certain cases, it provides a convenient way of looking at conditional probability and cannot, since it does not intervene in proofs, lead to any difficulties.

Properties of Conditional Probability

For any version of the conditional probability, $\int_G P\{M \parallel \mathcal{G}\} \, dP = P(M \cap G) \geq 0$ for $G \in \mathcal{G}$; since $P\{M \parallel \mathcal{G}\}$ is measurable $\mathcal{G}$, it follows that it is a.e. nonnegative. A similar argument shows that it is a.e. at most 1:

$(\mathrm{P_1})$ $$0 \leq P\{M \parallel \mathcal{G}\} \leq 1 \quad \text{a.e.}$$

If $P(M) = 1$, then $\int_G P\{M \parallel \mathcal{G}\} \, dP = P(G)$ for each $G \in \mathcal{G}$; hence

$(\mathrm{P_2})$ $$P\{M \parallel \mathcal{G}\} = 1 \quad \text{a.e.} \quad \text{if} \quad P(M) = 1.$$

Similarly,

$(\mathrm{P_2'})$ $$P\{M \parallel \mathcal{G}\} = 0 \quad \text{a.e.} \quad \text{if} \quad P(M) = 0.$$

Let us prove that

$(\mathrm{P_3})$ $P\{M_1 \cup M_2 \parallel \mathcal{G}\} =$

$$P\{M_1 \parallel \mathcal{G}\} + P\{M_2 \parallel \mathcal{G}\} \quad \text{a.e.} \quad \text{if} \quad M_1 \cap M_2 = 0.$$

We must show that the right-hand member of $(\mathrm{P_3})$ has the two properties required of a version of $P\{M_1 \cup M_2 \parallel \mathcal{G}\}$. Clearly it is measurable $\mathcal{G}$.

---

* In this particular case the difficulty can be avoided by admitting versions that are a.e. equal to some function that is measurable with respect to $\mathcal{G}$. More complicated examples (the same ones that demonstrate the occasional nonexistence of conditional probability measures—see the end of this section) show that this does not always help.

Since M_1 and M_2 are disjoint, if $G \in \mathcal{G}$ then

$$\int_G (P\{M_1 \parallel \mathcal{G}\} + P\{M_2 \parallel \mathcal{G}\})\, dP$$

$$= \int_G P\{M_1 \parallel \mathcal{G}\}\, dP + \int_G P\{M_2 \parallel \mathcal{G}\}\, dP$$

$$= P(M_1 \cap G) + P(M_2 \cap G)$$

$$= P((M_1 \cup M_2) \cap G),$$

so the functional equation is satisfied.

Similar arguments prove the following three results.

(P_3') $P\{M_1 - M_2 \parallel \mathcal{G}\} = P\{M_1 \parallel \mathcal{G}\} - P\{M_2 \parallel \mathcal{G}\}$ a.e.   if $M_2 \subset M_1$.

(P_3'') $P\{M^c \parallel \mathcal{G}\} = 1 - P\{M \parallel \mathcal{G}\}$ a.e.

(P_3''') $|P\{M_1 \parallel \mathcal{G}\} - P\{M_2 \parallel \mathcal{G}\}| \leq P\{M_1 + M_2 \parallel \mathcal{G}\}$ a.e.*

Suppose now that $\{M_n\}$ is a nonincreasing sequence of sets with intersection M, which we indicate by writing $M_n \downarrow M$. By (P_3') and (P_1), the sequence $P\{M_n \parallel \mathcal{G}\}_\omega$ is a.e. nonincreasing and hence has a limit $f(\omega)$ a.e. Now f is measurable $\mathcal{G}$ and, by (P_1) and the bounded convergence theorem,

$$\int_G f\, dP = \lim_{n \to \infty} \int_G P\{M_n \parallel \mathcal{G}\}\, dP = \lim_{n \to \infty} P(M_n \cap G) = P(M \cap G)$$

for any $G \in \mathcal{G}$. Therefore f is a version of $P\{M \parallel \mathcal{G}\}$:

(P_4) $P\{M_n \parallel \mathcal{G}\} \downarrow P\{M \parallel \mathcal{G}\}$ a.e.   if $M_n \downarrow M$.

Similarly,

(P_4') $P\{M_n \parallel \mathcal{G}\} \uparrow P\{M \parallel \mathcal{G}\}$ a.e.   if $M_n \uparrow M$.

Finally, by (P_3) and (P_4'),

(P_5) $P\left\{\bigcup_n M_n \parallel \mathcal{G}\right\} = \sum_n P\{M_n \parallel \mathcal{G}\}$ a.e.   if $M_m \cap M_n = 0\ (m \neq n)$.

Example 9.7.   The relations (9.8) and (9.9) for Markov chains imply that

$$P\{x_0 = i \parallel \cdots, x_{-2}, x_{-1}\} = P\{x_0 = i \parallel x_{-1}\}   \text{a.e.}$$

---

* As usual, the $+$ stands for symmetric difference.

A similar argument shows that if M is any cylinder depending on non-negative coordinates, then

(9.13) $\qquad P\{M \parallel \cdots, x_{-2}, x_{-1}\} = P\{M \parallel x_{-1}\}$ a.e.

Let us use the properties just derived to show that, more generally, (9.13) holds if M is any set in the σ-field generated by $x_0, x_1, \ldots$. For any such M and any positive ϵ there exists a cylinder M_ϵ, depending on nonnegative coordinates only, such that $P(M + M_\epsilon) < \epsilon$. By (P_3'''),

$$\Delta = |P\{M \parallel x_{-1}\} - P\{M_\epsilon \parallel x_{-1}\}| \leq P\{M + M_\epsilon \parallel x_{-1}\} \quad \text{a.e.}$$

Since $P\{M + M_\epsilon \parallel x_{-1}\}$ has expected value $P(M + M_\epsilon) < \epsilon$,

$$P\{\Delta > \lambda\} \leq E\{\Delta\}/\lambda \leq \epsilon/\lambda.$$

Similarly, $|P\{M \parallel \ldots, x_{-2}, x_{-1}\} - P\{M_\epsilon \parallel \ldots, x_{-2}, x_{-1}\}|$ has probability at most ϵ/λ of exceeding λ. Therefore the two sides of (9.13) differ by more than 2λ with probability at most $2\epsilon/\lambda$. Letting $\epsilon \to 0$, and then $\lambda \to 0$, we get (9.13).

Functions vs. Measures

We have, throughout this section, taken a "global" point of view. We have attached to each fixed M in $\mathscr{F}$ a function (actually a family of functions) $P\{M \parallel \mathscr{G}\}$ defined over all of Ω. What happens if we change our point of view, fixing ω and letting M vary over $\mathscr{F}$? Will we have a probability measure on $\mathscr{F}$? If so, of course, the results $(P_1), \ldots, (P_5)$ just proved reduce to standard facts about measures.

Suppose $\mathscr{G}$ is a finite field with atoms $G_1, \ldots, G_r$. If $P(G_1) = 0$ and if $P(G_i) > 0$ for the other i, then one version of $P\{M \parallel \mathscr{G}\}$ is

$$P\{M \parallel \mathscr{G}\}_\omega = \begin{cases} P(M \cap G_i)/P(G_i) & \text{if } \omega \in G_i, i = 2, \ldots, r, \\ 0 & \text{if } \omega \in G_1. \end{cases}$$

With this choice of version for each M, $P\{M \parallel \mathscr{G}\}_\omega$ is, as a function of M, a probability measure on $\mathscr{F}$ if $\omega \in G_2 \cup \cdots \cup G_r$, but not if $\omega \in G_1$. We have chosen the "wrong" versions. If we take, say, the versions

$$P\{M \parallel \mathscr{G}\}_\omega = \begin{cases} P(M \cap G_i)/P(G_i) & \text{if } \omega \in G_i, i = 2, \ldots, r, \\ P(M) & \text{if } \omega \in G_1, \end{cases}$$

then $P\{M \parallel \mathcal{G}\}_\omega$ *is* a probability measure in M for each ω. Clearly versions like this exist whenever $\mathcal{G}$ is finite.

It might be thought that, for any σ-field $\mathcal{G}$, versions of the various $P\{M \parallel \mathcal{G}\}$ can be so chosen that $P\{M \parallel \mathcal{G}\}_\omega$ is a probability measure in M for each* ω in Ω. It can be shown by counterexample that this is not so.†

Suppose, though, that a point ω_0 has the property that $P(G) > 0$ for any G in $\mathcal{G}$ that contains ω_0. This will be true, for example, if the one-point set $\{\omega_0\}$ lies in $\mathcal{F}$ and has positive measure. Fix any versions of the $P\{M \parallel \mathcal{G}\}$ for all M in $\mathcal{F}$. For any M, the set $\{\omega: P\{M \parallel \mathcal{G}\}_\omega < 0\}$ lies in $\mathcal{G}$ and has measure 0, by (P_1), and hence cannot contain ω_0. Thus $P\{M \parallel \mathcal{G}\}_{\omega_0} \geq 0$. Similarly, $P\{\Omega \parallel \mathcal{G}\}_{\omega_0} = 1$, and, if the M_n are disjoint, $P\{\bigcup_n M_n \parallel \mathcal{G}\}_{\omega_0} = \Sigma_n P\{M_n \parallel \mathcal{G}\}_{\omega_0}$. Therefore $P\{M \parallel \mathcal{G}\}_{\omega_0}$ is a probability measure as M ranges over $\mathcal{F}$.

Thus conditional probabilities behave properly at points having positive probability. That they may misbehave at points of probability 0 causes no problem, because individual such points have no effect on the probabilities of sets. Of course, *sets* of points individually having measure 0 do have an effect—but here we return to the global point of view with which we started.

Remarks. Kolmogorov (1933) first introduced the general notion of conditional probability. The present account owes all to Doob (1953).

10. CONDITIONAL EXPECTATION

Definition

Suppose that x is an integrable random variable on $(\Omega, \mathcal{F}, P)$ and that $\mathcal{G}$ is a σ-subfield of $\mathcal{F}$. Define a set function ϕ on $\mathcal{G}$ by

$$\phi(G) = \int_G x \, dP \qquad G \in \mathcal{G}.$$

---

* If this can be done for almost all ω, then clearly it can also be done for all ω.
† See Doob (1953, p. 624).

Then ϕ is finite-valued (even bounded) and completely additive. Moreover, it is absolutely continuous with respect to P (restricted to $\mathscr{G}$). By the Radon–Nikodym theorem, there exists a function $E\{x \parallel \mathscr{G}\}$ that is integrable, measurable $\mathscr{G}$, and satisfies $\phi(G) = \int_G E\{x \parallel \mathscr{G}\}\, dP$ for all $G \in \mathscr{G}$. We denote by $E\{x \parallel \mathscr{G}\}_\omega$ the value of $E\{x \parallel \mathscr{G}\}$ at the point ω.

This function we call the conditional expectation (or expected value) of x with respect to $\mathscr{G}$. It is specified by the requirements that (i) $E\{x \parallel \mathscr{G}\}$ is integrable and measurable $\mathscr{G}$ and (ii) $E\{x \parallel \mathscr{G}\}$ satisfies the functional equation

$$(10.1) \qquad \int_G E\{x \parallel \mathscr{G}\}\, dP = \int_G x\, dP, \qquad G \in \mathscr{G}.$$

There are in general many such functions, which we call versions of the conditional expectation. Any two versions agree a.e.

If $\mathscr{G} = 2$, then the function identically equal to $E\{x\}$ is a version of $E\{x \parallel \mathscr{G}\}$. If $\mathscr{G} = \mathscr{F}$, then x itself is a version of $E\{x \parallel \mathscr{G}\}$. For any $\mathscr{G}$, the function identically equal to $E\{x\}$ satisfies condition (i) above (which becomes more stringent as $\mathscr{G}$ decreases), and x itself satisfies condition (ii) (which becomes more stringent as $\mathscr{G}$ increases). The two conditions work in opposite directions and between them delimit the class of versions of $E\{x \parallel \mathscr{G}\}$.

We interpret $E\{x \parallel \mathscr{G}\}_\omega$ as the experimenter's new expected value for the random variable x when Tyche reports to him which sets in $\mathscr{G}$ do and which do not contain the ω she has drawn. Conditions (i) and (ii) parallel the corresponding ones in the definition of conditional probability. According to the first, the experimenter can compute the value of $E\{x \parallel \mathscr{G}\}$ upon receipt of Tyche's report. If, after the report, she offers to pay him x dr. in return for an entry fee, the fair entry fee is $E\{x \parallel \mathscr{G}\}$ dr., if this is to satisfy the intuitive requirements of a conditional expected value. If the experimenter's strategy is to bet if G occurs but not otherwise (where $G \in \mathscr{G}$), then his expected gain is $\int_G (x - E\{x \parallel \mathscr{G}\})\, dP$. And (10.1) requires that such a strategy favor neither Tyche nor the experimenter.

If $\mathscr{G}$ is a finite field then $E\{x \parallel \mathscr{G}\}_\omega$ must be $\int_{G_i} x\, dP / P(G_i)$ for ω in an atom G_i of positive probability, while $E\{x \parallel \mathscr{G}\}$ may take any constant value over an atom of probability 0. This links our general definition to the classical concept of conditional expectation given a set G:

$$E\{x \mid G\} = \frac{1}{P(G)} \int_G x \, dP \quad (P(G) > 0).$$

Note that for a set $M \in \mathscr{F}$, the defining properties of $E\{I_M \parallel \mathscr{G}\}$ and $P\{M \parallel \mathscr{G}\}$ coincide. Thus we have

$$E\{I_M \parallel \mathscr{G}\} = P\{M \parallel \mathscr{G}\} \quad \text{a.e.,}$$

which generalizes the relation $E\{I_M\} = P(M)$.

Example 10.1. If $x = \Sigma_i a_i I_{A_i}$ is a simple function, then

$$E\{x \parallel \mathscr{G}\} = \sum_i a_i P\{A_i \parallel \mathscr{G}\} \quad \text{a.e.}$$

Example 10.2. Let us identify the limit function $\hat{f}$ in the ergodic theorem. If f is integrable, then, according to the ergodic theorem,

$$(10.2) \qquad \lim_{n \to \infty} \frac{1}{n} \sum_{k=0}^{n-1} f(T^k \omega) = \hat{f}(\omega) \quad \text{a.e.}$$

Now, for any set A, the product $I_A f$ has its own "hat function" $(I_A f)\hat{\ }$, to which its averages converge:

$$(10.3) \qquad \lim_{n \to \infty} \frac{1}{n} \sum_{k=0}^{n-1} I_A(T^k \omega) f(T^k \omega) = (I_A f)\hat{\ }(\omega) \quad \text{a.e.}$$

If A is invariant, so that $I_A(T^k \omega) = I_A(\omega)$ a.e., (10.2) and (10.3) imply that $I_A(\omega) \hat{f}(\omega) = (I_A f)\hat{\ }(\omega)$ a.e. Since $(I_A f)\hat{\ }$ and $I_A f$ have the same expected value, we have

$$\int I_A \hat{f} \, dP = \int (I_A f)\hat{\ } \, dP = \int I_A f \, dP,$$

or

$$(10.4) \qquad \int_A \hat{f} \, dP = \int_A f \, dP.$$

Clearly the class $\mathscr{I}$ of sets invariant under T forms a σ-subfield of $\mathscr{F}$, and $\hat{f}$, being invariant, is measurable $\mathscr{I}$. Since (10.4) holds for all $A \in \mathscr{I}$, $\hat{f}$ is a version of $E\{f \parallel \mathscr{I}\}$.

Example 10.3. It is easy to show, by a change-of-variable argument, that if $y(\omega) = x(T\omega)$, then

$$(10.5) \qquad E\{y \parallel T^{-1}\mathscr{G}\}_\omega = E\{x \parallel \mathscr{G}\}_{T\omega} \quad \text{a.e.}$$

In particular,

$$(10.6) \qquad P\{T^{-1}M \parallel T^{-1}\mathscr{G}\}_\omega = P\{M \parallel \mathscr{G}\}_{T\omega} \quad \text{a.e.}$$

Basic Properties

Most of the examples and results of the preceding section carry over immediately. Theorem 9.1 has an obvious analogue, for example. Moreover, the same methods used to prove (P_1), (P_2), and (P_3) suffice for proving the following three results. We assume throughout that the variables x, y, etc., are integrable.

(E_1) If $x = a$ a.e., where a is a constant, then $E\{x \parallel \mathscr{G}\} = a$ a.e.

(E_2) If $x \leq y$ a.e. then $E\{x \parallel \mathscr{G}\} \leq E\{y \parallel \mathscr{G}\}$ a.e.

(E_3) If a and b are constants then $E\{ax + by \parallel \mathscr{G}\} = aE\{x \parallel \mathscr{G}\} + bE\{y \parallel \mathscr{G}\}$ a.e.

These propositions have the obvious consequence that $x = y$ a.e. implies $E\{x \parallel \mathscr{G}\} = E\{y \parallel \mathscr{G}\}$ a.e.

Since $-|x| \leq x \leq |x|$, we have, by (E_2) and (E_3),

$$-E\{|x| \parallel \mathscr{G}\} \leq E\{x \parallel \mathscr{G}\} \leq E\{|x| \parallel \mathscr{G}\} \quad \text{a.e.,}$$

and hence

(E_4) $|E\{x \parallel \mathscr{G}\}| \leq E\{|x| \parallel \mathscr{G}\}$ a.e.

We shall need the following extension of Lebesgue's dominated convergence theorem.

(E_5) If $\lim x_n = x$ a.e. and $|x_n| \leq y$ a.e., where y is integrable, then $\lim_n E\{x_n \parallel \mathscr{G}\} = E\{x \parallel \mathscr{G}\}$ a.e.

To prove this, consider $z_n = \sup_{k \geq n} |x_k - x|$. Now $z_n \downarrow 0$ a.e., and, by (E_3) and (E_4), $|E\{x_n \parallel \mathscr{G}\} - E\{x \parallel \mathscr{G}\}| \leq E\{z_n \parallel \mathscr{G}\}$ a.e. It suffices, therefore, to show that $E\{z_n \parallel \mathscr{G}\} \downarrow 0$ a.e. By (E_2), the sequence $E\{z_n \parallel \mathscr{G}\}$ is a.e. nonincreasing and hence has a.e. a limit g. We must prove that $g = 0$ a.e., or, since g is nonnegative, that $E\{g\} = 0$. However, by the dominated convergence theorem applied to z_n ($|z_n| \leq 2y$),

$$E\{g\} \leq \int E\{z_n \parallel \mathscr{G}\} \, dP = \int z_n \, dP \to 0.$$

If x is measurable $\mathscr{G}$ then of course $E\{x \parallel \mathscr{G}\} = x$ a.e. The following generalization of this is used constantly.

THEOREM 10.1   *If x is measurable $\mathscr{G}$, and if y and xy are integrable, then*

(10.7) $$E\{xy \parallel \mathscr{G}\} = xE\{y \parallel \mathscr{G}\} \quad \text{a.e.}$$

Proof. Suppose first that $x = I_{G_0}$ with $G_0 \in \mathscr{G}$. We must show that $I_{G_0}E\{y \parallel \mathscr{G}\}$ is a version of $E\{I_{G_0}y \parallel \mathscr{G}\}$. Since $I_{G_0}E\{y \parallel \mathscr{G}\}$ is clearly measurable $\mathscr{G}$, we need only verify the functional equation

$$\int_G I_{G_0}E\{y \parallel \mathscr{G}\} \, dP = \int_G I_{G_0}y \, dP, \qquad G \in \mathscr{G}.$$

But this reduces to

$$\int_{G \cap G_0} E\{y \parallel \mathscr{G}\} \, dP = \int_{G \cap G_0} y \, dP,$$

which holds by the definition of $E\{y \parallel \mathscr{G}\}$. Thus (10.7) is true if x is the indicator of an element of $\mathscr{G}$. It follows by (E$_3$) that (10.7) holds if x is a step function measurable $\mathscr{G}$. Now for any x that is measurable $\mathscr{G}$, there exist step functions x_n, measurable $\mathscr{G}$, such that $|x_n| \leq |x|$ and $\lim_n x_n = x$. Since $|x_n y| \leq |xy|$ and $|xy|$ is integrable, (E$_5$) implies $\lim_n E\{x_n y \parallel \mathscr{G}\} = E\{xy \parallel \mathscr{G}\}$ a.e. But $E\{x_n y \parallel \mathscr{G}\} = x_n E\{y \parallel \mathscr{G}\}$ by the case already proved, and, of course, $\lim_n x_n E\{y \parallel \mathscr{G}\} = xE\{y \parallel \mathscr{G}\}$. Therefore $E\{xy \parallel \mathscr{G}\} = xE\{y \parallel \mathscr{G}\}$. Note that we have not assumed x integrable.

Iterated Conditional Expectations

Taking a conditional expected value can be thought of as an averaging operation, or a smoothing operation. In passing from x to $E\{x \parallel \mathscr{G}\}$, we make x "more nearly constant." This can be seen graphically on the unit interval with Lebesgue measure, if $\mathscr{G}$ is finite and has sub-intervals for its atoms. We are led to expect, therefore, that averaging x with respect to a σ-field $\mathscr{G}_2$, and then averaging the result with respect to a coarser (smaller) σ-field $\mathscr{G}_1$, should lead to the same result as averaging with respect to $\mathscr{G}_1$ in the first place would.

THEOREM 10.2 *If x is integrable and the σ-fields $\mathscr{G}_1$ and $\mathscr{G}_2$ satisfy $\mathscr{G}_1 \subset \mathscr{G}_2$, then*

$$(10.8) \qquad E\{E\{x \parallel \mathscr{G}_2\} \parallel \mathscr{G}_1\} = E\{x \parallel \mathscr{G}_1\} \quad \text{a.e.}$$

Proof. We prove that $E\{E\{x \parallel \mathscr{G}_2\} \parallel \mathscr{G}_1\}$ is a version of $E\{x \parallel \mathscr{G}_1\}$. Of course $E\{E\{x \parallel \mathscr{G}_2\} \parallel \mathscr{G}_1\}$ is measurable $\mathscr{G}_1$. If $G \in \mathscr{G}_1$ then

$$\int_G E\{E\{x \parallel \mathscr{G}_2\} \parallel \mathscr{G}_1\} \, dP = \int_G E\{x \parallel \mathscr{G}_2\} \, dP;$$

but, since G also lies in $\mathscr{G}_2$, the right-hand member of this equation is $\int_G x \, dP$. Thus $E\{E\{x \parallel \mathscr{G}_2\} \parallel \mathscr{G}_1\}$ satisfies the functional equation for versions of $E\{x \parallel \mathscr{G}_1\}$.

As a second proof, we show that $E\{x \parallel \mathscr{G}_1\}$ is a version of $E\{E\{x \parallel \mathscr{G}_2\} \parallel \mathscr{G}_1\}$. Since $E\{x \parallel \mathscr{G}_1\}$ is measurable $\mathscr{G}_1$, we need only verify the functional equation

$$\int_G E\{x \parallel \mathscr{G}_1\} \, dP = \int_G E\{x \parallel \mathscr{G}_2\} \, dP \qquad G \in \mathscr{G}_1.$$

However, if $G \in \mathscr{G}_1$, then $G \in \mathscr{G}_2$ as well, and each member of the equation coincides with $\int_G x \, dP$.

If $\mathscr{G}_2 = \mathscr{F}$, then $E\{x \parallel \mathscr{G}_2\} = x$ a.e., so that (10.8) is trivial. If $\mathscr{G}_1 = 2$, then (10.8) becomes $E\{E\{x \parallel \mathscr{G}_2\}\} = E\{x\}$—a special case of (10.1).

If $\mathscr{G}_1 \subset \mathscr{G}_2$, then $E\{x \parallel \mathscr{G}_1\}$, being measurable $\mathscr{G}_1$, is also measurable $\mathscr{G}_2$; taking an expected value with respect to $\mathscr{G}_2$ does not alter it:

$$E\{E\{x \parallel \mathscr{G}_1\} \parallel \mathscr{G}_2\} = E\{x \parallel \mathscr{G}_1\} \quad \text{a.e.}$$

This complement to (10.8) is useless.

Jensen's Inequality

For ordinary integrals or expected values, Jensen's inequality states that if ϕ is real and convex,* then

$$(10.9) \qquad \phi(E\{x\}) \leq E\{\phi(x)\},$$

provided the expected values exist. The extension to conditional expected values is: if x and $\phi(x)$ are integrable, then

$$(10.10) \qquad \phi(E\{x \,\|\, \mathscr{G}\}) \leq E\{\phi(x) \,\|\, \mathscr{G}\} \quad \text{a.e.}$$

If $\mathscr{G} = 2$, (10.10) reduces to (10.9); if $\phi(t) = |t|$, it reduces to (E$_4$).

We shall prove (10.10) for the only case we need, namely that in which the random variable x takes its values in a finite closed interval $[a, b]$, and ϕ is defined over all of this interval. In this case ϕ is continuous and bounded. If $A_1, \ldots, A_r$ is an $\mathscr{F}$-decomposition of Ω, then $\Sigma P\{A_i \,\|\, \mathscr{G}\}_\omega = 1$ for almost all ω. For any such ω and any numbers $\alpha_1, \ldots, \alpha_r$ from $[a, b]$, we have

$$\phi(\textstyle\sum \alpha_i P\{A_i \,\|\, \mathscr{G}\}_\omega) \leq \sum_i \phi(\alpha_i) P\{A_i \,\|\, \mathscr{G}\}_\omega,$$

by the basic property of convex functions. Therefore (10.10) holds for simple random variables. But any x with values in $[a, b]$ is the limit of simple random variables x_n taking values in $[a, b]$. Since the sequences $\{x_n\}$ and $\{\phi(x_n)\}$ are both uniformly bounded, (10.10) follows by (E$_5$).

A Special Formula

We shall later need the fact that if $\mathscr{A}$ is a finite field with atoms $A_1, \ldots, A_r$, then

$$(10.11) \qquad P\{M \,\|\, \mathscr{A} \vee \mathscr{G}\} = \sum_{i=1}^{r} I_{A_i} \frac{P\{M \cap A_i \,\|\, \mathscr{G}\}}{P\{A_i \,\|\, \mathscr{G}\}} \quad \text{a.e.}$$

For almost any ω at which the denominator on the right vanishes, so does the numerator, and we take the ratio to be 0. If $\mathscr{G} = 2$, (10.11)

---

* See Chapter 1 of Zygmund (1959) for an elegant treatment of convexity.

reduces to the original formula for conditional probabilities with respect to a finite field $\mathscr{A}$.

We shall show that the sum on the right in (10.11) is a version of $P\{M \parallel \mathscr{A} \vee \mathscr{G}\}$. Since this sum is measurable $\mathscr{A} \vee \mathscr{G}$, we need only verify the functional equation. But $\mathscr{A} \vee \mathscr{G}$ consists of the finite, disjoint unions of sets $A_j \cap G$ with $G \in \mathscr{G}$; hence it suffices to check

$$(10.12) \qquad \int_{A_j \cap G} \sum_i I_{A_i} g_i \, dP = P(M \cap A_j \cap G),$$

where $g_i = P\{M \cap A_i \parallel \mathscr{G}\}/P\{A_i \parallel \mathscr{G}\}$. Since the A_i are disjoint and g_j is measurable $\mathscr{G}$, the left side of (10.12) is

$$\int_{A_j \cap G} I_{A_j} g_j \, dP = \int_G I_{A_j} g_j \, dP = \int_G E\{I_{A_j} g_j \parallel \mathscr{G}\} \, dP$$

$$= \int_G g_j P\{A_j \parallel \mathscr{G}\} \, dP = \int_G P\{M \cap A_j \parallel \mathscr{G}\} \, dP$$

$$= P(M \cap A_j \cap G).$$

Example 10.4. Let A be a set with $P(A) > 0$ and define a measure P_1 by

$$(10.13) \qquad P_1(B) = P(B \mid A), \qquad B \in \mathscr{F}.$$

We shall prove a formula related to (10.11):

$$(10.14) \qquad P_1\{M \parallel \mathscr{G}\} = \frac{P\{M \cap A \parallel \mathscr{G}\}}{P\{A \parallel \mathscr{G}\}} \quad \text{a.e. } P_1$$

(equality holds except on a set of P_1-measure 0). Note that, since P_1 is absolutely continuous with respect to P, each side of (10.14) is determined up to a set of P_1-measure 0. The right-hand member of (10.14) is measurable $\mathscr{G}$; we must show that it satisfies

$$\int_G \frac{P\{M \cap A \parallel \mathscr{G}\}}{P\{A \parallel \mathscr{G}\}} \, dP_1 = P_1(M \cap G), \qquad G \in \mathscr{G},$$

which is equivalent to

$$\int_{G \cap A} \frac{P\{M \cap A \parallel \mathscr{G}\}}{P\{A \parallel \mathscr{G}\}} \, dP = P(M \cap A \cap G), \qquad G \in \mathscr{G}.$$

But, if $G \in \mathcal{G}$, the left side of this equation is

$$\int_G I_A \frac{P\{M \cap A \parallel \mathcal{G}\}}{P\{A \parallel \mathcal{G}\}} \, dP = \int_G E\left\{I_A \frac{P\{M \cap A \parallel \mathcal{G}\}}{P\{A \parallel \mathcal{G}\}} \parallel \mathcal{G}\right\} dP$$

$$= \int_G \frac{P\{M \cap A \parallel \mathcal{G}\}}{P\{A \parallel \mathcal{G}\}} E\{I_A \parallel \mathcal{G}\} \, dP = \int_G P\{M \cap A \parallel \mathcal{G}\} \, dP$$

$$= P(M \cap A \cap G),$$

which proves (10.14). If A happens to lie in $\mathcal{G}$, then (10.14) becomes

(10.15) $$P_1\{M \parallel \mathcal{G}\} = P\{M \parallel \mathcal{G}\} \quad \text{a.e. } P_1.$$

Example 10.5. If T is a nonergodic shift, then it fails to respect some cylinder C. Since the limit function

(10.16) $$\lim_{n \to \infty} \frac{1}{n} \sum_{k=0}^{n-1} I_C(T^k \omega) = \hat{I}_C(\omega)$$

is then not constant a.e., there exists some a such that the invariant set $A_0 = \{\omega : \hat{I}_C(\omega) < a\}$ satisfies $0 < P(A) < 1$. Since C is a cylinder, A_0 lies in the σ-field generated by $x_n, x_{n+1}, \ldots$ for each n, as follows by (10.16). By reversing the time scale (consider T^{-1}), we see that there also exists a nontrivial invariant A that lies, for each n, in the σ-field generated by $\ldots, x_{n-1}, x_n$.

Define P_1 by (10.13); by (10.15) we then have

$$P_1\{M \parallel \ldots, x_{n-1}, x_n\} = P\{M \parallel \ldots, x_{n-1}, x_n\} \quad \text{a.e. } P_1$$

for each $n = 0, \pm 1, \ldots$, and for each M in $\mathcal{F}$. In particular,

(10.17)
$$P_1\{x_{n+1} = i \parallel \ldots, x_{n-1}, x_n\} = P\{x_{n+1} = i \parallel \ldots, x_{n-1}, x_n\} \quad \text{a.e. } P_1.$$

If T is not ergodic under P, therefore, there exists a probability measure P_1 on $\mathcal{F}$ that is distinct from P and absolutely continuous with respect to it, and has the same transition structure as P (in the sense of (10.17)).

Suppose now that T is a nonergodic Markov shift under P, with transition matrix Π and stationary distribution p. It follows by (10.17) that, under P_1, T is also a Markov shift with transition matrix Π. If P_1 is to differ from P, it must have a different stationary distribution.

Thus T is ergodic if there is only one stationary distribution for Π, a fact derived differently in Section 3.

Remarks. See Doob (1953) for further information about conditional expectation.

11. A CONVERGENCE THEOREM

We may ask whether $E\{x \parallel \mathscr{G}\}$ is in any sense continuous as $\mathscr{G}$ varies. Suppose that $\mathscr{G}_1 \subset \mathscr{G}_2 \subset \cdots$, and that $\mathscr{G} = \bigvee_{n=1}^{\infty} \mathscr{G}_n$, which we indicate by writing $\mathscr{G}_n \uparrow \mathscr{G}$. In this section, we prove that

$$\lim_{n \to \infty} E\{x \parallel \mathscr{G}_n\} = E\{x \parallel \mathscr{G}\} \quad \text{a.e.}$$

in this case.

The Theorem

We first prove a result which serves the same purpose as the maximal ergodic theorem does.

THEOREM 11.1 *Suppose that x is integrable and that $\mathscr{G}_1 \subset \mathscr{G}_2 \subset \cdots$. Then, for all positive λ,*

$$(11.1) \qquad P\left\{\sup_{n \geq 1} E\{|x| \parallel \mathscr{G}_n\} > \lambda\right\} \leq \frac{1}{\lambda} E\{|x|\}.$$

Proof. It is enough to show that for each n we have

$$(11.2) \qquad P\left\{\max_{1 \leq k \leq n} E\{|x| \parallel \mathscr{G}_k\} > \lambda\right\} \leq \frac{1}{\lambda} E\{|x|\}.$$

For $n = 1$, this is an inequality of the Chebyshev type, since $E\{|x| \parallel \mathscr{G}_1\}$ is a random variable with expected value $E\{|x|\}$.

To treat the general case, consider the ω-set M_k $(k \leq n)$ where $E\{|x| \parallel \mathscr{G}_i\} \leq \lambda$ for $i < k$ and $E\{|x| \parallel \mathscr{G}_k\} > \lambda$. Then $M_1, \ldots, M_n$ are disjoint sets whose union M is the set appearing in (11.2). If $i \leq k$, then $E\{|x| \parallel \mathscr{G}_i\}$, being measurable $\mathscr{G}_i$, is also measurable $\mathscr{G}_k$ (here we use the assumption $\mathscr{G}_1 \subset \mathscr{G}_2 \subset \cdots$). Since M_k is defined in terms of the $E\{|x| \,\|\, \mathscr{G}_i\}$ with $i \le k$, it lies in $\mathscr{G}_k$. Therefore,

$$\lambda P(M) = \sum_{k=1}^{n} \int_{M_k} \lambda \, dP \le \sum_{k=1}^{n} \int_{M_k} E\{|x| \,\|\, \mathscr{G}_k\} \, dP$$

$$= \sum_{k=1}^{n} \int_{M_k} |x| \, dP \le E\{|x|\}.$$

This proves the theorem.*

By a continuity argument for λ, one can replace the $>$ in (11.1) by $\ge$. And one can replace $E\{|x| \,\|\, \mathscr{G}_n\}$ by $|E\{x \,\|\, \mathscr{G}_n\}|$ or by $E\{x \,\|\, \mathscr{G}_n\}$, since $E\{x \,\|\, \mathscr{G}_n\} \le |E\{x \,\|\, \mathscr{G}_n\}| \le E\{|x| \,\|\, \mathscr{G}_n\}$.

THEOREM 11.2   *Suppose that* $\mathscr{G}_n \uparrow \mathscr{G}$. *Then for any integrable x, we have*

$$(11.3) \qquad \lim_{n \to \infty} E\{x \,\|\, \mathscr{G}_n\} = E\{x \,\|\, \mathscr{G}\} \quad \text{a.e.,}$$

and for any $M \in \mathscr{F}$, we have

$$(11.4) \qquad \lim_{n \to \infty} P\{M \,\|\, \mathscr{G}_n\} = P\{M \,\|\, \mathscr{G}\} \quad \text{a.e.}$$

Proof.   Of course (11.4) is a special case of (11.3). If (11.3) holds whenever x is integrable and measurable $\mathscr{G}$, then, even if x is not measurable $\mathscr{G}$, (11.3) holds with $E\{x \,\|\, \mathscr{G}\}$ in place of x:

$$(11.5) \qquad \lim_{n \to \infty} E\{E\{x \,\|\, \mathscr{G}\} \,\|\, \mathscr{G}_n\} = E\{E\{x \,\|\, \mathscr{G}\} \,\|\, \mathscr{G}\} \quad \text{a.e.}$$

But (11.5) reduces to (11.3) by Theorem 10.2. Hence we may assume that x is measurable $\mathscr{G}$, in which case (11.3) becomes

$$(11.6) \qquad \lim_{n \to \infty} E\{x \,\|\, \mathscr{G}_n\} = x \quad \text{a.e.†}$$

If x is measurable with respect to some $\mathscr{G}_k$, then $E\{x \,\|\, \mathscr{G}_n\} = x$ a.e. for $n \ge k$, and (11.6) follows immediately. We shall prove (11.6) for the general x measurable $\mathscr{G}$ by approximating to x by these random

---

* The inequality (11.1) and Kolmogorov's inequality for sums of independent random variables, which it resembles, are both special cases of a martingale inequality. See Doob (1953, p. 314).

† In what follows, we shall need only (11.4). Even so, the step just taken carries us from (11.4) to (11.6) with x measurable $\mathscr{G}$ and, in this case, bounded. In other words, it is no easier, using the techniques here, to prove (11.4) than to prove (11.3).

variables. Given ϵ, choose a random variable x_ϵ, measurable with respect to some $\mathcal{G}_k$, such that

$$E\{|x - x_\epsilon|\} < \epsilon.^*$$

Now

(11.7) $\quad |E\{x \,\|\, \mathcal{G}_m\} - E\{x \,\|\, \mathcal{G}_n\}|$

$$\leq |E\{x_\epsilon \,\|\, \mathcal{G}_m\} - E\{x_\epsilon \,\|\, \mathcal{G}_n\}| + 2 \sup_{k \geq 1} E\{|x - x_\epsilon| \,\|\, \mathcal{G}_k\}.$$

Since $E\{x_\epsilon \,\|\, \mathcal{G}_n\} \to x_\epsilon$ a.e., the first term on the right in (11.7) goes to 0 a.e. as $m, n \to \infty$. Therefore, by Theorem 11.1,

$$P\left\{ \limsup_{m,n \to \infty} |E\{x \,\|\, \mathcal{G}_m\} - E\{x \,\|\, \mathcal{G}_n\}| > \lambda \right\} \leq \frac{2}{\lambda} E\{|x - x_\epsilon|\} < \frac{2\epsilon}{\lambda}.$$

Letting $\epsilon \to 0$, we see that the probability on the left is 0. Thus the sequence $E\{x \,\|\, \mathcal{G}_n\}$ is a.e. fundamental.†

Therefore, the limit $y = \lim_n E\{x \,\|\, \mathcal{G}_n\}$ exists a.e. We must identify y with x. Assuming that y is integrable and that we may integrate the sequence $E\{x \,\|\, \mathcal{G}_n\}$ to the limit, we have

(11.8) $$\int_A y \, dP = \lim_{n \to \infty} \int_A E\{x \,\|\, \mathcal{G}_n\} \, dP.$$

If $A \in \mathcal{G}_k$, then $\int_A E\{x \,\|\, \mathcal{G}_n\} \, dP = \int_A x \, dP$ for $n \geq k$, so that

$$\int_A y \, dP = \int_A x \, dP.$$

But if this holds for all A in the field $\bigcup_k \mathcal{G}_k$, then it holds for all A in $\mathcal{G}$, so that, since x and y are measurable g, $y = x$ a.e.

Therefore we need only prove y integrable and justify (11.8).‡ Since

$$\int |y| \, dP \leq \liminf_{n \to \infty} \int |E\{x \,\|\, \mathcal{G}_n\}| \, dP$$

$$\leq \liminf_{n \to \infty} \int E\{|x| \,\|\, \mathcal{G}_n\} \, dP \leq E\{|x|\},$$

---

* This is possible because x can be approximated (in the mean) by a step function measurable $\mathcal{G}$, and each set involved in the step function can be approximated by a set in the field $\bigcup_n \mathcal{G}_n$.

† This argument parallels the first of the proofs of the ergodic theorem in Section 2.

‡ This is obvious if x is bounded; hence (11.4) follows already. The argument below parallels the last part of the second of our proofs of the ergodic theorem.

by Fatou's lemma, y is integrable. To establish (11.8), it suffices to prove

$$(11.9) \qquad \lim_{n \to \infty} \int |E\{x \parallel \mathscr{G}_n\} - y| \, dP = 0.$$

If $x_n = E\{x \parallel \mathscr{G}_n\}$, then

$$\int |x_n - y| \, dP \leq \int_{\{|x_n| \leq \lambda\}} |x_n - y| \, dP$$
$$+ \int_{\{|x_n| > \lambda\}} E\{|x| \parallel \mathscr{G}_n\} \, dP + \int_{\{|x_n| > \lambda\}} |y| \, dP.$$

Since $\{|x_n| > \lambda\}$ lies in $\mathscr{G}_n$, the middle term on the right is $\int_{\{|x_n| > \lambda\}} |x| \, dP$; writing $N_\lambda = \{\sup_n |x_n| > \lambda\}$, we have

$$\int |x_n - y| \, dP \leq \int_{\{|x_n| \leq \lambda\}} |x_n - y| \, dP + \int_{N_\lambda} (|x| + |y|) \, dP.$$

For fixed λ, the first term on the right goes to 0 as $n \to \infty$, by the dominated convergence theorem. Since $P(N_\lambda) \to 0$ as $\lambda \to \infty$, by Theorem 11.1, (11.9) follows.

Examples

Example 11.1. If $A \in \mathsf{V}_{n=1}^{\infty} \mathscr{A}_n$, where the $\mathscr{A}_n$ are finite fields with $\mathscr{A}_1 \subset \mathscr{A}_2 \subset \cdots$, then

$$(11.10) \qquad \text{p} \lim_{n \to \infty} P\{A \parallel \mathscr{A}_n\} = I_A$$

(convergence in probability). This much-weakened version of (11.4) has a direct proof involving entropy. If $\mathscr{A}$ is the finite field with atoms A and A^c, then, as the proof of Theorem 7.1 shows, $H(\mathscr{A} \mid \mathscr{A}_n) \to 0$. But $H(\mathscr{A} \mid \mathscr{A}_n)$ is the expected value of

$$\eta(P\{A \parallel \mathscr{A}_n\}) + \eta(P\{A^c \parallel \mathscr{A}_n\}),$$

which thus converges to 0 in probability. Since $\eta(t)$ vanishes only at 0 and 1, it follows that

$$P\{\epsilon \leq P\{A \parallel \mathscr{A}_n\} \leq 1 - \epsilon\} \to 0.$$

But

$$P(A \cap \{P\{A \parallel \mathscr{A}_n\} < \epsilon\}) = \int_{\{P\{A \parallel \mathscr{A}_n\} < \epsilon\}} P\{A \parallel \mathscr{A}_n\} \, dP \leq \epsilon.$$

From these two relations, it follows that

$$P(A \cap \{P\{A \| \mathscr{A}_n\} \leq 1 - \epsilon\}) < 2\epsilon$$

for large n. Similarly

$$P(A^c \cap \{P\{A^c \| \mathscr{A}_n\} \leq 1 - \epsilon\}) < 2\epsilon$$

for large n. Now (11.10) follows easily.

Example 11.2. Let P be Lebesgue measure on the class $\mathscr{F}$ of Borel sets in $\Omega = [0, 1)$, and take $\mathscr{G}_n$ to be the finite field having as atoms the dyadic intervals $[(k - 1)/2^n, k/2^n)$ of rank n. Then $\mathscr{G}_n \uparrow \mathscr{F}$, so that if $x(\omega)$ is Borel measurable and Lebesgue integrable, $E\{x \| \mathscr{G}_n\} \to x$ a.e. A version of $E\{x \| \mathscr{G}_n\}_\omega$ is $(\int_{u_n(\omega)} x(\omega') \, d\omega')/2^{-n}$, where $u_n(\omega)$ is the dyadic interval of rank n that contains ω. Thus

$$\frac{1}{2^{-n}} \int_{u_n(\omega)} x(\omega') \, d\omega' \to x(\omega)$$

for almost all ω. This is essentially the fundamental theorem of calculus.

Example 11.3. Let $\{x_n\}$ be the coordinate variables corresponding to a shift with state space ρ. If $\mathscr{G}_n$ is the σ-field generated by $x_{-n}, \ldots, x_{-1}$ and $\mathscr{G}$ is that generated by $\ldots, x_{-2}, x_{-1}$, then $\mathscr{G}_n \uparrow \mathscr{G}$, so that, by Theorem 11.2,

$$\lim_{n \to \infty} P\{x_0 = i \| x_{-n}, \ldots, x_{-1}\} = P\{x_0 = i \| \ldots, x_{-2}, x_{-1}\} \quad \text{a.e.}$$

If $\{x_n\}$ is a Markov chain, this is obvious by (9.8) and (9.9).

Example 11.4. Theorem 11.2 provides a new derivation of the ergodicity criterion for the Markov shift. We first show that if A is invariant then $P(A + M) = 0$ for some M that lies in all the σ-fields $\mathscr{F}_n$, where $\mathscr{F}_n$ is generated by $x_n, x_{n+1}, \ldots$. Indeed, A can be approximated (in the sense of small symmetric difference) by a cylinder E. But $T^{-m}E$ approximates $T^{-m}A = A$, and $T^{-m}E \in \mathscr{F}_n$ if m is taken large enough. Thus A can be approximated by elements of $\mathscr{F}_n$. It follows easily that $P(A + B_n) = 0$ for some set B_n in $\mathscr{F}_n$. Take M to be, say, $\lim \sup_n B_n$.

Since M lies in $\mathscr{F}_{n+1}$, it follows by an obvious generalization of (9.13) that

$$P\{M \parallel \ldots, x_{n-1}, x_n\} = P\{M \parallel x_n\} \quad \text{a.e.}$$

Since $P(A + M) = 0$, A and M have conditional probabilities which are a.e. equal, and hence

$$P\{A \parallel \cdots x_{n-1}, x_n\} = P\{A \parallel x_n\} \quad \text{a.e.}$$

Since the σ-fields $\mathscr{G}_n$ generated by the sequences $\ldots, x_{n-1}, x_n$ satisfy $\mathscr{G}_n \uparrow \mathscr{F}$, where $\mathscr{F}$ is the full σ-field generated by all the coordinate variables, Theorem 11.2 now implies

$$\lim_{n \to \infty} P\{A \parallel x_n\} = I_A \quad \text{a.e.}$$

Thus

(11.11) $$\lim_{n \to \infty} P\{|P\{A \parallel x_n\} - I_A| > \epsilon\} = 0.$$

By (10.6) and the fact that A is invariant,

$$P\{A \parallel x_{n+1}\}_\omega = P\{A \parallel x_n\}_{T\omega}.$$

And, again because A is invariant, $I_A(\omega) = I_A(T\omega)$. Therefore, if H_n is the set whose probability appears in (11.11), $T^{-1}H_n = H_{n+1}$. Since T preserves P, this probability is actually 0 for all n. Thus

$$P\{A \parallel x_0\} = I_A \quad \text{a.e.}$$

It follows that there exists a cylinder B, depending only on the coordinate x_0, such that $P(A + B) = 0$. Thus T is ergodic if and only if no such set B can satisfy $P(B + T^{-1}B) = 0$, unless $P(B)$ is 0 or 1. This immediately gives the criterion of Section 3: T is ergodic if and only if the transition matrix Π is irreducible (assuming all the stationary probabilities p_i are positive). The new derivation has the advantage that it goes through even if the state space ρ is not discrete.[*]

Decreasing σ-fields.[†]

If $\mathscr{G}_1 \subset \mathscr{G}_2 \subset \cdots$, and $x_n = E\{x \parallel \mathscr{G}_n\}$, then

$$E\{x_{n+1} \parallel x_1, \ldots, x_n\} = x_n \quad \text{a.e.}$$

---

[*] See Doob (1953, p. 460).
[†] The rest of this section may be omitted.

Any sequence of integrable random variables satisfying this relation is called a *martingale*. Doob has a famous theorem about the a.e. convergence of martingales which contains Theorem 11.2 as a special case.

Suppose now that $\mathcal{G}_1 \supset \mathcal{G}_2 \supset \cdots$ and $\mathcal{G} = \bigcap_{n=1}^{\infty} \mathcal{G}_n$, which we indicate by writing $\mathcal{G}_n \downarrow \mathcal{G}$. The following result is another corollary of Doob's general theorem.

If $\mathcal{G}_n \downarrow \mathcal{G}$, then

$$(11.12) \qquad \lim_{n \to \infty} E\{x \, \| \, \mathcal{G}_n\} = E\{x \, \| \, \mathcal{G}\} \quad \text{a.e.}$$

for any integrable x, and

$$(11.13) \qquad \lim_{n \to \infty} P\{M \, \| \, \mathcal{G}_n\} = P\{M \, \| \, \mathcal{G}\} \quad \text{a.e.}$$

We shall not prove this result, but shall illustrate it by using it to prove that any Kolmogorov shift is mixing.

Recall (see Section 8) that T is a Kolmogorov shift if each set in the σ-field $\mathcal{F}_{\infty} = \bigcap_{n=1}^{\infty} \mathcal{F}_n$ has measure either 0 or 1, where $\mathcal{F}_n$ is the σ-field generated by the coordinate variables $x_n, x_{n+1}, \ldots$. To prove T mixing, it is enough, by Theorem 1.2, to show that

$$(11.14) \qquad \lim_{n \to \infty} P(A \cap T^{-n}B) = P(A)P(B)$$

holds whenever B is a cylinder. There is no loss of generality in assuming that B depends only on nonnegative coordinates, in which case $T^{-n}B \in \mathcal{F}_n$ for all n. Since $\mathcal{F}_n \downarrow \mathcal{F}_{\infty}$, we have, by (11.13),

$$\lim_{n \to \infty} P\{A \, \| \, \mathcal{F}_n\} = P\{A \, \| \, \mathcal{F}_{\infty}\} \quad \text{a.e.}$$

Since every set in $\mathcal{F}_{\infty}$ has measure either 0 or 1, $P\{A \, \| \, \mathcal{F}_{\infty}\} = P(A)$ a.e., so that

$$\Delta_n = P\{A \, \| \, \mathcal{F}_n\} - P(A) \to 0 \quad \text{a.e.}$$

But, since $T^{-n}B \in \mathcal{F}_n$,

$$|P(A \cap T^{-n}B) - P(A)P(B)| = \left| \int_{T^{-n}B} \Delta_n \, dP \right| \leq E\{|\Delta_n|\}.$$

Since $|\Delta_n| \leq 2$, $E\{|\Delta_n|\} \to 0$, by the bounded convergence theorem, which proves (11.14).

At the end of Section 4, on the continued-fraction transformation, we showed that if $\mathscr{G}_n$ is the σ-field generated by $a_n(\omega), a_{n+1}(\omega), \ldots,$ then $\mathscr{G}_\infty = \cap_{n=1}^\infty \mathscr{G}_n$ contains only sets of measure 0 and 1. The argument just given clearly also proves the continued-fraction transformation to be mixing.

The proof in Section 4 that $\mathscr{G}_\infty$ is trivial depends only on the relation (4.15). This leads easily to the following criterion. Suppose that T is a shift with the special property that there exists a positive constant C such that

$$(11.15) \qquad \frac{1}{C} P(B) \le P(B \mid A) \le CP(B)$$

holds whenever A and B are cylinders

$$(11.16) \qquad \begin{aligned} A &= \{x_m = i_m, \ldots, x_n = i_n\} \\ B &= \{x_u = j_u, \ldots, x_v = j_v\} \end{aligned}$$

with $m \le n < u \le v$. Then T is a Kolmogorov shift, and hence mixing.

If T is a Markov shift corresponding to a transition matrix Π with positive entries, (11.15) certainly holds. If Π is irreducible and aperiodic, then there is some integer k such that Π^k has only positive entries. In this case (11.15) holds if $u - n \ge k$ in (11.16), and it is not hard to see that the proof still goes through. Thus we have another proof that a Markov shift with an irreducible, aperiodic transition matrix is a Kolmogorov shift and hence mixing.

Remarks. The relation (11.4) is due to Lévy (1937). See Doob (1953) for martingale theory.

CHAPTER 4

Convergence of Entropy

12. A GENERALIZATION OF CONDITIONAL ENTROPY*

Definition

If $\mathscr{A}$ is a finite subfield of $\mathscr{F}$, and if $\mathscr{G}$ is a σ-subfield of $\mathscr{F}$, put

$$(12.1) \qquad H(\mathscr{A} \mid \mathscr{G}) = E\left\{\sum_A \eta(P\{A \parallel \mathscr{G}\})\right\},$$

where the sum extends over the atoms of $\mathscr{A}$, and η is defined as usual by (5.11). In case $\mathscr{G}$ is finite, the quantity (12.1), which we call the conditional entropy of $\mathscr{A}$ given $\mathscr{G}$, reduces to the definition (6.1) used throughout Chapter 2.

Tyche draws an ω according to the distribution P and reports to the experimenter which elements of $\mathscr{G}$ contain ω and which do not. According to the heuristics of the preceding chapter, $P\{A \parallel \mathscr{G}\}$ is the experimenter's new probability for A, so that the entropy $\Sigma_A \eta(P\{A \parallel \mathscr{G}\})$ measures his remaining uncertainty about the outcome of $\mathscr{A}$. And $H(\mathscr{A} \mid \mathscr{G})$ is the mean of this remaining uncertainty. We can regard $\mathscr{G}$ as a complicated experiment. If the experimenter knows the outcome

---

* The reader may pass over this section if he will assume that certain shifts in the following sections are Markov shifts.

of $\mathcal{G}$, he is still to a degree uncertain about the outcome of $\mathcal{A}$ and will gain some information when he learns the outcome of $\mathcal{A}$. The uncertainty remaining and the additional information to be gained have $H(\mathcal{A} \mid \mathcal{G})$ as their common measure.

There is an alternative form for $H(\mathcal{A} \mid \mathcal{G})$:

$$(12.2) \qquad H(\mathcal{A} \mid \mathcal{G}) = E\left\{- \sum_A I_A \log P\{A \parallel \mathcal{G}\}\right\}.$$

In fact, the right-hand member of (12.2) is (recall that $E\{E\{x \parallel \mathcal{G}\}\} = E\{x\}$)

$$E\left\{E\left\{- \sum_A I_A \log P\{A \parallel \mathcal{G}\} \parallel \mathcal{G}\right\}\right\}$$

$$= E\left\{- \sum_A E\{I_A \parallel \mathcal{G}\} \log P\{A \parallel \mathcal{G}\}\right\} = H(\mathcal{A} \mid \mathcal{G}),$$

by Theorem 10.1.

Properties of $H(\mathcal{A} \mid \mathcal{G})$.

This extended notion of conditional entropy has the same properties as the earlier one.*

(C$_1$) $H(\mathcal{A} \vee \mathcal{B} \mid \mathcal{G}) = H(\mathcal{A} \mid \mathcal{G}) + H(\mathcal{B} \mid \mathcal{A} \vee \mathcal{G})$.

(C$_2$) $H(\mathcal{A} \mid \mathcal{G}) \leq H(\mathcal{B} \mid \mathcal{G})$ if $\mathcal{A} \subset \mathcal{B}$.

(C$_3$) $H(\mathcal{A} \mid \mathcal{G}_1) \leq H(\mathcal{A} \mid \mathcal{G}_2)$ if $\mathcal{G}_1 \supset \mathcal{G}_2$.

(C$_4$) $H(\mathcal{A} \vee \mathcal{B} \mid \mathcal{G}) \leq H(\mathcal{A} \mid \mathcal{G}) + H(\mathcal{B} \mid \mathcal{G})$.

(C$_5$) $H(T^{-1}\mathcal{A} \mid T^{-1}\mathcal{G}) = H(\mathcal{A} \mid \mathcal{G})$.

We prove properties (C$_1$), (C$_3$), and (C$_5$); the other two follow as before.

According to (10.11),

$$(12.3) \qquad P\{B \parallel \mathcal{A} \vee \mathcal{G}\} = \sum_A I_A \frac{P\{B \cap A \parallel \mathcal{G}\}}{P\{A \parallel \mathcal{G}\}} \qquad \text{a.e.,}$$

---

* These properties are therefore not listed separately on the endpaper at the back of the book nor on the page following the index.

where the summation extends over the atoms of $\mathscr{A}$. For any point ω, all but one of the summands in (12.3) vanish. Therefore,

$$(12.4) \qquad \log P\{B \parallel \mathscr{A} \vee \mathscr{G}\} = \sum_A I_A \log \frac{P\{A \cap B \parallel \mathscr{G}\}}{P\{A \parallel \mathscr{G}\}} \quad \text{a.e.}$$

But now

$$\sum_{A,B} I_{A \cap B} \log P\{A \cap B \parallel \mathscr{G}\}$$

$$= \sum_{A,B} I_A I_B \log P\{A \parallel \mathscr{G}\} + \sum_{A,B} I_A I_B \log \frac{P\{A \cap B \parallel \mathscr{G}\}}{P\{A \parallel \mathscr{G}\}}$$

$$= \sum_A I_A \log P\{A \parallel \mathscr{G}\} + \sum_B I_B \log P\{B \parallel \mathscr{A} \vee \mathscr{G}\}.$$

Taking expected values and applying (12.2), we get (C_1).

To prove (C_3), we use Jensen's inequality (10.10). Let $x = P\{A \parallel \mathscr{G}_1\}$; since η is concave, we have

$$E\{\eta(x) \parallel \mathscr{G}_2\} \leq \eta(E\{x \parallel \mathscr{G}_2\}) = \eta(P\{A \parallel \mathscr{G}_2\}),$$

the equality following from Theorem 10.2. Taking expected values on both sides, we obtain

$$E\{\eta(P\{A \parallel \mathscr{G}_1\})\} \leq E\{\eta(P\{A \parallel \mathscr{G}_2\})\};$$

summing over the atoms of $\mathscr{A}$, we have (C_3). The proof of (A_3) in Section 6 is a disguised form of this conditional probability argument.

It follows from (10.6) that

$$\eta(P\{T^{-1}A \parallel T^{-1}\mathscr{G}\}_\omega) = \eta(P\{A \parallel \mathscr{G}\}_{T\omega});$$

integration leads to

$$E\{\eta(P\{T^{-1}A \parallel T^{-1}\mathscr{G}\})\} = E\{\eta(P\{A \parallel \mathscr{G}\})\},$$

and summation over the atoms of $\mathscr{A}$ yields (C_5).

Consider σ-fields $\mathscr{G}_n$ and $\mathscr{G}$.

THEOREM 12.1 *If $\mathscr{G}_n \uparrow \mathscr{G}$, then $\lim_n H(\mathscr{A} \mid \mathscr{G}_n) = H(\mathscr{A} \mid \mathscr{G})$.*
Proof. By Theorem 11.2,

$$\lim_{n \to \infty} P\{A \parallel \mathscr{G}_n\} = P\{A \parallel \mathscr{G}\} \quad \text{a.e.}$$

Since $\eta(t)$ is continuous and bounded, the result follows from the definition (12.1) and the bounded convergence theorem.

We can use Theorem 12.1 to give a new proof of Theorem 7.1, the basic Kolmogorov-Sinai result. The central step of that proof consists in showing that if $\mathscr{A}_n$ are finite fields satisfying $\mathscr{A}_1 \subset \mathscr{A}_2 \subset \ldots$, and if $\mathscr{A} \subset \mathsf{V}_{n=1}^{\infty}\mathscr{A}_n$, then $\lim_n H(\mathscr{A} \mid \mathscr{A}_n) = 0$. But

$$\lim_{n \to \infty} H(\mathscr{A} \mid \mathscr{A}_n) = H\left(\mathscr{A} \,\middle|\, \bigvee_{n=1}^{\infty} \mathscr{A}_n\right) \leq H(\mathscr{A} \mid \mathscr{A}) = 0,$$

by Theorem 12.1 and property (C_3). Compare Example 11.1.

Theorem 12.1 and property (B_1) of Section 6 imply

$$(12.5) \qquad\qquad h(\mathscr{A}, T) = H\left(\mathscr{A} \,\middle|\, \bigvee_{i=1}^{\infty} T^{-i}\mathscr{A}\right).$$

Similarly, if T is invertible,

$$(12.6) \qquad\qquad h(\mathscr{A}, T) = H\left(\mathscr{A} \,\middle|\, \bigvee_{i=1}^{\infty} T^{i}\mathscr{A}\right).$$

In Section 6, we interpreted $h(\mathscr{A}, T)$ as the approximate amount of information in one performance of the experiment $\mathscr{A}$, given the results of a long, finite series of previous performances. *We may now interpret it as the exact amount in one performance given the entire past history.*

*Two Special Formulas** *

Write $\mathscr{A}^- = \mathsf{V}_{i=1}^{\infty} T^{-i}\mathscr{A}$ and $\mathscr{B}^- = \mathsf{V}_{i=1}^{\infty} T^{-i}\mathscr{B}$.

THEOREM 12.2　*Suppose T is invertible. If either $\mathscr{B} \subset \mathscr{A}$ or $\mathscr{A} \subset \mathscr{B}$, then*

$$(12.7) \qquad \lim_{n \to \infty} \frac{1}{n} H\left(\bigvee_{k=0}^{n-1} T^{k}\mathscr{A} \,\middle|\, \mathscr{B}^-\right) = H(\mathscr{A} \mid \mathscr{A}^-).$$

Proof.　Consider the first case, $\mathscr{B} \subset \mathscr{A}$. By (C_1) (extended inductively)

---

* The last two results of this section are used only in the proof of Theorem 17.3. It is perhaps best to return to them when they are needed.

and (C_5),

$$\frac{1}{n} H\left(\bigvee_{k=0}^{n-1} T^k \mathscr{A} \mid \mathscr{B}^-\right)$$

$$= \frac{1}{n} \sum_{k=0}^{n-1} H\left(T^k \mathscr{A} \mid \mathscr{B}^- \vee \bigvee_{i=0}^{k-1} T^i \mathscr{A}\right)$$

$$= \frac{1}{n} \sum_{k=0}^{n-1} H\left(\mathscr{A} \mid T^{-k}\left(\mathscr{B}^- \vee \bigvee_{i=0}^{k-1} T^i \mathscr{A}\right)\right)$$

$$= \frac{1}{n} \sum_{k=0}^{n-1} H(\mathscr{A} \mid T^{-1}\mathscr{A} \vee \cdots \vee T^{-k}\mathscr{A} \vee T^{-(k+1)}\mathscr{B} \vee T^{-(k+2)}\mathscr{B} \vee \cdots).$$

Theorem 12.1 implies, if $\mathscr{B} \subset \mathscr{A}$,

$$\lim_{k \to \infty} H(\mathscr{A} \mid T^{-1}\mathscr{A} \vee \cdots \vee T^{-k}\mathscr{A} \vee T^{-(k+1)}\mathscr{B} \vee \cdots) = H(\mathscr{A} \mid \mathscr{A}^-).$$

And now (12.7) follows by the thoerem on arithmetic means.

Consider now the second case, $\mathscr{A} \subset \mathscr{B}$. Since $\mathscr{A}^- \subset \mathscr{B}^-$, we have, by (C_3) and by the first case (with $\mathscr{A} = \mathscr{B}$),

$$(12.8) \quad \lim_{n \to \infty} \frac{1}{n} H\left(\bigvee_{k=0}^{n-1} T^k \mathscr{A} \mid \mathscr{B}^-\right)$$

$$\leq \lim_{n \to \infty} \frac{1}{n} H\left(\bigvee_{k=0}^{n-1} T^k \mathscr{A} \mid \mathscr{A}^-\right) = H(\mathscr{A} \mid \mathscr{A}^-).$$

On the other hand, using in turn (C_1), (C_3), and (C_1), each followed by an application of the first case, we have

$$\lim_{n \to \infty} \frac{1}{n} H\left(\bigvee_{k=0}^{n-1} T^k \mathscr{A} \mid \mathscr{B}^-\right)$$

$$= \lim_{n \to \infty} \left[\frac{1}{n} H\left(\bigvee_{k=0}^{n-1} T^k \mathscr{B} \mid \mathscr{B}^-\right) - \frac{1}{n} H\left(\bigvee_{k=0}^{n-1} T^k \mathscr{B} \mid \bigvee_{k=0}^{n-1} T^k \mathscr{A} \vee \mathscr{B}^-\right)\right]$$

$$\geq H(\mathscr{B} \mid \mathscr{B}^-) - \lim_{n \to \infty} \frac{1}{n} H\left(\bigvee_{k=0}^{n-1} T^k \mathscr{B} \mid \bigvee_{k=0}^{n-1} T^k \mathscr{A} \vee \mathscr{A}^-\right)$$

$$= \lim_{n \to \infty} \left[\frac{1}{n} H\left(\bigvee_{k=0}^{n-1} T^k \mathscr{B} \mid \mathscr{A}^-\right) - \frac{1}{n} H\left(\bigvee_{k=0}^{n-1} T^k \mathscr{B} \mid \bigvee_{k=0}^{n-1} T^k \mathscr{A} \vee \mathscr{A}^-\right)\right]$$

$$= \lim_{n \to \infty} \frac{1}{n} H\left(\bigvee_{k=0}^{n-1} T^k \mathscr{A} \mid \mathscr{A}^-\right) = H(\mathscr{A} \mid \mathscr{A}^-).$$

This, together with (12.8), yields (12.7).

THEOREM 12.3   *If T is invertible, then*

$$H(\mathscr{A} \vee \mathscr{B} \mid \mathscr{A}^- \vee \mathscr{B}^-) = H\left(\mathscr{A} \mid \mathscr{A}^- \vee \bigvee_{i=-\infty}^{\infty} T^i \mathscr{B}\right) + H(\mathscr{B} \mid \mathscr{B}^-).$$

Proof.   Theorem 12.1 implies

$$(12.9) \quad \lim_{n \to \infty} H\left(\mathscr{A} \mid \mathscr{A}^- \vee \mathscr{B}^- \vee \bigvee_{k=0}^{n-1} T^k \mathscr{B}\right) = H\left(\mathscr{A} \mid \mathscr{A}^- \vee \bigvee_{i=-\infty}^{\infty} T^i \mathscr{B}\right).$$

By (C_1) and (C_5),

$$H\left(\bigvee_{k=0}^{n-1} T^k \mathscr{A} \mid \mathscr{A}^- \vee \mathscr{B}^- \vee \bigvee_{i=0}^{n-1} T^i \mathscr{B}\right)$$

$$= \sum_{k=0}^{n-1} H\left(T^k \mathscr{A} \mid \mathscr{A}^- \vee \mathscr{B}^- \vee \bigvee_{i=0}^{n-1} T^i \mathscr{B} \vee \bigvee_{j=0}^{k-1} T^j \mathscr{A}\right)$$

$$= \sum_{k=0}^{n-1} H\left(\mathscr{A} \mid \mathscr{A}^- \vee \mathscr{B}^- \vee \bigvee_{i=0}^{n-k-1} T^i \mathscr{B}\right)$$

$$= \sum_{k=1}^{n} H\left(\mathscr{A} \mid \mathscr{A}^- \vee \mathscr{B}^- \vee \bigvee_{i=0}^{k-1} T^i \mathscr{B}\right).$$

By this, (12.9), and the theorem on arithmetic means,

$$\lim_{n \to \infty} \frac{1}{n} H\left(\bigvee_{k=0}^{n-1} T^k \mathscr{A} \mid \mathscr{A}^- \vee \mathscr{B}^- \vee \bigvee_{k=0}^{n-1} T^k \mathscr{B}\right) = H\left(\mathscr{A} \mid \mathscr{A}^- \vee \bigvee_{i=-\infty}^{\infty} T^i \mathscr{B}\right).$$

On the other hand, by (C_1) and by two applications of the preceding theorem (first with $\mathscr{A} \vee \mathscr{B}$ in the roles of both $\mathscr{A}$ and $\mathscr{B}$, and then with $\mathscr{B}$ in the role of $\mathscr{A}$ and $\mathscr{A} \vee \mathscr{B}$ in the role of $\mathscr{B}$),

$$\lim_{n \to \infty} \frac{1}{n} H\left(\bigvee_{k=0}^{n-1} T^k \mathscr{A} \mid \mathscr{A}^- \vee \mathscr{B}^- \vee \bigvee_{k=0}^{n-1} T^k \mathscr{B}\right)$$

$$= \lim_{n \to \infty} \left[\frac{1}{n} H\left(\bigvee_{k=0}^{n-1} T^k \mathscr{A} \vee \bigvee_{k=0}^{n-1} T^k \mathscr{B} \mid \mathscr{A}^- \vee \mathscr{B}^-\right)\right.$$

$$\left. - \frac{1}{n} H\left(\bigvee_{k=0}^{n-1} T^k \mathscr{B} \mid \mathscr{A}^- \vee \mathscr{B}^-\right)\right]$$

$$= H(\mathscr{A} \vee \mathscr{B} \mid \mathscr{A}^- \vee \mathscr{B}^-) - H(\mathscr{B} \mid \mathscr{B}^-).$$

Remarks.   Theorems 12.2 and 12.3 are due to Rohlin and Sinai (1962).

13. THE SHANNON-McMILLAN-BREIMAN THEOREM

If T is the general shift (Example 1.2) with state space ρ, and if $H(x_0, \ldots, x_{n-1})$ denotes the entropy of the finite field having as atoms the r^n (r is the size of ρ) sets $\{\omega : x_0(\omega) = i_0, \ldots, x_{n-1}(\omega) = i_{n-1}\}$, then, by the Kolmogorov-Sinai theorem,

$$(13.1) \qquad h(T) = \lim_{n \to \infty} \frac{1}{n} H(x_0, \ldots, x_{n-1}).$$

Recall that (13.1) is a theorem and not a definition.

For any sequence $(i_0, \ldots, i_{n-1})$ of elements of ρ, let $p(i_0, \ldots, i_{n-1}) = P\{x_0 = i_0, \ldots, x_{n-1} = i_{n-1}\}$. Then $p(x_0(\omega), \ldots, x_{n-1}(\omega))$ is the probability of the sequence $(x_0(\omega), \ldots, x_{n-1}(\omega))$ actually observed. Since $-\log p(x_0(\omega), \ldots, x_{n-1}(\omega))$ has expected value $H(x_0, \ldots, x_{n-1})$, (13.1) implies

$$(13.2) \qquad \lim_{n \to \infty} E\left\{ -\frac{1}{n} \log p(x_0(\omega), \ldots, x_{n-1}(\omega)) \right\} = h(T).$$

The Result

In the ergodic case, according to the following theorem, successively sharper versions of which were proved by Shannon, by McMillan, and by Breiman, the integrands in (13.2) actually converge to $h(T)$ almost everywhere. For large n the probability $p(x_0(\omega), \ldots, x_{n-1}(\omega))$ of the observed sequence is thus bound to be near $e^{-nh(T)}$.

THEOREM 13.1 *If T is an ergodic shift then*

$$(13.3) \qquad \lim_{n \to \infty} \left\{ -\frac{1}{n} \log p(x_0(\omega), \ldots, x_{n-1}(\omega)) \right\} = h(T) \quad \text{a.e.}$$

Proof. We first prove two instructive special cases. If T is the Bernoulli shift $(p_1, \ldots, p_r)$, then $p(i_0, \ldots, i_{n-1}) = p_{i_0} \cdots p_{i_{n-1}}$, so that

$$-\frac{1}{n} \log p(x_0(\omega), \ldots, x_{n-1}(\omega)) = -\frac{1}{n} \sum_{k=0}^{n-1} \log p_{x_k(\omega)}.$$

The ergodic theorem (which in this application reduces to the strong law of large numbers for independent Bernoulli trials) now implies that the left side of this equation converges a.e. to $E\{-\log p_{x_0(\omega)}\} = -\Sigma_i p_i \log p_i = h(T)$.

If T is an ergodic Markov shift generated by initial probabilities p_i and transition probabilities p_{ij}, then

$$-\frac{1}{n} \log p(x_0(\omega), \ldots, x_{n-1}(\omega))$$

$$= -\frac{1}{n} \log p_{x_0(\omega)} - \frac{1}{n} \sum_{k=1}^{n-1} \log p_{x_{k-1}(\omega), x_k(\omega)};$$

(13.3) follows in this special case by another application of the ergodic theorem.

The proof in the general case rests on a combination of the ergodic theorem and the convergence theorem (Theorem 11.2) for conditional probabilities. We shall use the functions

$$g_0(\omega) = -\log p(x_0(\omega))$$

$$g_k(\omega) = -\log \frac{p(x_{-k}(\omega), \ldots, x_{-1}(\omega), x_0(\omega))}{p(x_{-k}(\omega), \ldots, x_{-1}(\omega))}$$

$$f_k^{(i)}(\omega) = -\log \frac{p(x_{-k}(\omega), \ldots, x_{-1}(\omega), i)}{p(x_{-k}(\omega), \ldots, x_{-1}(\omega))}.$$

Note that $f_k^{(i)}(\omega)$ is the negative of the logarithm of

$$P\{x_0 = i \,\|\, x_{-k}, \ldots, x_{-1}\}_\omega.$$

Note also that these functions are all nonnegative.

Direct computation shows that

(13.4) $\qquad -\frac{1}{n} \log p(x_0(\omega), \ldots, x_{n-1}(\omega)) = \frac{1}{n} \sum_{k=0}^{n-1} g_k(T^k \omega).$

If $g_k(\omega)$ did not depend on k then the right number of (13.4) would be the kind of average to which the ergodic theorem applies, and (13.3) would follow. Although $g_k(\omega)$ does in general depend on k, we shall show, by using Theorem 11.2, that it converges to a function $g(\omega)$ as $k \to \infty$. The idea of the proof is then to show that the average in (13.4) is close to the corresponding average with $g_k(\omega)$ replaced by $g(\omega)$. (The Bernoulli case goes through easily just because, for all nonnegative

k, $g_k(\omega)$ is identical with this limit $g(\omega)$. The Markov case is easy for the reason that $g_k(\omega) = g(\omega)$ so long as k is strictly positive.)

By Theorem 11.2, $P\{x_0 = i \,\|\, x_{-k} \cdots x_{-1}\}$ converges a.e. to

$$P\{x_0 = i \,\|\, \cdots x_{-2}, x_{-1}\}.$$

The continuity of the logarithm function implies $f_k^{(i)}(\omega)$ converges a.e. (the limit may be $+\infty$); since $g_k(\omega)$ agrees with $f_k^{(i)}(\omega)$ on the cylinder $\{\omega \colon x_0(\omega) = i\}$, the limit

$$(13.5) \qquad\qquad g(\omega) = \lim_{k \to \infty} g_k(\omega)$$

exists a.e. The $g_k(\omega)$ being nonnegative, the same is true of $g(\omega)$, although, for all we know at this point, it may be $+\infty$ on a set of positive measure.

We next show that

$$(13.6) \qquad\qquad E\Big\{\sup_k g_k(\omega)\Big\} < \infty.$$

It will follow in particular that $g(\omega)$ is integrable and hence finite a.e. If

$$E_k = \Big\{\omega \colon \max_{1 \le j < k} g_j(\omega) \le \lambda < g_k(\omega)\Big\},$$

then

$$P(E_k) = \sum_i P(\{x_0 = i\} \cap E_k)$$

$$= \sum_i P(\{x_0 = i\} \cap F_k^{(i)}),$$

where

$$F_k^{(i)} = \Big\{\omega \colon \max_{1 \le j < k} f_j^{(i)}(\omega) \le \lambda < f_k^{(i)}(\omega)\Big\}.$$

Since $F_k^{(i)}$ is in the σ-field generated by $x_{-k}, \ldots, x_{-1}$,

$$P(\{x_0 = i\} \cap F_k^{(i)}) = \int_{F_k^{(i)}} P\{x_0 = i \,\|\, x_{-k} \cdots x_{-1}\} \, dP$$

$$= \int_{F_k^{(i)}} e^{-f_k^{(i)}(\omega)} P(d\omega) \le e^{-\lambda} P(F_k^{(i)}).$$

The $F_k^{(i)}$ being disjoint for different k,

$$\sum_k P(E_k) \le \sum_i e^{-\lambda} \sum_k P(F_k^{(i)}) \le r e^{-\lambda},$$

where r is the size of ρ. Hence

$$P\left\{\omega: \sup_k g_k(\omega) > \lambda\right\} \leq re^{-\lambda},$$

from which (13.6) follows. Thus g is integrable and we may integrate to the limit; by (13.4) and the change-of-variable formula,

$$E\{g\} = \lim_{k \to \infty} E\{g_k\} = \lim_{n \to \infty} E\left\{\frac{1}{n} \sum_{k=0}^{n-1} g_k(T^k\omega)\right\} = h(T).$$

Write

$$(13.7) \quad \frac{1}{n} \sum_{k=0}^{n-1} g_k(T^k\omega) = \frac{1}{n} \sum_{k=0}^{n-1} g(T^k\omega) + \frac{1}{n} \sum_{k=0}^{n-1} (g_k(T^k\omega) - g(T^k\omega)).$$

The ergodic theorem implies (recall that T is ergodic)

$$(13.8) \quad \lim_{n \to \infty} \frac{1}{n} \sum_{k=0}^{n-1} g(T^k\omega) = E\{g\} = h(T) \quad \text{a.e.}$$

If $G_N(\omega) = \sup_{k \geq N} |g_k(\omega) - g(\omega)|$, then, for any N,

$$\limsup_{n \to \infty} \left| \frac{1}{n} \sum_{k=0}^{n-1} (g_k(T^k\omega) - g(T^k\omega)) \right|$$

$$\leq \limsup_{n \to \infty} \frac{1}{n} \sum_{k=0}^{n-1} |g_k(T^k\omega) - g(T^k\omega)|$$

$$\leq \limsup_{n \to \infty} \frac{1}{n} \sum_{k=0}^{n-1} G_N(T^k\omega) = E\{G_N\} \quad \text{a.e.}$$

But the $G_N(\omega)$ converge to 0 a.e. and are dominated by the integrable function $g(\omega) + \sup_k g_k(\omega)$, so that $\lim_N E\{G_N\} = 0$. It follows that the second term on the right in (13.7) goes to 0 a.e., which, together with (13.8), implies in turn that

$$\lim_{n \to \infty} \frac{1}{n} \sum_{k=0}^{n-1} g_k(T^k\omega) = h(T) \quad \text{a.e.}$$

And now (13.3) follows via (13.4), which completes the proof of the theorem.

Other Versions of the Theorem

If T is not necessarily ergodic, then (13.8) must be replaced by

$$\lim_{n \to \infty} \frac{1}{n} \sum_{k=0}^{n-1} g(T^k \omega) = \hat{g}(\omega) \quad \text{a.e.,}$$

where $\hat{g}$ is an invariant function with $E\{\hat{g}\} = h(T)$. Similarly, the inequality following must be replaced by

$$\limsup_{n \to \infty} \left| \frac{1}{n} \sum_{k=0}^{n-1} g_k(T^k \omega) - g(T^k \omega)) \right| \le \hat{G}_N(\omega) \quad \text{a.e.,}$$

where now $G_N(\omega) = \sup_{k \ge n} |g_k(\omega) - \hat{g}(\omega)|$ and $E\{\hat{G}_N\} = E\{G_N\}$. The left member of this inequality exceeds λ with probability at most $E\{G_N\}/\lambda$; letting $N \to \infty$ and then $\lambda \to 0$, we see that it is actually 0 a.e. It follows that

$$\lim_{n \to \infty} \left\{ -\frac{1}{n} \log p(x_0(\omega), \ldots, x_{n-1}(\omega)) \right\} = \hat{g}(\omega) \quad \text{a.e.}$$

If T is ergodic, we recover (13.3).

Theorem 13.1, which makes perfectly good sense if T is a one-sided shift rather than a two-sided one, it also true for a one-sided shift. Given an ergodic one-sided shift T, construct the two-sided shift $\tilde{T}$ with the same finite-dimensional measures; since ergodicity depends only on the finite-dimensional measures, $\tilde{T}$ is also ergodic. The mapping that takes the doubly infinite sequence $(\ldots, \omega_{-1}, \omega_0, \omega_1, \ldots)$ to $(\omega_0, \omega_1, \ldots)$ carries the relation (13.3) for $\tilde{T}$ into the corresponding relation for T. Thus Theorem 13.1 holds for one-sided shifts as well.

From Theorem 13.1 for the one-sided shift, we can deduce a superficially more general result: Suppose that T is any ergodic measure-preserving transformation on a probability space $(\Omega, \mathscr{F}, P)$ and that $\mathscr{A}$ is a finite subfield of $\mathscr{F}$. If $p_n(\omega)$ is the probability of that atom of $\bigvee_{k=0}^{n-1} T^{-k} \mathscr{A}$ that contains ω, then

$$(13.9) \qquad \lim_{n \to \infty} \left\{ -\frac{1}{n} \log p_n(\omega) \right\} = h(\mathscr{A}, T) \quad \text{a.e.}$$

(If $\bigvee_{k=0}^{\infty} T^{-k} \mathscr{A} = \mathscr{F}$, then $h(\mathscr{A}, T)$ can be identified with $h(T)$.) For this, we need only transfer the problem to one-sided sequence space via the mapping $\omega \rightarrow (f(\omega), f(T\omega), \ldots)$, where f is some function assuming distinct values on the different atoms of $\mathscr{A}$. From (13.9) we can, by taking $\mathscr{A}$ to be the time-0 field for the shift, recover Theorem 13.1.

A similar result holds if $\mathscr{A}$ is replaced by a σ-field corresponding to a countable (rather than finite) $\mathscr{F}$-decomposition of Ω. If $p_n(\omega)$ is again the probability of that atom of $\bigvee_{k=0}^{n-1} T^{-k}\mathscr{A}$ that contains ω, and if $\bigvee_{k=0}^{\infty} T^{-k}\mathscr{A} = \mathscr{F}$, then

$$\lim_{n \to \infty} \left\{ -\frac{1}{n} \log p_n(\omega) \right\} = h(T) \quad \text{a.e.*}$$

It follows, for example, that the continued-fraction transformation has entropy $\pi^2/6 \log 2$ (see (4.22)).

The Shannon-McMillan-Breiman theorem is connected with the Lipschitz conditions satisfied by certain distribution functions on the unit interval. Take for T the transformation $T\omega = r\omega$ (mod 1) on $[0, 1)$ (Example 3.5) and let P be a measure preserved by T. Let $\mathscr{A}$ be the finite field with atoms $[i/r, (i + 1)/r)$, $i = 0, 1, \ldots, r - 1$. In this case, $p_n(\omega)$ is the P-measure of that dyadic interval $u_n(\omega)$ of rank n that contains ω. If T is ergodic under P, it follows from (13.9) and the fact that $\bigvee_{k=0}^{\infty} T^{-k}\mathscr{A}$ is the σ-field $\mathscr{F}$ of all Borel sets, that

$$(13.10) \qquad \lim_{n \to \infty} \frac{\log p_n(\omega)}{\log r^{-n}} = \frac{h(T)}{\log r},$$

except on a set of P-measure 0. If (13.10) holds at ω, then

$$(13.11) \qquad \lim_{n \to \infty} \frac{p_n(\omega)}{(r^{-n})^{\alpha}} = \begin{cases} \infty & \text{if } \alpha > h(T)/\log r. \\ 0 & \text{if } \alpha < h(T)/\log r. \end{cases}$$

If $F(x) = P[0, x)$, then $p_n(\omega)$ is the increase of the distribution function F over the interval $u_n(\omega)$. Since this interval has length r^{-n}, (13.11) means that F satisfies a Lipschitz condition of order exactly $h(T)/\log r$ at ω. Thus F satisfies a Lipschitz condition of exact order $h(T)/\log r$ on a set of P-measure 1. (Recall from Section 3 that F is singular, unless $F(x) \equiv x$, in which case $h(T)/\log r = 1$.) It seems to be difficult to find the Lipschitz condition of F on a set of Lebesgue measure 1.

---

* See Chung (1961) for a proof.

The Equipartition Property

Let T be the two-sided shift once more. For any integer b, the mapping $\omega \to (x_1(\omega), \ldots, x_b(\omega))$ induces a probability measure on the set ρ^b of b-tuples of elements of ρ, the probability of such a b-tuple $u = (i_1, \ldots, i_b)$ being

$$p(u) = P\{(x_1, \ldots, x_b) = u\} = P\{(x_{n+1}, \ldots, x_{n+b}) = u\}.$$

According to Theorem 13.2, for large b the set ρ^b decomposes into two subsets, one of which has low total probability and the other of which consists of b-tuples with probabilities near $e^{-bh(T)}$—a fact known as the asymptotic equipartition property.

THEOREM 13.2 *Let T be an ergodic shift with entropy h. Then for any $\epsilon > 0$ there exists a positive integer $b_0(\epsilon)$ such that if $b \geq b_0(\epsilon)$ then ρ^b decomposes into two sets H and L such that*

$$\sum_{u \in L} p(u) = P\{(x_1, \ldots, x_b) \in L\} < \epsilon,$$

and such that

$$e^{-b(h+\epsilon)} < p(u) = P\{(x_1, \ldots, x_b) = u\} < e^{-b(h-\epsilon)}$$

for any b-tuple u in H.

Proof. Replacing (13.3) by a limit in probability leads to

$$\operatorname*{p\,lim}_{b \to \infty} \left\{ -\frac{1}{b} \log p(x_1(\omega), \ldots, x_b(\omega)) \right\} = h.$$

Choose $b_0(\epsilon)$ so that

$$P\left\{ \omega : \left| -\frac{1}{b} \log p(x_1(\omega), \ldots, x_b(\omega)) - h \right| \geq \epsilon \right\} < \epsilon$$

if $b \geq b_0(\epsilon)$. Let H, the high probability group, consist of those b-tuples u for which

$$\left| -\frac{1}{b} \log p(u) - h \right| < \epsilon,$$

and let L, the low probability group, be the complement of H in ρ^b. Clearly H and L have the properties required of them.

Remarks. Shannon (1948), McMillan (1953), and Breiman (1957) wrote the original papers in this area. See Thomasian (1960) for an alternative proof of Theorem 13.2.

14. A CONNECTION WITH DIMENSION THEORY*

The Classical Definition

In 1919, Hausdorff introduced a notion of dimension which turns out to have a curious connection with entropy.

Let M be a set in a metric space, say a Euclidean space. The α-*dimensional outer measure* $l_\alpha(M)$ is defined for positive α in this way: A ρ-covering of M is a countable covering of M by closed spheres S_i of diameter less than ρ; let

(14.1) $$l_\alpha(M, \rho) = \inf \sum_i (\operatorname{diam} S_i)^\alpha,$$

where the infimum extends over all ρ-coverings of M. As ρ decreases, the infimum in (14.1) extends over smaller and smaller classes of coverings and hence $l_\alpha(M, \rho)$ increases—or at least does not decrease. Therefore the limit (finite or infinite)

$$l_\alpha(M) = \lim_{\rho \to 0} l_\alpha(M, \rho)$$

exists.

Clearly $l_\alpha(\cdot)$ is monotone: $l_\alpha(M) \leq l_\alpha(M')$ if $M \subset M'$. Given a sequence of sets M_n, choose ρ-coverings $\{S_{ni}\}$ with $\Sigma_i (\operatorname{diam} S_{ni})^\alpha < l_\alpha(M_n, \rho) + \epsilon/2^n \leq l_\alpha(M_n) + \epsilon/2^n$. All the spheres S_{ni} together form a ρ-covering of $\cup_n M_n$ with $\Sigma_{in} (\operatorname{diam} S_{ni})^\alpha < \Sigma_n l_\alpha(M_n) + \epsilon$. Hence $l_\alpha(\cdot)$ is subadditive: $l_\alpha(\cup_n M_n) \leq \Sigma_n l_\alpha(M_n)$. Thus $l_\alpha(M)$ is, as a function of M, an outer measure.

The *Hausdorff dimension* of a set M is defined by considering the behavior of $l_\alpha(M)$ not as a function of M, but as a function of α. We show that if $l_\alpha(M)$ is finite then $l_{\alpha'}(M) = 0$ for any $\alpha' > \alpha$. If $\{S_i\}$ is some ρ-covering of M for which

$$\sum (\operatorname{diam} S_i)^\alpha \leq l_\alpha(M, \rho) + 1 \leq l_\alpha(M) + 1 = K < \infty,$$

---

* This section may be omitted.

then $l_{\alpha'}(M, \rho) \leq \Sigma (\text{diam } S_i)^{\alpha'} \leq \rho^{\alpha'-\alpha} \Sigma (\text{diam } S_i)^{\alpha} < \rho^{\alpha'-\alpha} K$. Since $\alpha' > \alpha$, we see, letting $\rho \to 0$, that $l_{\alpha'}(M) = 0$. If $l_{\alpha}(M)$ is finite for a particular value of α, then, it is 0 for all larger values. Therefore, there exists a "change-over point," a point α_0 such that $l_{\alpha}(M) = \infty$ for $\alpha < \alpha_0$ and $l_{\alpha}(M) = 0$ for $\alpha > \alpha_0$.
The value of $l_{\alpha}(M)$ at α_0 itself may be 0, positive and finite, or ∞. (The extreme cases $\alpha_0 = 0$ ($l_{\alpha}(M) = 0$ for all $\alpha > 0$) and $\alpha_0 = \infty$ ($l_{\alpha}(M) = \infty$ for all $\alpha > 0$) can arise, although the second one is impossible in a

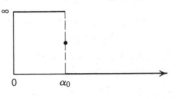

Euclidean space.) The uniquely defined number α_0 is the Hausdorff dimension of M; we denote it dim M.

We have

$$\text{dim } M = \sup \{\alpha : l_{\alpha}(M) = \infty\} = \inf \{\alpha : l_{\alpha}(M) = 0\}.$$

We constantly use four facts: $l_{\alpha}(M) > 0$ implies dim $M \geq \alpha$; dim $M > \alpha$ implies $l_{\alpha}(M) = \infty$; $l_{\alpha}(M) < \infty$ implies dim $M \leq \alpha$; and dim $M < \alpha$ implies $l_{\alpha}(M) = 0$.

We note two basic properties of Hausdorff dimension. First, it is obviously monotone:

(14.2) $\qquad \text{dim } M \leq \text{dim } M' \qquad \text{if} \qquad M \subset M'.$

Second,

(14.3) $\qquad \text{dim } \bigcup_n M_n = \sup_n \text{dim } M_n.$

For if dim $M_n < \alpha$ for all n then $l_{\alpha}(M_n) = 0$ so that, by the sub-additivity of $l_{\alpha}(\cdot)$, $l_{\alpha}(\bigcup_n M_n) = 0$ and hence dim $\bigcup_n M_n \leq \alpha$. Thus dim $\bigcup_n M_n \leq \sup_n \text{dim } M_n$. But the reverse inequality is obvious from (14.2).

As an indication that Hausdorff's definition makes sense, we shall show that the dimension of a reasonably smooth surface in 3-space is 2. Suppose, in fact, that M is defined by $z = f(x, y)$, with (x, y) ranging over the unit square in the plane. Without any further assumptions at all we can prove dim $M \geq 2$. For suppose M is covered by spheres S_i of diameter d_i. If p is the vertical projection on the (x, y)-plane, then the pS_i cover pM. Since pS_i is a disc of diameter d_i

(area $\pi d_i^2/4$) and pM is the unit square (area 1), $\Sigma \pi d_i^2/4 \geq 1$, or $\Sigma (\text{diam } S_i)^2 \geq 4/\pi$. Thus $l_2(M) > 0$, so that $\dim M \geq 2$.

We can prove the opposite inequality if we assume a Lipschitz condition $\omega_f(\delta) = O(\delta)$, where

$$\omega_f(\delta) = \sup \{|f(x, y) - f(x', y')| : |x - x'| \leq \delta, |y - y'| \leq \delta\}$$

is the modulus of continuity of f. This condition implies the continuity of f; on the other hand, if f is continuous and has bounded partial derivatives, for example, then the condition holds. We prove that $\dim M \leq 2$ by showing that $l_{2+\epsilon}(M) = 0$ for any $\epsilon > 0$. Choose $K > 1$ so that $\omega_f(\delta) < K\delta$. Now split the unit square into n^2 small squares of side $1/n$. Since the variation of f on one of these small squares is less than K/n, that part of the surface M lying over the small square can be enclosed in a cube of side K/n, which can in turn be enclosed in a sphere of diameter $\sqrt{3} K/n$. Thus M can be covered by n^2 spheres of diameter $\sqrt{3} K/n$; for this covering, $\Sigma (\text{diam } S_i)^{2+\epsilon} = (\sqrt{3} K)^{2+\epsilon}/n^\epsilon$. Choosing n so that $\sqrt{3} K/n < \rho$, we see that

$$l_{2+\epsilon}(M, \rho) \leq (\sqrt{3} K)^{2+\epsilon}/n^\epsilon$$

and, letting $n \to \infty$, that $l_{2+\epsilon}(M, \rho) = 0$. Thus $l_{2+\epsilon}(M) = 0$, so that $\dim M \leq 2$.

This sort of argument shows that reasonable sets get the dimensions they should. We do not pursue the matter further, since we shall be concerned with highly irregular sets whose dimensions are in fact not integers.

Dimension in the Unit Interval

From now on, M will be a subset of the unit interval. For such a set M it is not hard to see that $l_1(M)$ is the ordinary outer measure of M, so that $l_1(M) \leq 1$. Thus $\dim M$ must lie between 0 and 1. If M is a Borel set of positive Lebesgue measure then $l_1(M) > 0$, so that $\dim M = 1$. At the other end of the scale, every one-point set, and hence every countable set, has dimension 0.* In between lies the Cantor set, for

---

* Since the interval is a union of one-point sets, we see that (14.3) breaks down for uncountable unions.

example, which Hausdorff showed has dimension $\log 2/\log 3$. (We shall prove this result below.) Hausdorff dimension measures the magnitudes of subsets of the unit interval in such a way that two sets of measure 0 can be compared to see which is "larger."

Let $M(p)$ be the set of points of the unit interval that contain 1 in their dyadic expansions in the proportion p. That is, $\omega = .\omega_1\omega_2\cdots$ lies in $M(p)$ if and only if $\lim_n n^{-1} \sum_{k=1}^{n} \omega_k = p$. Since $M(\frac{1}{2})$ is the set of numbers that are normal in the base 2, its Lebesgue measure is 1. If $p \neq \frac{1}{2}$ then $M(p)$ consists of numbers which are nonnormal (in a particular way) and so has measure 0. Thus one asks for its dimension.* In 1949, Eggleston proved that

$$\dim M(p) = -\frac{1}{\log 2}[p \log p + (1-p) \log(1-p)],$$

a result closely related to that of Hausdorff on the Cantor set.

More generally, fix a base r and let $x_n(\omega)$ be the nth digit in the base–r expansion of ω; thus $\omega = \sum_{n=1}^{\infty} x_n(\omega)/r^n$. Let $N_i(\omega, n)$ be the number of occurrences of the digit i among $x_1(\omega), \ldots, x_n(\omega)$, and for a probability vector $(p_0, \ldots, p_{r-1})$, let $M(p_0, \ldots, p_{r-1})$ consist exactly of those ω for which $\lim_n N_i(\omega, n)/n = p_i$, $i = 0, 1, \ldots, r - 1$. Eggleston showed that

$$(14.4) \qquad \dim M(p_0, \ldots, p_{r-1}) = -\frac{1}{\log r} \sum_{i=0}^{r-1} p_i \log p_i.$$

We shall give a proof which shows why the dimension must involve entropy.

The Generalized Definition

In order to understand (14.4), we first give a different—equivalent— definition of Hausdorff dimension and then generalize it. In the unit interval, a sphere is an interval and its diameter is its length. Therefore (14.1) reduces to

$$l_\alpha(M, \rho) = \inf \sum_i |v_i|^\alpha,$$

---

* By (14.3) and the fact that the rationals have dimension 0, whether rational ω take the terminating or the nonterminating expansion has no effect on this dimension.

where the infimum extends over coverings of M by intervals v_i of length $|v_i| < \rho$. Now, an r-adic interval

$$v = \left[\frac{j}{r^n}, \frac{j+1}{r^n}\right), \quad n = 1, 2, \ldots, \quad j = 0, 1, \ldots, r^n - 1,$$

we shall call a cylinder, since it has the form

$$\{\omega : x_k(\omega) = i_k, k = 1, \ldots, n\}$$

for appropriate i's. (Here and in what follows, r is some fixed base.) If

$$(14.5) \qquad \lambda_\alpha(M, \rho) = \inf \sum_i |v_i|^\alpha,$$

where the infimum now extends only over coverings of M by *cylinders* of length less than ρ, then $\lambda_\alpha(M, \rho)$ differs from $l_\alpha(M, \rho)$, but not in any way that is significant for the computation of dimensions. Indeed, we shall show that

$$(14.6) \qquad l_\alpha(M, \rho) \leq \lambda_\alpha(M, \rho) \leq 2r l_\alpha(M, \rho),$$

from which it will follow that if $\lambda_\alpha(M) = \lim_{\rho \to \infty} \lambda_\alpha(M, \rho)$ then $\lambda_\alpha(M) = \infty$ for $\alpha < \dim M$ and $\lambda_\alpha(M) = 0$ for $\alpha > \dim M$, so that we can define $\dim M$ in terms of $\lambda_\alpha(M)$ just as well as in terms of $l_\alpha(M)$.

The left-hand inequality in (14.6) is obvious. We shall prove the right-hand one for the case $r = 2$ (the general proof is similar). It suffices to show that if u is any interval, then there exist four cylinders, each of length at most $|u|$, which cover u. Choose inside u a cylinder v_1 of maximal length $|v_1| = (\frac{1}{2})^n$—so that u contains no cylinder of length $(\frac{1}{2})^{n-1}$. If v_0 and v_2 are the cylinders of length $(\frac{1}{2})^n$ lying just to the left and just to the right of v_1, then one or the other of the intervals $v_0 \cup v_1$ and $v_1 \cup v_2$ is a cylinder of length $(\frac{1}{2})^{n-1}$; to be definite, assume the former. Since $v_0 \cup v_1$ cannot lie in u, v_0 extends beyond the left endpoint of u. If v_3 is the cylinder of length $(\frac{1}{2})^n$ next to v_2 on the right, then $v_2 \cup v_3$ is a cylinder of length $(\frac{1}{2})^{n-1}$ and hence cannot lie entirely within u. Thus v_3 extends beyond the right endpoint of u, and $v_0, \ldots, v_3$ cover u. And $|v_i| = (\frac{1}{2})^n \leq |u|$.

Thus we may redefine $\dim M$ as that α_0 such that $\lambda_\alpha(M) = \infty$ for $\alpha < \alpha_0$ and $\lambda_\alpha(M) = 0$ for $\alpha > \alpha_0$. This revised definition is useful for problems involving r-adic expansions, because it involves only coverings by r-adic intervals (or cylinders, as we are calling them here).*

Having recast the definition, we generalize it. If μ is a probability measure on the Borel sets of the unit interval, put

$$(14.7) \qquad \mu_\alpha(M, \rho) = \inf \sum_i \mu(v_i)^\alpha,$$

where the infimum extends over μ-ρ-coverings of M, a μ-ρ-covering being a covering by cylinders v_i with $\mu(v_i) < \rho$. In all that follows we assume, for simplicity, that μ is nonatomic, since otherwise there may be no μ-ρ-covering of M at all. If μ is Lebesgue measure, which we will denote by λ, (14.7) reduces to (14.5). As $\rho \to 0$, $\mu_\alpha(M, \rho)$ tends monotonically to a limit $\mu_\alpha(M)$. As before, we can show that $\mu_\alpha(M)$ is an outer measure as a function of M and that for fixed M there is an α_0 such that $\mu_\alpha(M) = \infty$ for $\alpha < \alpha_0$ and $\mu_\alpha(M) = 0$ for $\alpha > \alpha_0$. This α_0 we define to be the dimension of M with respect to μ, denoted $\dim_\mu M$.

Clearly $\dim_\lambda M$ coincides with our original $\dim M$ for any M in the unit interval. For any μ we have $0 \leq \dim_\mu M \leq 1$; moreover, $\dim_\lambda M = 0$ if M is countable, and $\dim_\mu M = 1$ if M is a Borel set with $\mu(M) > 0$. And the analogous of (14.2) and (14.3) hold.

The Main Result

Let $u_n(\omega)$ be that cylinder of length $(\frac{1}{2})^n$ that contains ω—that is, the unique interval of the form $\{\omega: x_k(\omega) = i_k, k = 1, \ldots, n\}$ containing ω. Note that ω' lies in $u_n(\omega)$ if and only if the base-r expansions of ω and ω' agree in the first n places. Let μ and ν be two probability measures on the interval.

THEOREM 14.1 *If*

$$(14.8) \qquad M \subset \left\{\omega: \lim_{n \to \infty} \frac{\log \nu(u_n(\omega))}{\log \mu(u_n(\omega))} = \delta\right\},$$

---

* Define a dimension starting from (14.5) with the infimum restricted to ρ-coverings by intervals in a given class $\mathscr{I}$. Under what conditions on $\mathscr{I}$ does this dimension coincide with Hausdorff's? We have proved it does if $\mathscr{I}$ is the class of r-adic intervals, but I know of no general conditions. See, however, Kinney and Pitcher (1965) for a result of this kind connected with continued fractions.

then

(14.9) $$\dim_\mu M = \delta \dim_\nu M.$$

To ensure that the ratio of logarithms in (14.8) is always defined, we adopt the convention that if $0 < \xi, \eta < 1$ then

(14.10) $$\begin{cases} \log \xi/\log 0 = \log 1/\log \eta = \log 1/\log 0 = 0, \\ \log 0/\log \eta = \log \xi/\log 1 = \log 0/\log 1 = \infty, \\ \log 0/\log 0 = \log 1/\log 1 = 1. \end{cases}$$

Before proving the theorem, we advance a heuristic argument in its favor and show how it implies Eggleston's result.

Let us pretend that for each ω in M not only does

$$\log \nu(u_n(\omega))/\log \mu(u_n(\omega))$$

approach δ, but that it actually equals δ for all n. If $\{v_i\}$ is any covering of M by cylinders each of which intersects M, then any v_i has the form $v_i = u_n(\omega)$ for some n and for some ω in M, and hence $\nu(v_i) = \mu(v_i)^\delta$. Thus $\Sigma_i \nu(v_i)^\alpha = \Sigma_i \mu(v_i)^{\alpha\delta}$ for any covering $\{v_i\}$. But then $\nu_\alpha(M) = \mu_{\alpha\delta}(M)$, which clearly implies (14.9). This argument makes the theorem plausible.

In order to apply Theorem 14.1 to prove Eggleston's result, take μ to be Lebesgue measure λ. Since $\lambda(u_n(\omega)) = r^{-n}$, it follows from the theorem (take $\delta = \theta/\log r$) that

(14.11) $$M \subset \left\{ \omega : \lim_{n\to\infty} \left[-\frac{1}{n} \log \nu(u_n(\omega)) \right] = \theta \right\}$$

implies

(14.12) $$\dim M = \frac{\theta}{\log r} \dim_\nu M.$$

If we construct a measure ν for which (14.11) holds and for which $\nu(M) > 0$, then $\dim_\nu M$ will be 1 and hence, by (14.12), $\dim M$ will be $\theta/\log r$. Let ν be that probability measure on the interval under which $\{x_n\}$ is an independent process with $\nu\{\omega : x_n(\omega) = i\} = p_i$, $i = 0$, $1, \ldots, r - 1$ (see Example 3.5). Since

$$-\frac{1}{n} \log \nu(u_n(\omega)) = -\sum_{i=0}^{r-1} \frac{N_i(\omega, n)}{n} \log p_i,$$

it is clear that (14.11) holds if $M = M(p_0, \ldots, p_{r-1})$ and $\theta = -\Sigma_{i=0}^{r-1} p_i \log p_i$. Since $M(p_0, \ldots, p_{r-1})$ has v-measure 1 by the strong law of large numbers, Eggeston's result follows.

As a further application, consider the number $N_{ij}(\omega, n)$ of $k \leq n$ for which $x_k(\omega) = i$ and $x_{k+1}(\omega) = j$. If

$$(14.13) \qquad \lim_{n \to \infty} \frac{1}{n} N_{ij}(\omega, n) = \pi_{ij}, \qquad i, j = 0, \ldots, r - 1,$$

then (π_{ij}) is an $r \times r$ matrix of nonnegative numbers such that if $p_i = \Sigma_j \pi_{ij}$, then $\Sigma_j \pi_{ji} = p_i$ and $\Sigma_j p_j = 1$. Let $p_{ij} = \pi_{ij}/p_i$; then (p_{ij}) is a stochastic matrix with the p_i as stationary probabilities. Suppose, for simplicity, that all p_{ij} are positive. If v is the measure under which $\{x_1, x_2, \ldots\}$ is the corresponding Markov process, then

$$\lim_{n \to \infty} \left[-\frac{1}{n} \log v(u_n(\omega)) \right] = -\sum_{ij} p_i p_{ij} \log p_{ij}$$

for any ω in the set $M(\pi)$ defined by (14.13). Since $v(M(\pi)) = 1$, it follows as before that

$$\dim M(\pi) = -\frac{1}{\log r} \sum_{ij} p_i p_{ij} \log p_{ij}.$$

Comparing these results with the Shannon-McMillan-Breiman theorem, we see why they involve entropies.

For a third application of Theorem 14.1, suppose that $r = 3$ and that $p_0 = p_2 = \frac{1}{2}, p_1 = 0$. Let v be the measure under which $\{x_1, x_2, \ldots\}$ is independent with $v\{x_n = i\} = p_i$ (v is the Cantor measure of Section 3). Now $-n^{-1} \log v(u_n(\omega))$ is $\log 2$ if the $x_n(\omega)$ are all 0's and 2's, that is, if ω lies in the Cantor set. Thus

$$M \subset \left\{ \omega : \lim_{n \to \infty} \left[-\frac{1}{n} \log v(u_n(\omega)) \right] = \log 2 \right\}$$

if M is the Cantor set, so that, since (14.11) implies (14.12),

$$\dim M = \frac{\log 2}{\log 3} \dim_v M.$$

Since $v(M) = 1$, we have Hausdorff's result $\dim M = \log 2/\log 3$.

We turn now to the proof of Theorem 14.1. It suffices to show that (14.8) implies

(14.14) $$\dim_\mu M \geq \delta \dim_\nu M,$$

since the reverse inequality will then follow upon interchange of μ and ν and replacement of δ by its reciprocal. We shall in fact show more, namely that (14.14) follows from

(14.15) $$M \subset \left\{\omega: \liminf_{n \to \infty} \frac{\log \nu(u_n(\omega))}{\log \mu(u_n(\omega))} \geq \delta\right\}.$$

We prove this result first under the assumption that $\mu(v) > 0$ for any cylinder v that intersects M; we shall indicate afterwards the trivial modifications needed to cover the general case.

It is enough to show that if $1/\delta < \eta$ and $\dim_\mu M < \xi$, then

$$\dim_\nu M \leq \eta\xi.$$

If $\omega \in M$, then, by (14.15), $\nu(u_n(\omega))^\eta \leq \mu(u_n(\omega))$ for all n exceeding some integer $N(\omega)$. Let M_ρ be the set of ω that lie in M and satisfy the disjunction

(14.16) $$\mu(u_n(\omega)) \geq \rho \quad \text{or} \quad \nu(u_n(\omega))^\eta \leq \mu(u_n(\omega))$$

for all n. Clearly M_ρ increases as ρ decreases; we shall show that $M_\rho \uparrow M$ as $\rho \downarrow 0$. If $\omega \in M$, take $\rho = \mu(u_{N(\omega)}(\omega)) > 0$ (it is here we need the assumption that cylinders meeting M have positive μ-measure); if $\mu(u_n(\omega)) < \rho$ then $n > N(\omega)$, so that $\nu(u_n(\omega))^\eta \leq \mu(u_n(\omega))$. Thus ω satisfies (14.16) for all n: $\omega \in M_\rho$.

Since $M_\rho \uparrow M$, it suffices, by (14.3) (let ρ decrease to 0 through a sequence), to prove

(14.17) $$\dim_\nu M_\rho \leq \eta\xi$$

for all positive ρ. Suppose $0 < \rho_1 < \rho$ and $\epsilon_1 > 0$. Since $\dim_\mu M_\rho < \xi$, we have

$$\sum_i \mu(v_i)^\xi < \epsilon_1$$

for some μ-ρ_1-covering $\{v_i\}$ of M_ρ. We may assume each v_i actually meets M_ρ. But then $v_i = u_n(\omega)$ for some $\omega \in M_\rho$, so that, since

$\mu(v_i) \leq \rho_1 < \rho$, we have $v(v_i)^\eta \leq \mu(v_i)$. Therefore

$$\sum_i v(v_i)^{\eta\xi} < \epsilon_1.$$

But $\{v_i\}$ is a $v\text{-}\rho_1^{1/\eta}$-covering of M_ρ, and hence, ϵ_1 and ρ_1 being arbitrarily small, $v_{\xi\eta}(M_\rho) = 0$, which proves (14.17).

It remains to remove the restriction that $\mu(v) > 0$ for all cylinders v intersecting M. Let E_μ be the union of all cylinders of μ-measure 0; since $\dim_\mu E_\mu = 0$, it follows that $\dim_\mu A = \dim_\mu B$ if the symmetric difference of A and B is contained in E_μ (use (14.3)). If ω lies in the set on the right in (14.15) (with $\delta > 0$) and if $\mu(u_n(\omega)) = 0$ for some n, then $v(u_m(\omega)) = 0$ for some m, by the convention (14.10). Thus $M \cap E_\mu \subset M \cap E_v$. We already know that (14.14) applies to $M - E_\mu$; hence

$$\dim_\mu M = \dim_\mu (M - E_\mu) \geq \delta \dim_v (M - E_\mu)$$
$$\geq \delta \dim_v (M - E_v) = \delta \dim_v M.$$

Remarks. See Hurewicz and Wallman (1948) for the connection between Hausdorff dimension and topological dimension.

Good (1941) conjectured (14.4); it was proved by Eggleston (1949). Billingsley (1960, 1961a) proves further results by the methods of this section, and Kinney and Pitcher (1965) apply these methods to dimensional problems connected with continued-fraction expansions. See Billingsley (1961b) for a connection with the coding theorem for the noiseless channel. Rényi (1959) treats a connection between dimension and entropy.

CHAPTER 5

Coding

15. THE CODING THEOREM FOR THE NOISELESS CHANNEL

Some Notation

Throughout this chapter, we shall deal with a number of shifts simultaneously, and a change of notation is in order. In addition to the finite set (state space) ρ, we need two more, which we denote σ and τ. The finite set $\rho[\sigma, \tau]$, consists of $r[s, t]$ elements, the generic one denoted $i[j, k]$. We call the sets *alphabets*, and their elements *letters*.

We denote by $X[Y, Z]$ the space of doubly infinite sequences $x = (\ldots, x_{-1}, x_0, x_1, \ldots)$ $[y = (\ldots, y_{-1}, y_0, y_1, \ldots), \; z = (\ldots, z_{-1}, z_0, z_1, \ldots)]$ of elements of $\rho[\sigma, \tau]$; $\mathscr{X}[\mathscr{Y}, \mathscr{Z}]$ stands for the σ-field generated by the cylinders. We indulge in the following abuse of notation: x_n (for fixed x) is the nth coordinate of x, but we use it also to denote (for fixed n) the coordinate variable. Moreover, we shall consider spaces like $X \times Y$; here, x_n denotes the function whose value at (x, y) is the nth coordinate of x. The same conventions apply to y_n and z_n. The shifts we denote by T_X, $T_{X \times Y}$, etc., or, if there is no danger of confusion, by T.

Always, $\rho^n[\sigma^n, \tau^n]$ denotes the set of n-tuples of elements of $\rho[\sigma, \tau]$.

If μ is a probability measure on $\mathscr{X}$ (we reserve the symbol P for other uses) that is preserved by T_X, we denote the whole structure $(X, \mathscr{X}, \mu, T_X)$ simply by $[X, \mu]$. The only variable element here is μ; we say that μ (or $[X, \mu]$) is ergodic [mixing, etc.] according as T_X is ergodic [mixing, etc.] under μ. The entropy of $[X, \mu]$ is that of T_X. Similar remarks apply to the spaces Y and Z.

We shall call $[X, \mu]$ a source, or information source (see Section 5). We view the x_n as letters emitted by the source and sequences $(x_m, \ldots, x_n)$ and $x = (\ldots x_{-1}, x_0, x_1, \ldots)$ as *messages*. The measure μ describes the structure of the source.

The Noiseless Channel

The coding theorem for the noiseless channel can be stated in terms of coding messages so as to make them shorter, or in terms of coding them in such a way that a smaller alphabet may be used. We develop the theorem from the latter point of view, as an introduction to the more complicated problems of the succeeding sections.

A *noiseless channel* consists of a sender and a receiver, each of which operates with the alphabet σ. Mathematically, the noiseless channel is simply the finite alphabet σ of size s, together with the associated space $(Y, \mathscr{Y})$ of sequences. (There is no measure involved.) If a message y is sent through the channel, it is received with perfect accuracy at the other end.

Suppose now that messages from a source $[X, \mu]$ must be sent through the channel to an addressee. The source and the addressee both operate with the alphabet ρ, but the channel operates with the alphabet σ. If ρ and σ are distinct, then clearly the message must be coded* in some way before transmission and decoded afterwards. We demand that if the source produces one letter per second (say), then one letter per second must be transmitted over the channel—it is not allowed to go faster or slower than the source.

---

* The word *code*, as used in this book, is unconnected with secret communication.

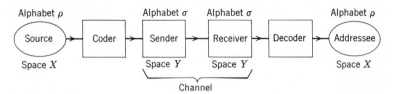

Suppose the sizes r and s of the alphabets ρ and σ satisfy $r \leq s$. For example, ρ might consist of the $r = 10$ digits $0, 1, \ldots, 9$ and σ of the $s = 26$ letters $A, B, \ldots, Z$. It is clear that the source can be coded (we postpone for the moment the precise mathematical definition of the notion of a code) in such a way that the messages it produces can be sent through the channel. In fact, take ψ to be some one-to-one mapping of ρ into σ; one exists if $r \leq s$. Encode x by replacing each symbol x_n by $y_n = \psi(x_n)$, and send the message consisting of these elements of σ through the channel. At the other end of the channel, ψ^{-1} can be applied to the received letters to recover the original message.

Even if $r > s$ it may be possible to send x through the channel. This is clear, for example, if there is some subset ρ_0 of ρ, of size at most s, such that $\mu\{x_n \in \rho_0\} = 1$. For a less trivial example, suppose that $r = 4$, that $s = 2$, and that the structure of μ is such that there is probability 1 that each letter is repeated, that is, $x_{2n} = x_{2n+1}$. (This source is not quite stationary, but the example can be modified so as to take care of this; see Example 3.3.) There are in ρ^2 only four possible values of (x_{2n}, x_{2n+1}). Let ψ be a one-to-one mapping of these elements onto the four elements of σ^2. If the message is encoded by defining $(y_{2n}, y_{2n+1}) = \psi(x_{2n}, x_{2n+1})$, then the x_n can be uniquely recovered from the y_n, and hence the code makes it possible to transmit x through the channel.

The problem, then, is to code x into y, preferably in a recoverable fashion. We must now define precisely what we mean by a code. A *code* is just a measurable mapping ϕ of X into Y. There are a number of desirable properties one can demand of a code.

1. *Stationary codes.* A code ϕ is stationary if

(15.1) $$\phi T_X x = T_Y \phi x$$

holds for all x in X. This means that the structure of the coding device does not change with time. We shall always demand that a code be stationary; from now on, stationary is part of the definition.

2. *Invertible codes.* A code ϕ is invertible if it is essentially one-to-one in the sense that there is in $\mathscr{X}$ a set X_0 such that $\mu(X_0) = 1$ and such that ϕ is one-to-one from X_0 to $Y_0 = \phi X_0$. We also demand that $T_X X_0 = X_0$, and that $\phi A \in \mathscr{Y}$ hold for any set A such that $A \subset X_0$ and $A \in \mathscr{X}$ (so that, in particular, $Y_0 \in \mathscr{Y}$). We call ϕ invertible in case such an X_0 exists. If a code is invertible, then the original message can be (essentially) uniquely recovered from the received one.

While the concept of code is defined without reference to any measure μ on X, whether a particular code is invertible does depend on what μ is involved. To stress the role of μ, we may say that ϕ is invertible *with respect to* μ.

Suppose that ϕ is invertible with respect to μ. Let us show that the shift T_X with the measure μ and the shift T_Y with the measure $\mu\phi^{-1}$ are isomorphic. (The value of $\mu\phi^{-1}$ at $B \in \mathscr{Y}$ is $\mu(\phi^{-1}B)$; recall that ϕ is always assumed measurable. The measure $\mu\phi^{-1}$ is the distribution of received messages.) Clearly $Y_0 \in \mathscr{Y}$, $\mu\phi^{-1}(Y_0) = 1$, and $T_Y Y_0 = Y_0$. Let ϕ_0 be the restriction of ϕ to X_0. Suppose that $A \subset X_0$, and put $B = \phi_0 A$. Then $A \in \mathscr{X}$ implies $B \in \mathscr{Y}$ by the definition of invertibility of ϕ, $B \in \mathscr{Y}$ implies $A = X_0 \cap \phi^{-1}B \in \mathscr{X}$ because ϕ is measurable, and $A \in \mathscr{X}$ certainly implies $\mu(A) = \mu\phi^{-1}(B)$. Since $\phi_0 T_X x = T_Y \phi_0 x$ holds for all x in X_0, the triple (X_0, Y_0, ϕ_0) fulfills the conditions $(\mathrm{I_i})$, $(\mathrm{I_{ii}})$, and $(\mathrm{I_{iii}})$ for isomorphism (see Section 5).

Suppose, on the other hand, that T_X, with the measure μ on X, is isomorphic to T_Y, with some measure γ on Y. Since T_X and T_Y are both invertible, it follows, by Remark 5 after the definition of isomorphism in Section 5, that they are isomorphic under a triple (X_0, Y_0, ϕ_0) having the special property that $T_X X_0 = X_0$ and $T_Y Y_0 = Y_0$. In this case, ϕ_0 is almost an invertible code, but not quite, since it maps from X_0 onto Y_0 instead of from X into Y. Extend ϕ_0 to a mapping ϕ with domain X by setting $\phi x = \phi_0 x$ for x in X_0 and by taking ϕx for x in $X - X_0$ to be some element $(\ldots, j, j, j, \ldots)$ of Y whose components are all the same (a common image point for all x in $X - X_0$). Then ϕ is invertible with respect to μ, its restriction to X_0 is ϕ_0 again, and $\mu\phi^{-1}$ is identical with γ.

Thus an invertible code is essentially an isomorphism. For this reason, coding theory ties in with the theory of Chapter 2.

3. *Nonanticipating codes.* A code ϕ is nonanticipating if, for all j in σ and all integers n, $\phi^{-1}\{y: y_n = j\} = \{x: (\phi x)_n = j\}$ lies in the σ-field generated by the random variables $\ldots, x_{n-1}, x_n$. (Referring to a measure μ on X, one might, more generally, require only that $\phi^{-1}\{y: y_n = j\}$ differ by a set of measure 0 from some element of this σ-field. We shall not need this wider definition.) If ϕ is nonanticipating, then the coding device need not be clairvoyant.

4. *Codes with nonanticipating inverses.* If ϕ is invertible, the restriction ϕ_0 of ϕ, which maps X_0 onto Y_0, has an inverse ϕ_0^{-1}, which maps Y_0 onto X_0. This ϕ_0^{-1} can be extended in one or more ways to an invertible code from Y to X. One can also demand that one of these extensions—they differ from one another only inessentially—be nonanticipating. In this case, the decoder at the receiving end can keep pace with the encoder.

The more of these conditions one imposes on the notion of code, the harder it becomes to prove the existence of codes with specified properties, and the easier it becomes to prove their nonexistence.

Coding Theorems

The problem of the noiseless channel is this. Given a source $[X, \mu]$ with alphabet ρ, and a noiseless channel with alphabet σ, find a code ϕ (from X to Y) that is invertible with respect to μ. If such a ϕ exists— and this is the premathematical idea lying back of the problem—then the message x can be put in coded form ϕx and sent through the channel to the receiver, where the original message can be reconstructed from ϕx. For each of the two examples preceding the definition of code, it seems intuitively clear that there does exist an invertible code. In the first of these examples, ρ is small (or at least the letters the source produces are confined to a small subset ρ_0 of ρ), and, in the second, the source repeats each letter twice. Each of these two characteristics restricts the rate at which the source produces information. The fact is, an invertible code exists if and only if the entropy of $[X, \nu]$ is at most $\log s$.

THEOREM 15.1 *If the entropy h of [X, μ] exceeds log s, then there is no code (from X to Y) invertible with respect to μ.*

Proof. If an invertible code ϕ exists, then T_X (with the measure μ) is isomorphic to T_Y (with the measure $\mu\phi^{-1}$). But then the entropy of T_Y is also h. Since the alphabet σ contains s letters, we must have (see (7.1)) $h = h(T_Y) \leq \log s$, which proves the theorem.

The central step in this proof consists in concluding $h(T_X) = h(T_Y)$ from the fact that T_X and T_Y are isomorphic; hence the importance of an invariant definition of entropy. On the other hand, the natural measure of the rate at which the source $[X, \mu]$ produces information is

$$\lim_{n \to \infty} \frac{1}{n} \sum_{i_0 \cdots i_{n-1}} \eta(\mu\{x_0 = i_0, \ldots, x_{n-1} = i_{n-1}\})$$

(that is, $h(\mathscr{A}, T_X)$ with $\mathscr{A}$ the time-0 field), and if $h(T_X)$ did not coincide with this quantity, it would be an unnatural measure of the information rate; hence the importance of the Kolmogorov-Sinai theorem. Thus the proof actually involves all of Chapter 2.

In the direction converse to that of Theorem 15.1, we prove only a hypothetical result.

HYPOTHESIS *The source [X, μ] has entropy h, and the shift T_X, with the measure μ, is isomorphic to any Bernoulli shift with entropy h.*

If entropy is complete (see Section 8) among the Bernoulli shifts [mixing Markov shifts, Kolmogorov shifts, etc.], then this hypothesis holds if the source $[X, \mu]$ is Bernoulli [mixing Markov, Kolmogorov, etc.]. It may be that the hypothesis is true of no source whatever.

"THEOREM" 15.2 *Under the above hypothesis, if $h \leq \log s$ then there exists a code (from X to Y) invertible with respect to μ.*

Proof. The function $\Sigma_j \eta(p_j)$ of probability vectors $(p_1, \ldots, p_s)$ assumes all the values between its minimum 0 and its maximum $\log s$ (as ξ runs from 0 to 1, $\Sigma_j (\xi s^{-1} + (1 - \xi)\delta_{j1})$ varies continuously from 0 to $\log s$, for example). If $h \leq \log s$, therefore, there exist probabilities $p_1, \ldots, p_s$ such that $\Sigma_j \eta(p_j) = h$. If γ is the measure on Y that makes T_Y the Bernoulli shift $(p_1, \ldots, p_s)$, then T_Y has entropy exactly h. By the hypothesis, T_X with the measure μ is isomorphic to T_Y with the measure γ; hence there exists a code ϕ that is invertible with respect to μ (and incidentally has the property that $\mu\phi^{-1} = \gamma$).

This result is true, but it may well be vacuous; hence the quotation marks. The question of whether it is nonvacuous is equivalent to the question of the extent to which entropy is complete. If one makes the "theorem" harder by insisting that the code be nonanticipating, one is in effect making the questions posed in Section 8 harder by requiring that the isomorphism mapping depend only on the past—compare Sinai's results on weak isomorphism.

Remarks. Shannon (1948) originated these coding problems. Theorem 15.1 is homemade—at least I have not seen it in the literature. It is of course a very simple consequence of the Kolmogorov-Sinai theory. Nor have I seen "Theorem" 15.2. For accounts of the coding theorem for the noiseless channel from other points of view, see Feinstein (1958), Khinchine (1957), and Billingsley (1961b). These references have versions of Theorem 15.1 which are unsatisfactory in various ways, but they contain constructive versions of "Theorem" 15.2.

16. THE NOISY CHANNEL

Definitions

We now consider a channel which is affected by noise—that is to say, one in which the received message may not be a faithful copy of the one transmitted. The sender and receiver may even operate with different alphabets.

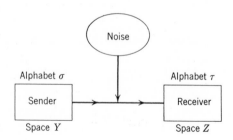

For the mathematical formalization, consider the spaces $(Y, \mathscr{Y})$ and $(Z, \mathscr{Z})$. Suppose that for each $y \in Y$ we have a probability measure $\nu_y(\cdot)$ on $\mathscr{Z}$. For technical reasons, we assume that for each set C in $\mathscr{Z}$, $\nu_y(C)$ is measurable $\mathscr{Y}$, as a function of y. The triple $[Y, \nu_y, Z]$ is called a *channel*; the function $\nu_y(\cdot)$ is called the *kernel* of the channel. The idea is that if the message y is put into the channel then the received message, which will in general have been affected by some sort of random noise, has probability $\nu_y(C)$ of lying in the subset C of Z. The problem of the noisy channel is to code a given source $[X, \mu]$ into Y in such a way as to use the channel effectively. For example, we can ask whether it would pay to combat the noise by repeating each letter twice. (We assume the structure of the channel and the source to be known perfectly—no problem of statistical inference is involved.)

Although there is no real loss of generality at this point in taking the alphabets for the source, the sender, and the receiver to be identical, we take them to be ρ, σ, and τ, respectively, because this helps to order the notation.

If $Y = Z$ and if ν_y is a unit mass at y, we have in effect the noiseless channel of the preceding section. If ν_y is a unit mass for each y (Z being perhaps distinct from Y), we have in effect a code from Y to Z.

The channel is *stationary* if

$$\nu_{T_Y y}(T_Z C) = \nu_y(C).$$

As usual, this means that the properties of the channel do not change with time. We shall always assume the channel is stationary, and we incorporate this requirement into the definition.

The channel is *nonanticipating* if for each n and each $k \in \tau$, $\nu_y\{z : z_n = k\}$ is measurable with respect to the σ-field generated by $\cdots y_{n-1}, y_n$. (A code is a special kind of channel. The notion of a nonanticipating channel specializes to that of a nonanticipating code.)

The Channel without Memory

Consider this very special kind of channel: Let (c_{jk}) be an $s \times t$ matrix of nonnegative numbers, the rows and columns indexed by the elements of σ and τ, respectively, and the rows summing to 1. The kernel $\nu_y(\cdot)$ is specified by

$$\nu_y\{z_l = k_l, m \leq l \leq n\} = \prod_{l=m}^{n} c_{y_l k_l}.$$

This channel treats the letters of the input message independently; if the letter j is put into the channel, the letter k is received with probability c_{jk}. (Of course, the input letters are not themselves assumed independent; indeed, measures on the space Y do not intervene in the specification of the structure of any channel.) A channel of this sort—clearly it is stationary and nonanticipating—we call a channel *without memory*.* Notice that if $\sigma = \tau$ and $c_{jj} = 1$ for all j, then we effectively have the noiseless channel of the preceding section.

In proving that good—good according to some specified desideratum—codes *do not* exist, we shall impose on the channel no restrictions at all. In proving that good codes *do* exist, we shall confine our attention to the channel without memory.

The Input-Output Measure

Suppose now that there is a measure μ on Y, so that $[Y, \mu]$ is a source. We want to define on the product space $(Y \times Z, \mathscr{Y} \times \mathscr{Z})$ a probability measure P that will describe the joint distribution of the input and output of the channel. Clearly we want

(16.1) $$P(B \times C) = \int_B \nu_y(C)\, \mu(dy)$$

for $B \in \mathscr{Y}$ and $C \in \mathscr{Z}$. This integral is well defined because of the assumption that $\nu_y(C)$ is measurable in y. For M in $\mathscr{Y} \times \mathscr{Z}$, put

$$P(M) = \int_Y \nu_y\{z \colon (y, z) \in M\}\, \mu(dy),$$

which reduces to (16.1) if $M = B \times C$. The class of sets M in $\mathscr{Y} \times \mathscr{Z}$

---

* See Khinchine (1957), for example, for the more general notion of a channel with *finite memory*. (See also Takano (1958), who corrects an error in Khinchine's treatment.)

for which the integrand here is measurable $\mathcal{Y}$ contains the finite, disjoint unions of rectangles $B \times C$; since it is also a monotone class, it coincides with $\mathcal{Y} \times \mathcal{Z}$. Thus the integral is defined. It is now easy to verify that P is a probability measure, and that it is the only one satisfying (16.1).

If the source and the channel are both stationary—and we always assume they are—then we also expect the shift $T_{Y \times Z}$ to preserve P.

THEOREM 16.1 *The measure P is preserved by $T_{Y \times Z}$.*

Proof. It is enough to show that $T = T_{Y \times Z}$ preserves the measures of rectangles $B \times C$. But, by (16.1),

$$P(T^{-1}(B \times C)) = \int_{T_Y^{-1}B} \nu_y(T_Z^{-1}C)\, \mu(dy)$$

$$= \int_B \nu_{T_Y^{-1}y}(T_Z^{-1}C)\, \mu(dy)$$

$$= \int_B \nu_y(C)\, \mu(dy) = P(B \times C).$$

The marginal distribution P induces on Y is just μ. The one induced on Z is the distribution of the output of the channel; as follows by Theorem 16.1, it is preserved by T_Z.

Rate of Transmission

We now define the *rate of transmission* of the source $[Y, \mu]$ over the channel $[Y, \nu_y, Z]$. An entropy attaches to each of the three shifts $T_{Y \times Z}$ (with measure P), T_Y (with the measure $\mu(B) = P(B \times Z)$), and T_Z (with the measure $P(Y \times C)$). The rate is defined by

$$R = h(T_Y) + h(T_Z) - h(T_{Y \times Z}).$$

The intuitive meaning of this will be given in a moment.

The rate can be given more explicitly by means of the Kolmogorov–Sinai theorem. Let $\mathcal{B}[\mathcal{C}]$ denote the finite field in $\mathcal{Y} \times \mathcal{Z}$ with atoms $\{(y, z): y_0 = j\}$, $j \in \sigma$ $[\{(y, z): z_0 = k\}, k \in \tau]$. The field $\mathcal{B} \vee \mathcal{C}$ is the time-0 field for $Y \times Z$. It is not difficult to see that if $\mathcal{B}_0$, say, is the finite field in $\mathcal{Y}$ with atoms $\{y: y_0 = j\}$, $j \in \sigma$, then $H(\bigvee_{l=0}^{n-1} T_Y^{-l} \mathcal{B}_0) = H(\bigvee_{l=0}^{n-1} T^{-l} \mathcal{B})$, where $T = T_{Y \times Z}$. Therefore, by the Kolmogorov–Sinai theorem, $h(T_Y) = h(T_Y, \mathscr{B}_0) = h(T, \mathscr{B})$. Using a similar argument for T_Z, we see that if we write

$$H\left(\bigvee_{k=0}^{n-1} T^{-k}\mathscr{B}\right) = H(y_0, \ldots, y_{n-1})$$

$$H\left(\bigvee_{k=0}^{n-1} T^{-k}\mathscr{C}\right) = H(z_0, \ldots, z_{n-1})$$

$$H\left(\bigvee_{k=0}^{n-1} T^{-k}(\mathscr{B} \vee \mathscr{C})\right) = H(y_0, \ldots, y_{n-1}, z_0, \ldots, z_{n-1}),$$

then

$$(16.2) \quad R = \lim_{n \to \infty} \frac{1}{n}\{H(y_0, \ldots, y_{n-1}) + H(z_0, \ldots, z_{n-1})$$
$$- H(y_0, \ldots, y_{n-1}, z_0, \ldots, z_{n-1})\}.$$

Using property (A_1') of Section 6, we can rewrite the quantity in brackets in (16.2) in two ways. In an obvious notation, we have

(16.3)

$$\begin{cases} H(y_0, \ldots, y_{n-1}) + H(z_0, \ldots, z_{n-1}) - H(y_0, \ldots, y_{n-1}, z_0, \ldots, z_{n-1}) \\ = H(y_0, \ldots, y_{n-1}) - H(y_0, \ldots, y_{n-1} \mid z_0, \ldots, z_{n-1}) \\ = H(z_0, \ldots, z_{n-1}) - H(z_0, \ldots, z_{n-1} \mid y_0, \ldots, y_{n-1}). \end{cases}$$

The middle member of (16.3) has the following interpretation. If we were in receipt of the message $y_0, \ldots, y_{n-1}$, our (mean) amount of information would be $H(y_0, \ldots, y_{n-1})$—information gained equals uncertainty removed. If, however, the message $y_0, \ldots, y_{n-1}$ has been sent through the channel, so that we have, instead, the perturbed message $z_0, \ldots, z_{n-1}$, then we are to a certain extent uncertain as to what the original message $y_0, \ldots, y_{n-1}$ actually was—the (mean) amount of this uncertainty being $H(y_0, \ldots, y_{n-1} \mid z_0, \ldots, z_{n-1})$. The difference of these two quantities—that is, the middle member of (16.3)—is therefore a reasonable measure of the (mean) amount of information received. We have the "formula"

> information *received*
> = information *in* the message sent
>   minus uncertainty *about* the message sent.

Thus

$$R = \lim_{n \to \infty} \frac{1}{n} \{H(y_0, \ldots, y_{n-1}) - H(y_0, \ldots, y_{n-1} \mid z_0, \ldots, z_{n-1})\}$$

represents the amount of information received *per letter*. Hence the term *rate*. The quantity

$$\lim_{n \to \infty} \frac{1}{n} H(y_0, \ldots, y_{n-1} \mid z_0, \ldots, z_{n-1}) = h(T_Y) - R$$
$$= h(T_{Y \times Z}) - h(T_Z)$$

is called the *equivocation* (per letter). If the entropy of the source is fixed, an increase in the rate of transmission corresponds to an equal decrease in the equivocation.

If we accept the interpretations given to entropy and conditional entropy in Chapter 2, then these definitions are the natural ones: a high rate (low equivocation) is good, and a low rate (high equivocation) is bad. An alternative way to approach the question of measuring the efficiency of the source-channel pair is to consider the problem of actually constructing an efficient decision procedure for recovering the original message from the received one. Although this second approach does bear indirectly on the discussion in Sections 18 and 19, we shall not study it systematically.*

Only in special cases can we compute the rate explicitly. Let (c_{jk}) be the $s \times t$ matrix describing a channel without memory. Since

$$H(z_0, \ldots, z_{n-1} \mid y_0, \ldots, y_{n-1})$$

$$= - \int_Y \left\{ \sum_{k_0 \cdots k_{n-1}} (c_{y_0 k_0} \cdots c_{y_{n-1} k_{n-1}}) \log (c_{y_0 k_0} \cdots c_{y_{n-1} k_{n-1}}) \right\} \mu(dy),$$

we have

(16.4) $$H(z_0, \ldots, z_{n-1} \mid y_0, \ldots, y_{n-1}) = nH(z_0 \mid y_0),$$

no matter what the distribution of the y_n is. For any set of probabilities $p_1, \ldots, p_s$ on σ, define a second set $q_1, \ldots, q_t$ on τ by

$$q_k = \sum_j p_j c_{jk},$$

---

* For a comparison of the two approaches, see Feinstein (1958, Chapter 3).

and put

(16.5) $r(p_1, \ldots, p_s) = \sum_j \eta(p_j) - \sum_k q_k \sum_j \eta(p_j c_{jk}/q_k)$

$= \sum_k \eta(q_k) - \sum_j p_j \sum_k \eta(c_{jk})$

$= \sum_j \eta(p_j) + \sum_k \eta(q_k) - \sum_{jk} \eta(p_j c_{jk}).$

If

(16.6) $\mu\{y : y_0 = j\} = p_j, \qquad j \in \sigma,$

then, even if the y_n are not independent under μ,

(16.7) $r(p_1, \ldots, p_s) = H(y_0) - H(y_0 \mid z_0)$

$= H(z_0) - H(z_0 \mid y_0)$

$= H(y_0) + H(z_0) - H(y_0, z_0).$

If (16.6) holds, and *if the y_n are independent*, then

$H(y_0, \ldots, y_{n-1}) + H(z_0, \ldots, z_{n-1}) - H(y_0, \ldots, y_{n-1}, z_0, \ldots, z_{n-1})$

$= nH(y_0) + nH(z_0) - nH(y_0, z_0) = nr(p_1, \ldots, p_s),$

so that the rate is

(16.8) $R = r(p_1, \ldots, p_s).$

This relation need not hold if the y_n are not independent.

Example 16.1.   In the channel without memory, suppose that $s = 2$, $t = 3$, and that the matrix (c_{jk}) is

$$\begin{bmatrix} 1 & 0 & 0 \\ 0 & \frac{1}{2} & \frac{1}{2} \end{bmatrix}.$$

For any input probabilities (p_1, p_2), the matrix $(p_j c_{jk}/q_k)$ is

$$\begin{bmatrix} 1 & 0 & 0 \\ 0 & 1 & 1 \end{bmatrix},$$

so that $H(y_0 \mid z_0) = 0$. Even if the y_n are not independent, we have, by

(A_4) and (A_3) of Section 6,

$$H(y_0, \ldots, y_{n-1} \mid z_0, \ldots, z_{n-1}) \leq \sum_{i=0}^{n-1} H(y_i \mid z_0, \ldots, z_{n-1})$$

$$\leq \sum_{i=0}^{n-1} H(y_i \mid z_i) = 0,$$

so that the equivocation vanishes. For this channel, the rate always coincides with the entropy of the input.*

Example 16.2. In the channel without memory, suppose the rows of (c_{jk}) are all the same: c_{jk} does not depend on j. Then $H(z_0 \mid y_0) = H(z_0)$, and hence, by (16.4),

$$H(z_0, \ldots, z_{n-1}) - H(z_0, \ldots, z_{n-1} \mid y_0, \ldots, y_{n-1})$$

$$= H(z_0, \ldots, z_{n-1}) - nH(z_0).$$

By (A_4) of Section 6, this quantity vanishes. The rate is always 0, no matter what the input; no information at all can be transmitted through this channel.†

An example in between the two extremes represented by Examples 16.1 and 16.2 shows that the rate generally depends not on the source alone, and not on the channel alone, but on how the two interact with one another.

Example 16.3. In the channel without memory, suppose that $s = t = 4$, and that the matrix (c_{jk}) is

$$\begin{bmatrix} 1 & 0 & 0 & 0 \\ 0 & 1 & 0 & 0 \\ 0 & 0 & \frac{1}{2} & \frac{1}{2} \\ 0 & 0 & \frac{1}{2} & \frac{1}{2} \end{bmatrix}.$$

It follows by (16.5) that

$$(16.9) \qquad r(p_1, \ldots, p_4) = \eta(p_1) + \eta(p_2) + \eta(p_3 + p_4).$$

---

* A channel like this one, though noisy, is *lossless*. See Feinstein (1958, p. 26).

† See Feinstein (1958, p. 27) for a characterization of channels without memory that have this property.

Suppose now that the y_n are independent under μ, so that (16.9) is the rate of transmission and

$$(16.10) \qquad \eta(p_1) + \eta(p_2) + \eta(p_3) + \eta(p_4)$$

is the entropy of the source $[Y, \mu]$. If $p_1 = p_2 = 0$, then the rate (16.9) is 0, while the entropy (16.10) may be as high as $\log 2$; such a source fits badly with the channel. On the other hand, if $p_4 = 0$, then the rate (16.9) and the entropy (16.10) coincide, although their common value may be as low as 0; such a source fits well with the channel.

Channel Capacity

The rate of transmission depends on both the source $[Y, \mu]$ and the channel $[Y, \nu_y, Z]$; for a fixed channel $[Y, \nu_y, Z]$, it is a function R_μ of the measure μ describing the probability structure of the source. The *capacity* is the supremum of these rates:

$$(16.11) \qquad C = \sup R_\mu.$$

The capacity is the rate at which information can be sent over the channel if it is used in the most efficient way—by selecting a source that "matches" the channel. (Actually, we do not know in general whether the supremum is achieved.) For technical reasons, we must distinguish two capacities. If the supremum in (16.11) extends over all μ preserved by T_Y, we have the *stationary capacity* C_s. If it only extends over those μ under which T_Y is ergodic, we have the *ergodic capacity* C_e. Clearly $C_e \leq C_s$.

Note that $C_e = C_s = \log s$ for the noiseless channel of the preceding section. Although it is difficult to compute capacities in general, this can be done for the channel without memory.

THEOREM 16.2   *For the channel without memory, we have*

$$C_s = C_e = \max r(p_1, \ldots, p_s),$$

with $(p_1, \ldots, p_s)$ *ranging over probability distributions on* σ.

Proof. Choosing $p_1, \ldots, p_s$ so as to maximize $r(p_1, \ldots, p_s)$ (compactness), and recalling that the Bernoulli shift is ergodic, we see by (16.8) that $C_e \geq \max r(p_1, \ldots, p_s)$.

To prove $C_s \leq \max r(p_1, \ldots, p_s)$, it is enough to show that for any input measure μ, and for any n, we have

$$H(z_0, \ldots, z_{n-1}) - H(z_0, \ldots, z_{n-1} \mid y_0, \ldots, y_{n-1})$$
$$\leq nH(z_0) - nH(z_0 \mid y_0).$$

Since clearly

$$H(z_0, \ldots, z_{n-1}) \leq H(z_0) + \cdots + H(z_{n-1}) = nH(z_0),$$

the result follows by (16.4).

This proof shows that the suprema in the definitions of C_s and C_e are achieved for the channel without memory, which is difficult to prove for more complicated channels.

In Example 16.1, the channel capacity is $\log s = \log 2$; in Example 16.2, it is 0; in Example 16.3, it is $\log 3$.

Ergodicity of the Input-Output Process

One can ask for conditions on the channel $[Y, \nu_y, Z]$ which ensure that the input-output measure P (defined by (16.1)) is ergodic whenever μ is. Necessary and sufficient conditions are not known; we content ourselves with the following result, which will not be used in what follows.

THEOREM 16.3 *A channel without memory has the property that P is ergodic whenever μ is.*

Proof. It is enough to show (Theorem 1.4) that

$$(16.12) \qquad \lim_{n \to \infty} \frac{1}{n} \sum_{l=0}^{n-1} P(E \cap T^{-l}E') = P(E)P(E')$$

for cylinders E and E'. We shall prove (16.9) assuming that $E = \{(y, z) : y_0 = j, z_0 = k\}$ and $E' = \{(y, z) : y_0 = j', z_0 = k'\}$; the proof in the more general case follows the same pattern. The left side of (16.12) is

$$\lim_{n \to \infty} \frac{1}{n} \sum_{l=0}^{n-1} P\{y_0 = j, z_0 = k, y_l = j', z_l = k'\}$$

$$= \lim_{n \to \infty} \frac{1}{n} \sum_{l=0}^{n-1} \mu\{y_0 = j, y_l = j'\} c_{jk} c_{j'k'}$$

$$= \mu\{y_0 = j\}\mu\{y_0 = j'\} c_{jk} c_{j'k'} = P(E)P(E'),$$

where the next-to-last equality holds because of the ergodicity of μ.

Remarks. The ideas here originated with Shannon (1948). McMillan (1953), Feinstein (1954), and Khinchine (1957) gave them their precise mathematical formulation.

Breiman (1960) has extended Theorem 16.2 by proving that $C_e = C_s$, and that the suprema are achieved, for a class of channels with finite memory. See Adler (1961) for extensions of Theorem 16.3.

17. THE CODING THEOREM FOR THE NOISY CHANNEL

The Problem

In general terms, the coding problem for the noisy channel can be described in the following way. Messages from a source $[X, \mu]$ are to be sent through a given noisy channel $[Y, \nu_y, Z]$ to an addressee. We are to insert a coder that will make the operation efficient. We measure the efficiency by the rate at which information is sent from the source

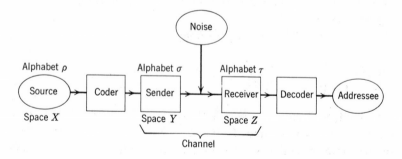

to the receiver, ignoring the problem of how to use the information at the receiver to reconstruct the original message.

A code ϕ from X to Y gives rise to a compound channel from X to Z; that is, the message x is sent through the coder, and then the coded message y is sent through the channel, the received message being z. Let the entropy of the source be h and the capacity—say the stationary capacity—of the channel be C. The direct coding theorem says roughly that if $h \leq C$ then there exists a code ϕ such that the rate through the compound channel is h. The converse coding theorem says roughly that if $h > C$ then no such code ϕ exists. There are various versions of each of these theorems.

Suppose then that we are given a channel $[Y, \nu_y, Z]$ and a code ϕ from X to Y. Clearly $\nu_{\phi(x)}(\cdot)$ is a kernel, and hence $[X, \nu_{\phi(x)}, Z]$ is a channel—the compound channel. For a given measure μ on X, consider the measure P on $X \times Y \times Z$ defined by

(17.1) $$P(A \times B \times C) = \int_{A \cap \phi^{-1}B} \nu_{\phi(x)}(C) \, \mu(dx).$$

The measure P induces marginal distributions P_X, $P_{X \times Y}$, etc., on the various component spaces. Note that $P_X = \mu$, that $P_Y = P_X \phi^{-1} = \mu \phi^{-1}$ (because $P(A \times B \times C) = P(A \cap \phi^{-1}B \times Y \times C)$), and that $P_{X \times Z}$ gives the joint input-output distribution for the source $[X, \mu]$ together with the compound channel $[X, \nu_{\phi(x)}, Z]$.

Let h be the entropy of the source; let C_s be the stationary capacity of the channel $[Y, \nu_y, Z]$. With the measures P_X, P_Z, and $P_{X \times Z}$,

$$R_\mu = h(T_X) + h(T_Z) - h(T_{X \times Z})$$

is the rate of transmission of the source $[X, \mu]$ over the compound channel $[X, \nu_{\phi(x)}, Z]$. The equivocation is the deficit

$$h(T_X) - R_\mu = h(T_{X \times Z}) - h(T_Z)$$

by which this rate falls below the entropy of the source $[X, \mu]$. To find a code for which the rate is high (and the equivocation low)—this we take as our task, ignoring, as already mentioned, the decision problems involved in inferring x from z.

A Simple Converse

The following result is a special case of Theorem 17.3.

THEOREM 17.1   *If ϕ is invertible with respect to μ, then $R_\mu \leq C_s$. If $h > C_s$, therefore, there exists no code, invertible with respect to μ, for which $R_\mu = h$.*

Proof. The rate of transmission of the source $[Y, \mu\phi^{-1}]$ over $[Y, \nu_y, Z]$ is

$$h(T_Y) + h(T_Z) - h(T_{Y \times Z}),$$

a quantity which does not exceed C_s, by the definition of stationary capacity. It is enough, then, to prove

$$h(T_X) + h(T_Z) - h(T_{X \times Z}) = h(T_Y) + h(T_Z) - h(T_{Y \times Z}).$$

(Here the measure for T_Z is P_Z.) Since ϕ is by assumption invertible, T_X and T_Y are isomorphic and hence $h(T_X) = h(T_Y)$. Thus we need only prove

$$h(T_{X \times Z}) = h(T_{Y \times Z}).$$

But if T_X is isomorphic to T_Y under the triple (X_0, Y_0, ϕ_0), then, as follows without difficulty, $T_{X \times Z}$ is isomorphic to $T_{Y \times Z}$ under $(X_0 \times Z, Y_0 \times Z, \psi_0)$, where $\psi_0(x, z) = (\phi_0 x, z)$. This proves the theorem.

Theorem 17.1 reduces to Theorem 15.1 in case $[Y, \nu_y, Z]$ is noiseless. Again the proof would not work without an invariant definition of entropy.

If we assume that μ is ergodic, then so is $\mu\phi^{-1}$, and we may replace C_s in the theorem by C_e. Note that we have not assumed that ϕ is nonanticipating.

In practice, the problem of decoding is not to infer x from y, but to infer x from z, so the assumption of invertibility in Theorem 17.1 is not natural. This assumption is removed in Theorem 17.3.

Comments on the Direct Theorem for the Channel without Memory

It is tempting to try to prove for the channel without memory a hypothetical result like "Theorem" 15.2. The hypothesis was this:

HYPOTHESIS *The source $[X, \mu]$ has entropy h, and the shift T_X, with the measure μ, is isomorphic to any Bernoulli shift with entropy h.*

With the explicit understanding that we shall not succeed in giving for the following "theorem" any proof at all—hypothetical or otherwise—let us state the result and examine the difficulties, which are instructive.

Recall that the structure of a channel without memory is specified by the $s \times t$ matrix (c_{jk}) described in Section 16, and that the capacity $C = C_e = C_s$ is given by the maximum of (16.5).

"THEOREM" 17.2 *If $[X, \mu]$ satisfies the above hypothesis, if the channel is without memory, and if $h \leq C$, then there exists a code ϕ, invertible with respect to μ, such that the rate R_μ over the compound channel satisfies $R_\mu = h$.*

Consider first a special channel without memory $[Y, \nu_y, Z]$ for which it is possible to carry through a proof—the channel in Example 16.3. This channel has capacity $\log 3$. If $h \leq \log 3$, then, for $p_4 = 0$ and for appropriate choices of $p_1, p_2,$ and p_3, the quantities (16.9) and (16.10) have the common value h. Let γ be the measure on Y that makes T_Y the Bernoulli shift $(p_1, \ldots, p_4)$; then $h(T_Y) = h$, the rate of transmission of $[Y, \gamma]$ over $[Y, \nu_y, Z]$ is h, and the equivocation vanishes. By the hypothesis, there exists a code ϕ (from X to Y), invertible with respect to μ, such that $\gamma = \mu\phi^{-1}$. Since ϕ is invertible, it follows as in the proof of Theorem 17.1 that the rate of transmission of $[X, \mu]$ over the compound channel has the same value as the rate of transmission of $[Y, \mu\phi^{-1}]$ over $[Y, \nu_y, Z]$—namely h.

This argument works whenever the channel has the special property that if $h \leq C$ then there exists on Y a measure γ satisfying these three conditions:

(i) T_Y is a Bernoulli shift under γ.

(ii) $[Y, \gamma]$ has entropy h.

(iii) The rate of transmission of $[Y, \gamma]$ over the channel is h (or, equivalently, in view of (ii), the equivocation is 0).

This property holds for the channel in Example 16.3, and it holds for any noiseless channel (hence "Theorem" 15.2), but it fails for the general channel without memory—it fails, for example, if the c_{jk} are all strictly positive.

It might be possible to prove for the general channel without memory that if $h \leq C$ then there exists on Y a measure γ satisfying conditions (ii) and (iii). In order to carry through the above proof, however, it would, even then, be necessary, in the absence of condition (i), to strengthen the basic hypothesis so as to ensure the isomorphism of T_X (with the measure μ) and T_Y (with the measure γ). To convert "Theorem" 15.2 into a genuine theorem for (say) a mixing Markov source $[X, \mu]$ would require proving the completeness of entropy among the mixing Markov shifts; to convert "Theorem" 17.2 into a genuine theorem for the same source would require proving the completeness of entropy for some broader class of shifts—one broad enough to include T_Y under the measure γ.

These remarks in effect outline a possible program for proving the direct coding theorem for the channel without memory. Sections 18 and 19 can be regarded as a finite, constructive approximation to this program: there we construct a γ approximately satisfying (ii) and (iii), and then we construct a nearly invertible ϕ that carries μ into γ.

A Refinement of the Converse*

Theorem 17.1 shows that if an invertible code is inserted between the source and the sender, then the rate of transmission from source to receiver cannot exceed the capacity of the channel. It is intuitively clear that this should also be true if the code is not invertible or if it is a *stochastic code*. A stochastic code is simply a channel $[X, \zeta_x, Y]$; if the kernel $\zeta_x(\cdot)$ is a unit mass at ϕx, we have again an ordinary code ϕ. The compound channel which results from inserting the stochastic code is the channel $[X, \beta_x, Z]$, where the kernel $\beta_x(\cdot)$ is defined by

$$\beta_x(C) = \int_Y \zeta_x(dy)\, \nu_y(C).$$

(Note that $\beta_x(C)$ is measurable in x.) We shall show that the rate of transmission of $[X, \mu]$ over $[X, \beta_x, Z]$ cannot exceed the rate of transmission of $[Y, \lambda]$ over $[Y, \nu_y, Z]$, where $\lambda(B) = \int_X \mu(dx)\, \zeta_x(B)$; of

---

* The rest of this section may be omitted.

course, this second rate cannot exceed the stationary capacity C_s of $[Y, \nu_y, Z]$.

Define a measure P on $X \times Y \times Z$ by

$$(17.2) \qquad P(A \times B \times C) = \int_A \int_B \int_C \mu(dx)\, \zeta_x(dy)\, \nu_y(dz)$$

$$= \int_A \int_B \mu(dx)\, \zeta_x(dy)\, \nu_y(C).$$

(If the code $[X, \zeta_x, Y]$ is nonstochastic, (17.2) reduces to (17.1).) Let $\mathscr{A}$ be the time-0 field for X, as embedded in $X \times Y \times Z$—that is, $\mathscr{A}$ is the finite subfield of $\mathscr{X} \times \mathscr{Y} \times \mathscr{Z}$ with atoms $\{(x, y, z): x_0 = i\}$, $i \in \rho$. Similarly, let $\mathscr{B}$ and $\mathscr{C}$ be the time-0 fields for Y and Z, as embedded in $X \times Y \times Z$. If T is the shift on $X \times Y \times Z$ (with the measure P defined by (17.2)), then the two rates mentioned above are

$$R(x \to z) = h(\mathscr{A}, T) + h(\mathscr{C}, T) - h(\mathscr{A} \vee \mathscr{C}, T)$$

and

$$R(y \to z) = h(\mathscr{B}, T) + h(\mathscr{C}, T) - h(\mathscr{B} \vee \mathscr{C}, T).$$

We want to prove the intuitively obvious relationship $R(x \to z) \le R(y \to z)$, which reduces to

$$(17.3) \qquad h(\mathscr{A} \vee \mathscr{C}, T) - h(\mathscr{A}, T) \ge h(\mathscr{B} \vee \mathscr{C}, T) - h(\mathscr{B}, T).$$

Let $\mathscr{X}_0 = \vee_{n=-\infty}^{\infty} T^n \mathscr{A}$, $\mathscr{Y}_0 = \vee_{n=-\infty}^{\infty} T^n \mathscr{B}$, and $\mathscr{Z}_0 = \vee_{n=-\infty}^{\infty} T^n \mathscr{C}$; note that $\mathscr{X}_0$, for example, consists of the sets $A \times Y \times Z$ with A in $\mathscr{X}$. The basic fact we use is that $M \in \mathscr{Z}_0$ implies

$$(17.4) \qquad P\{M \,\|\, \mathscr{X}_0 \vee \mathscr{Y}_0\} = P\{M \,\|\, \mathscr{Y}_0\} \quad \text{a.e.}$$

This relation, which is analogous to the Markov property, follows from (17.2)—if $M = X \times Y \times C$, the common value of the two sides of (17.4) at the point (x, y, z) is $\nu_y(C)$.

By (12.5), we have $h(\mathscr{A} \vee \mathscr{C}, T) = H(\mathscr{A} \vee \mathscr{C} \mid \mathscr{A}^- \vee \mathscr{C}^-)$, where $\mathscr{A}^- = \vee_{n<0} T^n \mathscr{A}$ and $\mathscr{C}^- = \vee_{n<0} T^n \mathscr{C}$. By Theorem 12.3, then,

$$h(\mathscr{A} \vee \mathscr{C}, T) = H(\mathscr{A} \vee \mathscr{C} \mid \mathscr{A}^- \vee \mathscr{C}^-)$$
$$= H(\mathscr{C} \mid \mathscr{C}^- \vee \mathscr{X}_0) + H(\mathscr{A} \mid \mathscr{A}^-).$$

Similarly,

$$h(\mathscr{B} \vee \mathscr{C}, T) = H(\mathscr{B} \vee \mathscr{C} \mid \mathscr{B}^- \vee \mathscr{C}^-)$$
$$= H(\mathscr{C} \mid \mathscr{C}^- \vee \mathscr{Y}_0) + H(\mathscr{B} \mid \mathscr{B}^-).$$

Finally, $h(\mathscr{A}, T) = H(\mathscr{A} \mid \mathscr{A}^-)$, and $h(\mathscr{B}, T) = H(\mathscr{B} \mid \mathscr{B}^-)$. Therefore, (17.3) is equivalent to

$$H(\mathscr{C} \mid \mathscr{C}^- \vee \mathscr{X}_0) \geq H(\mathscr{C} \mid \mathscr{C}^- \vee \mathscr{Y}_0).$$

Since, by (C_3) of Section 12,

$$H(\mathscr{C} \mid \mathscr{C}^- \vee \mathscr{X}_0) \geq H(\mathscr{C} \mid \mathscr{C}^- \vee \mathscr{X}_0 \vee \mathscr{Y}_0),$$

the whole problem reduces to that of proving

(17.5) $$H(\mathscr{C} \mid \mathscr{C}^- \vee \mathscr{X}_0 \vee \mathscr{Y}_0) = H(\mathscr{C} \mid \mathscr{C}^- \vee \mathscr{Y}_0).$$

If we show that

(17.6) $$H(\mathscr{C} \mid \mathscr{C}^{-n} \vee \mathscr{X}_0 \vee \mathscr{Y}_0) = H(\mathscr{C} \mid \mathscr{C}^{-n} \vee \mathscr{Y}_0),$$

where $\mathscr{C}^{-n} = \bigvee_{-n \leq k < 0} T^k \mathscr{C}$, then (17.5) will follow by an application of Theorem 12.1. But, by (C_1) of Section 12, (17.6) is the same as

$$H(\mathscr{C} \vee \mathscr{C}^{-n} \mid \mathscr{X}_0 \vee \mathscr{Y}_0) - H(\mathscr{C}^{-n} \mid \mathscr{X}_0 \vee \mathscr{Y}_0)$$
$$= H(\mathscr{C} \vee \mathscr{C}^{-n} \mid \mathscr{Y}_0) - H(\mathscr{C}^{-n} \mid \mathscr{Y}_0).$$

And, finally, we have $H(\mathscr{C}^{-n} \mid \mathscr{X}_0 \vee \mathscr{Y}_0) = H(\mathscr{C}^{-n} \mid \mathscr{Y}_0)$ and

$$H(\mathscr{C} \vee \mathscr{C}^{-n} \mid \mathscr{X}_0 \vee \mathscr{Y}_0) = H(\mathscr{C} \vee \mathscr{C}^{-n} \mid \mathscr{Y}_0)$$

by (17.4). We have proved the following result.

THEOREM 17.3   *For any stochastic code we have* $R(x \to z) \leq R(y \to z) \leq C_s$. *If* h, *the entropy of* $[X, \mu]$, *exceeds* C_s, *therefore, there is no stochastic code for which* $R(x \to z) = h$.

Remarks. Theorems 17.1 and 17.3 may lie hidden in the results of Pinsker (1960a).

18. FEINSTEIN'S THEOREM

We turn now to a sober analysis of the direct coding problem for the noisy channel. We limit ourselves to the channel without memory.

The theorem itself is given in Section 19; in this section we prove two preliminary results due to Feinstein.

The Decision Scheme

The channel without memory is specified by the $s \times t$ matrix (c_{jk}) of Section 16; its capacity $C = C_s = C_e$ is given by the maximum of (16.5).

THEOREM 18.1 *Consider a channel without memory and with capacity C. If $0 < \epsilon < C$, then there exists a positive integer $b_1(\epsilon)$ such that if $b \geq b_1(\epsilon)$, then σ^b contains N distinct points $u_1, \ldots, u_N$, and τ^b decomposes into N disjoint sets $V_1, \ldots, V_N$, such that the u_l and V_l satisfy*

$$(18.1) \quad P\{(z_1, \ldots, z_b) \in V_l \mid (y_1, \ldots, y_b) = u_l\} > 1 - \epsilon, l = 1, \ldots, N,$$

and such that N satisfies

$$(18.2) \qquad\qquad N > e^{b(C-\epsilon)}.$$

If u_l is the b-tuple $(j_1, \ldots, j_b)$ in σ^b, then the left-hand member of (18.1) is simply

$$\sum c_{j_1 k_1} \cdots c_{j_b k_b},$$

where the sum extends over those b-tuples $(k_1, \ldots, k_b)$ in the subset V_l of τ^b. Therefore the channel alone determines the conditional probabilities, so that the theorem, since it involves only the channel, applies for any input measure γ on Y.

The point of the theorem is this. Suppose the message $(y_1, \ldots, y_b)$ is sent and is received as $(z_1, \ldots, z_b)$. If $(y_1, \ldots, y_b)$ is known to be one of $u_1, \ldots, u_N$, and if $(z_1, \ldots, z_b)$ lies in V_l, then, because of (18.1), it appears reasonable to guess that $(y_1, \ldots, y_b)$ is in fact u_l. And if it is possible to encode the source invertibly, or nearly invertibly, in such a way that the transmitted message lies in $\{u_1, \ldots, u_N\}$ with high probability, then it should be possible to reconstruct the source's original message from the received one with good accuracy, and hence the equivocation should be low. The u_l and V_l provide a scheme for deciding what the transmitted message was. (See the discussion of rate and equivocation in Section 16.) This is the idea that lies at the base of the coding theorem in the next section.

As for the proof of Theorem 18.1, the idea is this. Suppose the alphabet σ contains just two letters, say 0 and 1. Assuming $b = 2a$ is even, let the sequence u_1 consist of a 0's followed by a 1's and let u_2 consist of a 1's followed by a 0's. If b is large, and if $(y_1, \ldots, y_b) = u_1$, then, with high conditional probability, the frequency count of $(z_1, \ldots, z_a)$ will closely match the first row of the matrix (c_{jk}), while the frequency count of $(z_{a+1}, \ldots, z_b)$ will closely match the second row. If $(y_1, \ldots, y_b) = u_2$, the same thing is true, but with the roles of the two rows of (c_{jk}) interchanged. Since these two rows are different (unless the capacity is 0), the distribution of $(z_1, \ldots, z_b)$ under the condition $(y_1, \ldots, y_b) = u_1$ is very different (for large b) from its distribution under the condition $(y_1, \ldots, y_b) = u_2$—and this is because the 0's and 1's are dissimilarly placed in u_1 and u_2—which permits us to find disjoint sets V_1 and V_2 satisfying (18.1). The proof that follows depends on a careful analysis of the conditional distributions of output frequency counts for *large* classes of dissimilar input sequences.

Since the conclusion of Theorem 18.1 becomes more stringent as ϵ decreases, we may, in proving it, assume that

$$0 < \epsilon < \tfrac{1}{2}.$$

Since the result is independent of a specification of the input measure γ, we may choose one that makes the proof easy. Choose γ so that the y_n are independent under γ, with $\gamma\{y_0 = j\} = p_j$, where $p_1, \ldots, p_s$ are chosen so as to maximize the function $r(p_1, \ldots, p_s)$ defined by (16.5). Then, by Theorem 16.2,

$$C = H(O) - H(O \mid I),$$

where, if $q_k = \sum_j p_j c_{jk}$,

$$H(O) = \sum_k \eta(q_k)$$

is the entropy of a single letter of the output of the channel, and

$$H(O \mid I) = \sum_{jk} p_j \eta(c_{jk})$$

is the conditional entropy of this letter given the input to the channel. (Throughout the proof, the index j ranges over σ and the index k ranges over τ.)

Choose λ so that

(18.3) $$\lambda > 1, \quad \frac{s}{\lambda^2} < \frac{\epsilon}{2},$$

where s is the size of σ. Now choose K so that

(18.4) $$-3s\lambda^{3/2} \sum_k \log q_k < K$$

and

(18.5) $$-3\lambda^{3/2} \sum_{jk} \log c_{jk} < K,$$

where the sums are restricted to those k for which $q_k > 0$ and to those (j, k) for which $c_{jk} > 0$. Finally, choose a positive integer $b_1(\epsilon)$ so that if $b \geq b_1(\epsilon)$ (as we assume from now on), then

(18.6) $$\frac{\log 4/\epsilon + 2K\sqrt{b}}{b} < \epsilon.$$

Let us denote by Π the measure on $\sigma^b \times \tau^b$ induced by $(y_1, \ldots, y_b, z_1, \ldots, z_b)$;

(18.7) $$\Pi(E) = P\{(y_1, \ldots, y_b, z_1, \ldots, z_b) \in E\}$$

for $E \subset \sigma^b \times \tau^b$. The measure Π assigns mass $p_{j_1} \cdots p_{j_b} c_{j_1 k_1} \cdots c_{j_b k_b}$ to the point $(j_1, \ldots, j_b, k_1, \ldots, k_b)$. If $B \subset \sigma^b [C \subset \tau^b]$, we shall write $\Pi(B)[\Pi(C)]$ where we really should write $\Pi(B \times \tau^b)[\Pi(\sigma^b \times C)]$; this should cause no confusion. Finally, for $C \subset \tau^b$ and $u \in \sigma^b$, we write

(18.8) $$\Pi_u(C) = P\{(z_1, \ldots, z_b) \in C \mid (y_1, \ldots, y_b) = u\}.$$

If $u = (j_1, \ldots, j_b)$, then, of course, $\Pi_u(C)$ is $c_{j_1 k_1} \cdots c_{j_b k_b}$ summed over the $(k_1, \ldots, k_b)$ in C.

For $u \in \sigma^b$ and $j \in \sigma$, let $N(j \mid u)$ be the number of components of u that equal j; similarly, for $v \in \tau^b$ and $k \in \tau$, let $N(k \mid v)$ be the number of components of v that equal k; finally, for $u \in \sigma^b$, $v \in \tau^b$, $j \in \sigma$, and $k \in \tau$, let $N(jk \mid uv)$ be the number of l, $1 \leq l \leq b$, for which the lth components of u and v are, respectively, j and k. Then

(18.9) $$\Pi(v) = \exp \sum_k N(k \mid v) \log q_k$$

and

(18.10) $$\Pi_u(v) = \exp \sum_{jk} N(jk \mid uv) \log c_{jk}.$$

We say that u is a *p-sequence* if

$$|N(j \mid u) - bp_j| < \lambda\sqrt{b}$$

for all $j \in \sigma$; we say that v is *generated* by u if

$$|N(jk \mid uv) - N(j \mid u)c_{jk}| < \lambda\sqrt{N(j \mid u)}$$

for all $j \in \sigma$ and $k \in \tau$.

We shall need the following four lemmas, of which the first two follow immediately from Chebyshev's inequality and (18.3).

LEMMA 1   *If S is the set of p-sequences, then*

$$\Pi(S) > 1 - \frac{\epsilon}{2} \geq \frac{1}{2}.$$

LEMMA 2   *If G_u is the set of sequences in τ^b generated by u, then*

$$\Pi_u(G_u) > 1 - \frac{\epsilon}{2}.$$

LEMMA 3   *If v is generated by some p-sequence, then*

$$\Pi(v) \leq e^{-bH(O) + K\sqrt{b}}.$$

LEMMA 4   *If B_u is the number of elements in G_u then, for each p-sequence u, we have*

$$B_u \leq e^{bH(O|I) + K\sqrt{b}}.$$

To prove Lemma 3, note that if u generates v then

$$N(k \mid v) = \sum_j N(jk \mid uv) \geq \sum_j [N(j \mid u)c_{jk} - \lambda\sqrt{N(j \mid u)}],$$

while, if u is a *p-sequence*,

$$bp_j - \lambda\sqrt{b} \leq N(j \mid u) \leq bp_j + \lambda\sqrt{b} \leq 2\lambda b,$$

so that

$$N(k \mid v) \geq b \sum_j p_j c_{jk} - s\lambda\sqrt{b} - 2s\lambda^{3/2}\sqrt{b} \geq bq_k - 3s\lambda^{3/2}\sqrt{b}.$$

The lemma follows from this together with (18.9) and (18.4).

To prove Lemma 4, observe that if u is a p-sequence and if u generates v, then

$$N(jk \mid uv) \leq N(j \mid u)c_{jk} + \lambda\sqrt{N(j \mid u)}$$

$$\leq (bp_j + \lambda\sqrt{b})c_{jk} + \lambda\sqrt{bp_j} + \lambda\sqrt{b}$$

$$\leq bp_j c_{jk} + 3\lambda^{3/2}\sqrt{b},$$

so that, by (18.10) and (18.5),

$$\Pi_u(v) \geq e^{-bH(0|I)-K\sqrt{b}}.$$

Since $\Pi_u(G_u) \leq 1$, the lemma follows.

To prove Theorem 18.1 itself, consider elements $u_1, \ldots, u_N$ of σ^b and subsets $V_1, \ldots, V_N$ of τ^b satisfying the following four conditions.

(i) Each u_l is a p-sequence.

(ii) For each l, $\Pi_{u_l}(V_l) > 1 - \epsilon$.

(iii) Each V_l consists of those sequences generated by u_l and not contained in $V_1 \cup \cdots \cup V_{l-1}$; that is, $V_l = G_{u_l} - (V_1 \cup \cdots \cup V_{l-1})$.

(iv) There are no u_{N+1} and V_{N+1} such that $u_1, \ldots, u_{N+1}$ and $V_1, \ldots, V_{N+1}$ satisfy (i), (ii), and (iii).

By Lemmas 1 and 2, there exist such u_l and V_l (perhaps with $N = 1$). Now if u is a p-sequence not in the set $u_1, \ldots, u_N$, then

(18.11) $$\Pi_u(G_u \cap (V_1 \cup \cdots \cup V_N)) \geq \frac{\epsilon}{2}.$$

For otherwise we could take $u_{N+1} = u$ and

$$V_{N+1} = G_u - (V_1 \cup \cdots \cup V_N),$$

contradicting (iv), since we would have $\Pi_{u_{N+1}}(V_{N+1}) = \Pi_u(G_u) - \Pi_u(G_u \cap (V_1 \cup \cdots \cup V_N)) > 1 - \epsilon/2 - \epsilon/2 = 1 - \epsilon$ by Lemma 2. On the other hand, if u is in $u_1, \ldots, u_N$, say $u = u_l$, then $\Pi_u(G_u \cap (V_1 \cup \cdots \cup V_N)) \geq \Pi_u(V_l) = \Pi_{u_l}(V_l) > 1 - \epsilon > \epsilon/2$. Thus (18.11) holds for any p-sequence u.

Therefore

$$\Pi(V_1 \cup \cdots \cup V_N) \geq \sum_{u \in S} \Pi(u)\Pi_u(V_1 \cup \cdots \cup V_N) \geq \frac{\epsilon}{2}\Pi(S) \geq \frac{\epsilon}{4}$$

by Lemma 1. It follows by Lemma 3 that the number of elements in $V_1 \cup \cdots \cup V_N$ is at least

$$\frac{\epsilon}{4} e^{bH(O)-K\sqrt{b}}.$$

But, by Lemma 4, the number of elements in $V_1 \cup \cdots \cup V_N$ is at most

$$N e^{bH(O|I)+K\sqrt{b}}.$$

Combining these estimates, we obtain, by (18.6),

$$N \geq \frac{\epsilon}{4} e^{bC-2K\sqrt{b}} > e^{b(C-\epsilon)},$$

which completes the proof. (If the V_l do not exhaust τ^b, enlarge one of them.)

Application

Recalling once more that Theorem 18.1 is true for any input measure γ on Y, let us suppose the input measure has the property that

(18.12)

$$P\{(y_1, \ldots, y_b) \in \{u_1, \ldots, u_N\}\} = \gamma\{(y_1, \ldots, y_b) \in \{u_1, \ldots, u_N\}\} = 1.$$

Our next result asserts that in this circumstance only small uncertainty attaches to the transmitted message $(y_1, \ldots, y_b)$, if the received one $(z_1, \ldots, z_b)$ is known. The remaining problem—that of constructing a nearly invertible code for which (18.12) holds; it is in this connection that (18.2) enters—is treated in the next section.

THEOREM 18.2 *With the u_l and V_l of Theorem* 18.1, *we have*

(18.13) $H(y_1, \ldots, y_b \mid z_1, \ldots, z_b) < \eta(\epsilon) + \eta(1 - \epsilon) + \epsilon \log t^b$,

provided (18.12) *holds and* $\epsilon < 1/e$.

Proof. Recall that t is the size of τ. We must bound from above the quantity $H(y_1, \ldots, y_b \mid z_1, \ldots, z_b) = H(\mathscr{B}' \mid \mathscr{C}')$, where $\mathscr{B}'$ is the finite subfield of $\mathscr{Y} \times \mathscr{Z}$ with atoms $\{(y, z) : (y_1, \ldots, y_b) = u\}$, $u \in \sigma^b$, and $\mathscr{C}'$ is the one with atoms $\{(y, z) : (z_1, \ldots, z_b) = v\}$, $v \in \tau^b$. Let $\mathscr{B}$ have atoms $B_l = \{(y, z) : (y_1, \ldots, y_b) = u_l\}$, $l = 1, \ldots, N$. Actually, these sets exhaust $Y \times Z$ only to within a set of measure 0; amalgamate this set of measure 0 with one of the B_l (this makes no difference to the computations). Finally, let $\mathscr{C}$ have atoms $C_l = \{(y, z): (z_1, \ldots, z_b) \in V_l\}, l = 1, \ldots, N$.

Because of (18.12), each nontrivial atom of $\mathscr{B}'$ differs by a set of measure 0 from some nontrivial atom of $\mathscr{B}$, and conversely. From this and the fact that $\mathscr{C} \subset \mathscr{C}'$, we obtain

(18.14)

$$H(y_1, \ldots, y_b \mid z_1, \ldots, z_b) = H(\mathscr{B}' \mid \mathscr{C}') = H(\mathscr{B} \mid \mathscr{C}') \le H(\mathscr{B} \mid \mathscr{C}).$$

For each l we have, by (18.1), $P(C_l \mid B_l) > 1 - \epsilon$. It follows that $\Sigma_l P(B_l)P(C_l{}^c \mid B_l) < \epsilon$, and hence, by Theorem 6.2, that

(18.15) $\qquad H(\mathscr{B} \mid \mathscr{C}) \le \eta(\epsilon) + \eta(1 - \epsilon) + \epsilon \log(N - 1),$

provided ϵ is small enough that $\eta(t)$ is nondecreasing in $[0, \epsilon]$ and nonincreasing in $[1 - \epsilon, 1]$, which is true if $\epsilon < 1/e$. The inequalities (18.14) and (18.15) combine to give (18.13).

Remarks. Feinstein (1954 and 1958) first proved the results of this section (for channels with finite memory, in fact). The proof of Theorem 18.1 given here is that of Wolfowitz (1961). In addition to generalizations of Theorem 18.1, Wolfowitz's detailed treatment includes results converse to it—results saying that if (18.1) holds then N cannot exceed a certain upper bound—through which he approaches the converse half of the coding theorem.

19. BLOCK CODES

Definition

Consider the channel of the preceding section—the channel without memory—together with an *ergodic* source $[X, \mu]$ of entropy h. The purpose of this section is to show that if $h < C$ and $\delta > 0$, then there exists a nonanticipating code ϕ from X to Y such that if x is sent through the compound channel (see Section 17), then the rate exceeds $h - \delta$.

Actually, we shall prove the theorem in terms of *b-block codes*. For each n let

$$\bar{x}_n = (x_{nb+1}, \ldots, x_{nb+b});$$

then $\bar{x} = (\dots, \bar{x}_{-1}, \bar{x}_0, \bar{x}_1, \dots)$ is an element of the space $\bar{X}$ of sequences of elements of ρ^b. Now define $\bar{y}$, $\bar{Y}$, $\bar{z}$, and $\bar{Z}$ similarly. By a b-block code, ϕ, we mean a mapping $\phi: X \to Y$ determined by a (measurable and stationary) code $\bar{\phi}: \bar{X} \to \bar{Y}$ via the formula

$$((\phi x)_{nb+1}, \dots, (\phi x)_{nb+b}) = (\bar{\phi}\bar{x})_n.$$

A b-block code is measurable, but not quite stationary, being stationary only in blocks of length b: $\phi T_X^b x = T_Y^b \phi x$. The b-block code ϕ is said to be nonanticipating if $\bar{\phi}$ is. (In this case the transmitter must lag b time units behind the source; given $\cdots x_{nb-1}, x_{nb}$—that is, given $\cdots \bar{x}_{n-2}, \bar{x}_{n-1}$—the coder can produce the block $\bar{y}_{n-1}$ of the coded message, and the letters $y_{(n-1)b+1}, \dots, y_{nb}$ in it can be transmitted during the following b units of time.) The code we shall produce depends only on the present, in that $(\bar{\phi}\bar{x})_n$ depends only on $\bar{x}_n$.

Since ϕ is not stationary, the previous definitions of rate and equivocation, etc., do not apply directly. We define these quantities for x, y, z by dividing by b the corresponding quantities for $\bar{x}$, $\bar{y}$, $\bar{z}$, although it is not hard to see that such limits as $\lim_n n^{-1}H(z_1, \dots, z_n)$ exist anyway.

The Direct Theorem by Block Codes

THEOREM 19.1 *Consider the channel without memory and an ergodic source* $[X, \mu]$. *Let C be the capacity of the channel and let h be the entropy of the source. If $h < C$ and $\delta > 0$, then there exists, for some b, a b-block code ϕ such that if x is transmitted through the compound channel, then the rate exceeds $h - \delta$.*
Proof. Choose ϵ so that

$$h + \epsilon < C - \epsilon$$

$$\eta(\epsilon) + \eta(1 - \epsilon) + \epsilon \log t < \delta/2$$

$$\epsilon \log r < \delta/2$$

$$\epsilon < 1/e.$$

(As usual, r and t are the sizes of ρ and τ.)

The calculations that follow are all based on probabilities

$$P(A \times B \times C) = \int_{A \cap \phi^{-1}B} \nu_{\phi(x)}(C)\, \mu(dx),$$

where ν_y is the kernel of the channel in question, and ϕ is the block code to be constructed.

If b exceeds the $b_0(\epsilon)$ of Theorem 13.2, then, no matter what ϕ may be, ρ^b decomposes into two sets H and L such that

$$P\{(x_1, \ldots, x_b) \in L\} < \epsilon,$$

and such that

(19.1) $$P\{(x_1, \ldots, x_b) = w\} > e^{-b(h+\epsilon)}$$

holds for each $w \in H$. If b exceeds the $b_1(\epsilon)$ of Theorems 18.1 and 18.2, then

(19.2) $$H(y_1, \ldots, y_b \mid z_1, \ldots, z_b) < \eta(\epsilon) + \eta(1 - \epsilon) + \epsilon b \log t,$$

provided ϕ is such that there is probability 1 that $(y_1, \ldots, y_b)$ is among the special elements $u_1, \ldots, u_N$ of σ^b. Recall (see (18.2)) that

$$N \geq e^{b(C-\epsilon)}.$$

Now choose and fix a b exceeding both $b_0(\epsilon)$ and $b_1(\epsilon)$. It follows from (19.1) that the number of elements in H is less than $e^{b(h+\epsilon)} < e^{b(C-\epsilon)} \leq N$. Therefore there exists a mapping ψ from ρ^b into σ^b such that H is carried in a one-to-one manner onto a proper subset $\psi(H)$ of $\{u_1, \ldots, u_N\}$, and all elements of L are carried onto some one u_l not in $\psi(H)$. Define $\bar{\phi}$, and hence ϕ, by

$$(\bar{\phi}\bar{x})_n = \psi(\bar{x}_n).$$

By construction, $\bar{y}_1 = \psi(\bar{x}_1)$ is in the set $\{u_1, \ldots, u_N\}$, so that, by (19.2),

(19.3) $$H(\bar{y}_1 \mid \bar{z}_1) < \eta(\epsilon) + \eta(1 - \epsilon) + \epsilon b \log t < \frac{b\delta}{2}.$$

If $\bar{y}_1$ lies in $\psi(H)$, then it completely determines $\bar{x}_1$; therefore, $u \in \psi(H)$ implies that the quantity

(19.4) $$\sum_{w \in \rho^b} \eta(P\{\bar{x}_1 = w \mid \bar{y}_1 = u\})$$

vanishes. Since ρ^b has r^b elements, (19.4) is in any case at most $\log r^b$. From the relation $P\{\bar{y}_1 \in \psi(H)\} = P\{\bar{x}_1 \in H\}$ it follows that

(19.5) $$H(\bar{x}_1 \mid \bar{y}_1) \leq \epsilon \log r^b \leq \frac{b\delta}{2}.$$

Now

$$H(\bar{x}_1 \mid \bar{z}_1) \leq H(\bar{x}_1, \bar{y}_1 \mid \bar{z}_1) = H(\bar{y}_1 \mid \bar{z}_1) + H(\bar{x}_1 \mid \bar{y}_1, \bar{z}_1)$$
$$\leq H(\bar{y}_1 \mid \bar{z}_1) + H(\bar{x}_1 \mid \bar{y}_1).$$

Applying (19.3) and (19.5) to this, we obtain

$$H(\bar{x}_1 \mid \bar{z}_1) < b\delta.$$

But

$$H(\bar{x}_1, \ldots, \bar{x}_n \mid \bar{z}_1, \ldots, \bar{z}_n) \leq \sum_{i=1}^{n} H(\bar{x}_i \mid \bar{z}_1, \ldots, \bar{z}_n)$$
$$\leq \sum_{i=1}^{n} H(\bar{x}_i \mid \bar{z}_i) = nH(\bar{x}_1 \mid \bar{z}_1),$$

so that

$$\frac{1}{n} H(\bar{x}_1, \ldots, \bar{x}_n \mid \bar{z}_1, \ldots, \bar{z}_n) < b\delta.$$

Passing to the limit, we see that the equivocation for the b-block process ($\bar{x}$ to $\bar{z}$ through the compound channel) is less than $b\delta$. Dividing by b, we see that the equivocation for the transmission of x itself is less than δ. Therefore the rate exceeds $h - \delta$.

Note that the ϕ constructed is in general not invertible. This is immaterial anyway, since the problem of decoding is to return from z to x, not to return from y to x. We have achieved our objective of bounding by δ the equivocation of the compound channel.

Throughout this chapter, we have measured the efficiency of a code linking a source with a channel by the rate of transmission of information from source to receiver. In Section 17, we ignored the problem of using the information at the receiver to recover the original message. In Theorem 19.1, on the other hand, we theoretically construct an efficient code by explicitly facing up to this problem, using Feinstein's theorem. The actual construction of codes in practical situations, however, is quite another matter.

It is clear that Theorems 17.1 and 17.3, on the impossibility of certain codes, could also be formulated in terms of *b*-block codes. On the other hand, it is not clear how to reformulate Theorem 19.1 so as to eliminate them.

Remarks. These theorems originated with Shannon (1948), although his proofs were incomplete. Feinstein (1954) gave the first complete proof. See also Feinstein (1958), Khinchine (1957), Takano (1958), Dobrushin (1959), and Pinsker (1960*a*). For broader treatments of communication theory, see Reza (1961) and Meyer-Eppler (1959).

Bibliography

While this list contains all the recent papers on the isomorphism problem that I know of, it hardly touches the literature of general ergodic theory or the huge literature of information theory.

Translations of Russian books and papers are indicated, except for papers in *Doklady*. The American Mathematical Society has translated all mathematical papers in this journal, starting with volume 130 (1960).

L. M. Abramov (1959*a*), "Entropy of induced automorphisms," *Dokl. Akad. Nauk SSSR* **128**, 647–650.

(1959*b*), "On the entropy of flows," *Dokl. Akad Nauk. SSSR* **128**, 873–876.

(1959*c*), "Entropy of automorphisms of a solenoid group," *Theory Prob. Appl.* **4**, 231–236.

(1960), "Some questions on the metric theory of dynamical systems," Dissertation, Moscow State University.

L. M. Abramov and V. A. Rohlin (1962), "Entropy of a skew product of mappings with invariant measure," *Vestnik Leningrad. Univ.* **17**, no. 7, 5–13.

Roy L. Adler (1961), "Ergodic and mixing properties of infinite memory channels," *Proc. Amer. Math. Soc.* **12**, 924–930.

(1962), "On a conjecture of Fomin," *Proc. Amer. Math. Soc.* **13**, 433–436.

(1963), "A note on the entropy of skew product transformations," *Proc. Amer. Math. Soc.* **14**, 665–669.

R. L. Adler, A. G. Konheim, and M. H. McAndrew (1965), "Topological entropy," to appear.

Patrick Billingsley (1960), "Hausdorff dimension in probability theory," *Ill. J. Math.* **4**, 187–209.

(1961*a*), "Hausdorff dimension in probability theory II," *Ill. J. Math.* **5**, 291–298.

(1961*b*), "On the coding theorem for the noiseless channel," *Ann. Math. Statist.* **32**, 594–601.

181

G. D. Birkhoff (1931), "Proof of the ergodic theorem," *Proc. Nat. Acad. U.S.A.* **17**, 656–660.

J. R. Blum and W. E. Franck (1965), "A strong mixing process which is not tail field trivial," to appear.

J. R. Blum and D. L. Hanson (1963), "On the isomorphism problem for Bernoulli schemes," *Bull. Amer. Math. Soc.* **69**, 221–223.

Leo Breiman (1957), "The individual ergodic theorem of information theory," *Ann. Math. Statist.* **28**, 809–811; Correction note, *ibid.* **31** (1960), 809–810.

(1960), "On achieving channel capacity in finite-memory channels," *Ill. J. Math.* **4**, 246–252.

Thomas A. Brown (1963), "Entropy and conjugacy," *Ann. Math. Statist.* **34**, 226–232.

K. L. Chung (1961), "A note on the ergodic theorem of information theory," *Ann. Math. Statist.* **32**, 612–614.

e. e. cummings (1958), *Eimi.* New York: Grove Press.

R. L. Dobrushin (1959), "General formulation of the Shannon theorems of information theory," *Uspehi Matem. Nauk* **14** (90), 3–104 (German translation in Arbeiten zur Informationstheorie IV).

W. Doeblin (1940), "Remarques sur la théorie métrique des fractions continues," *Compositio Math.* **7**, 353–371.

J. L. Doob (1953), *Stochastic Processes.* New York: John Wiley and Sons.

Nelson Dunford and Jacob T. Schwartz (1958), *Linear Operators, Part* I. New York: Interscience Publishers.

H. G. Eggleston (1949), "The fractional dimension of a set defined by decimal properties," *Quart. J. Math. Oxford Ser.* **20**, 31–36.

A. Feinstein (1954), "A new basic theorem of information theory," *I.R.E., Trans. P.G.I.T., September* 1954, 2–22.

(1958), *Foundations of Information Theory.* New York: McGraw-Hill.

William Feller (1957), *An Introduction to Probability Theory and Its Applications,* second edition. New York: John Wiley and Sons.

A. L. Genis (1961), "Metric properties of the endomorphisms of the *n*-dimensional torus," *Dokl. Akad. Nauk SSSR* **138**, 991–992.

I. J. Good (1941), "The fractional dimensional theory of continued fractions," *Proc. Camb. Phil. Soc.* **37**, 199–228.

Robert Graves (1955), *The Greek Myths,* two volumes. Baltimore: Penguin Books.

Edgar Guest (1917), *Just Folks.* Chicago: Reilly and Lee.

B. M. Gurevich (1960), "The entropy of a flux of oricycles," *Dokl. Akad. Nauk SSSR* **136**, 768–770.

Paul R. Halmos (1949), "Measurable transformations," *Bull. Amer. Math. Soc.* **55**, 1015–1034.

(1950), *Measure Theory.* New York: D. Van Nostrand.

(1956), *Lectures on Ergodic Theory.* Tokyo: The Mathematical Society of Japan.

(1959), "Entropy in ergodic theory," mimeographed notes, The University of Chicago.

(1961), "Recent progress in ergodic theory," *Bull. Amer. Math. Soc.* **67**, 70–80.

G. H. Hardy and E. M. Wright (1959), *An Introduction to the Theory of Numbers*, fourth edition. Oxford: Clarendon Press.

T. E. Harris (1955), "On chains of infinite order," *Pacific J. Math.* **5**, 707–724.

Eberhard Hopf (1937), *Ergodentheorie*, Erg. Math. **5**, no. 2. Berlin-Göttingen-Heidelberg: Springer-Verlag.

Withold Hurewicz and Henry Wallman (1948), *Dimension Theory*. Princeton: Princeton University Press.

Konrad Jacobs (1960), *Neuere Methoden und Ergebnisse der Ergodentheorie*. Erg. Math. (N.F.) **29**. Berlin-Göttingen-Heidelberg: Springer-Verlag.

(1962–1963), *Lecture Notes on Ergodic Theory*, University of Aarhus.

Mark Kac (1959), *Statistical Independence in Probability, Analysis and Number Theory*, Carus Mathematical Monographs 12. New York: John Wiley and Sons.

A. Ya. Khinchine (1935), "Metrische Kettenbruchprobleme," *Compositio Math.* **1**, 361–382.

(1936), "Zur metrischen Kettenbruchtheorie," *Compositio Math.*, **3**, 275–285.

(1957), *Mathematical Foundations of Information Theory*. New York: Dover Publications.

(1964), *Continued Fractions*. Chicago: University of Chicago Press.

John R. Kinney and Tom S. Pitcher (1965), "The dimension of some sets defined in terms of f-expansions," to appear.

A. N. Kolmogorov (1933), *Grundbegriffe der Wahrscheinlichkeitsrechnung*. Erg. Math. **2**, no. 3. Berlin-Göttingen-Heidelberg: Springer-Verlag.

(1958), "A new invariant for transitive dynamical systems," *Dokl. Akad. Nauk SSSR* **119**, 861–864.

(1959), "Entropy per unit time as a metric invariant of automorphisms," *Dokl. Akad. Nauk SSSR* **124**, 754–755.

R. O. Kuz'min (1928), "A problem of Gauss," *Dokl. Akad. Nauk, Ser. A*, 375–380.

Paul Lévy (1929), "Sur les lois de probabilité dont dépendent les quotients complets et incomplets d'une fraction continue," *Bull. Soc. Math.*, **57**, 178–194.

(1937), *Théorie de l'Addition des Variables Aléatoires*. Paris: Gauthier-Villars.

B. McMillan (1953), "The basic theorems of information theory," *Ann. Math. Stat.* **24**, 196–219.

L. D. Meshalkin (1959), "A case of isomorphism of Bernoulli schemes," *Dokl. Akad. Nauk SSSR* **128**, 41–44.

W. Meyer-Eppler (1959), *Grundlagen und Anwendungen der Informationstheorie*, Kommunikation und Kybernetik in Einzeldarstellungen, Vol. 1. Berlin-Göttingen-Heidelberg: Springer-Verlag.

M. S. Pinsker (1960a), *Information and Informational Stability of Random Variables and Processes.* Moscow: Academy of Science, U.S.S.R. (English translation 1964. San Francisco: Holden-Day).

(1960b), "Dynamical systems with completely positive or zero entropy," *Dokl. Akad. Nauk SSSR* 133, 1025–1026.

A. Rényi (1957), "Representations of real numbers and their ergodic properties," *Acta. Math. Acad. Sci. Hungar.* 8, 477–493.

(1959), "Dimension, entropy and information," *Transactions of the Second Prague Conference on Information Theory, Statistical Decision Functions, Random Processes,* 545–556.

Tazlollah M. Reza (1961), *An Introduction to Information Theory.* New York: McGraw-Hill.

F. Riesz (1945), "Sur la théorie ergodique," *Comm. Math. Helvetici* 17, 221–239.

V. A. Rohlin (1959), "On the entropy of metric automorphisms," *Dokl. Akad. Nauk SSSR* 128, 980–983.

(1960), "New progress in the theory of measure-preserving transformations," *Uspehi Matem. Nauk* 15, 3–26. (Translation: Russian Mathematical Surveys, 15, No. 4, 1–22.)

(1961a), "Exact endomorphisms of Lebesgue spaces," *Izv. Akad. Nauk SSSR* 25, 499–530.

(1961b), "On the entropy of automorphisms of a commutative compact group," *Theory Prob. Appl.* 6, 322–323.

(1963), "Axiomatic determination of the entropy in a transformation with invariant measure," *Dokl. Akad. Nauk SSSR* 148, 779–781.

V. A. Rohlin and Ya. G. Sinai (1962), "Construction and properties of invariant measurable partitions," *Dokl. Akad. Nauk SSSR* 141, 1038–1041.

Murray Rosenblatt (1962), *Random Processes.* New York: Oxford University Press.

C. Ryll-Nardzewski (1951), "On the ergodic theorems II," *Studia Math.* 12, 74–79.

C. Shannon (1948), "A mathematical theory of communication," *Bell System Tech. J.* 27, 379–423, 623–656.

Ya. G. Sinai (1959a), "On the notion of the entropy of a dynamical system," *Dokl. Akad. Nauk SSSR* 124, 768–771.

(1959b), "On flows with finite entropy," *Dokl. Akad. Nauk SSSR* 125, 1200–1202.

(1960a), "Dynamical systems and stationary Markov processes," *Theory Prob. Appl.* 5, 305–308.

(1960b), "Geodesic flows in manifolds with constant negative curvature," *Dokl. Akad. Nauk SSSR* 131, 752–756.

(1961a), "Geodesic flows on compact surfaces of negative curvature," *Dokl. Akad. Nauk SSSR* 136, 549–552.

(1961b), "Dynamical systems with countable Lebesgue spectrum," *Izv. Akad. Nauk SSSR Ser. Mat.* 25, 899–924.

(1962*a*), "Probabilistic ideas in ergodic theory," *Proceedings of the International Congress of Mathematicians in Stockholm*, 540–559 (Translation: Amer. Math. Soc. Translations, Series 2, **31**, 62–84).

(1962*b*), "A weak isomorphism of transformations having an invariant measure," *Dokl. Akad. Nauk SSSR* **147**, 797–800.

K. Takano (1958), "On the basic theorems of information theory," *Ann. Inst. Stat. Math.* **9**, 53–77.

A. J. Thomasian (1960), "An elementary proof of the AEP of information theory," *Ann. Math. Statist.* **31**, 452–456.

J. V. Uspenski (1937), *Introduction to Mathematical Probability*. New York: McGraw-Hill.

J. von Neumann (1932*a*), "Proof of the quasiergodic hypothesis," *Proc. Nat. Acad. U.S.A.* **18**, 70–82.

(1932*b*), "Einige Sätze über messbare Abbildungen," *Ann. Math.* **33**, 574–586.

Fred B. Wright, editor (1963), *Ergodic Theory*. New York: Academic Press.

J. Wolfowitz (1961), *Coding Theorems of Information Theory*. Erg. Math. (N.F.) **31**. Berlin-Göttingen-Heidelberg: Springer-Verlag.

A. Zygmund (1959), *Trigonometric Series*, two volumes. Cambridge: Cambridge University Press.

Index of Examples

The examples from Chapter 1 are here briefly defined and their properties indicated. Absence of an assertion of ergodicity or nonergodicity, say, means the transformation may be ergodic or not, depending on how it is specialized.

For the examples in Chapters 2 through 5, all that is given is the number of the page on which the example is introduced.

Example 1.1 (p. 3). *The (two-sided) Bernoulli shift.*

Ω: $\omega = (\ldots, \omega_{-1}, \omega_0, \omega_1, \ldots)$ with $x_n(\omega) = \omega_n$ in the finite set ρ,

$T\omega = (\ldots, \omega_0, \omega_1, \omega_2, \ldots)$, i.e., $x_n(T\omega) = x_{n+1}(\omega)$,

$P\{\omega: x_l(\omega) = i_l, n \leq l < n + k\} = \Pi_{l=n}^{n+k-1} p_{i_l}.$

PROPERTIES: Invertible (p. 5); ergodic (p. 13); mixing (p. 13); $h(T) = -\Sigma_i p_i \log p_i$ (pp. 66 and 85).

Example 1.2 (p. 5). *The general (two-sided) shift.*

Ω: $\omega = (\ldots, \omega_{-1}, \omega_0, \omega_1, \ldots)$ with $x_n(\omega) = \omega_n$ in the finite set ρ,

$T\omega = (\ldots, \omega_0, \omega_1, \omega_2, \ldots)$; i.e., $x_n(T\omega) = x_{n+1}(\omega)$,

P: any probability measure preserved by T.

PROPERTIES: Invertible.

Example 1.3 (p. 6). *Noncyclic permutation.*

$\Omega = \{a, b, c, d, e\}$,

$T = (a, b, c)(d, e)$,

$P(a) = P(b) = P(c)$ and $P(d) = P(e)$.

PROPERTIES: Invertible; nonergodic unless $P(a) = P(b) = P(c)$ vanishes or $P(d) = P(e)$ vanishes (p. 8); not mixing (p. 13); $h(T) = 0$.

Example 1.4 (p. 6).   *Cyclic permutation.*
$\Omega = \{a, b, c, d, e\}$,
$T = (a, b, c, d, e)$,
$P(a) = P(b) = P(c) = P(d) = P(e) = 1/5$.

PROPERTIES: Invertible; ergodic (p. 8); not mixing (p. 13); $h(T) = 0$.

Example 1.5 (p. 6).   *The rotation of the circle.*
Ω: the unit circle in the complex plane,
$T\omega = c\omega$ with c in Ω,
P: normalized circular Lebesgue measure.

PROPERTIES: Invertible; ergodic if and only if c is not a root of unity (p. 9); not mixing (p. 13); $h(T) = 0$ (pp. 86 and 87).

Example 1.6 (p. 6).   *The dyadic transformation.*
$\Omega = [0,1)$,
$T\omega = 2\omega$ (mod 1),
P: Lebesgue measure.

PROPERTIES: Noninvertible; ergodic (pp. 11 and 102); mixing (p. 13); $h(T) = \log 2$.

Example 1.7 (p. 18).   *The shift for a real-valued process.*
Ω: $\omega = (\ldots, \omega_{-1}, \omega_0, \omega_1, \ldots)$ with $x_n(\omega) = \omega_n$ in the real line,
$T\omega = (\ldots, \omega_0, \omega_1, \omega_2, \ldots)$; i.e., $x_n(T\omega) = x_{n+1}(\omega)$,
P: any probability measure preserved by T.

PROPERTIES: Invertible.

Example 3.1 (p. 30).   *The Markov shift.*
Specialization of the general two-sided shift (Example 1.2) given by

$$P\{\omega: x_{n+l-1}(\omega) = i_l, l = 1, \ldots, k\} = p_{i_1}p_{i_1 i_2} \ldots p_{i_{k-1} i_k},$$

with the p_i stationary for the transition matrix (p_{ij}) and strictly positive.

PROPERTIES: Invertible; ergodic if and only if (p_{ij}) is irreducible (pp. 31, 114, and 119); mixing if and only if (p_{ij}) is irreducible and aperiodic (pp. 33 and 122); $h(T) = -\Sigma_{ij}p_i p_{ij} \log p_{ij}$ (p. 86).

Example 3.2 (p. 33).   *The general one-sided shift.*
Ω:$\omega = (\omega_1, \omega_2, \ldots)$ with $x_n(\omega) = \omega_n$ in the finite set ρ,
$T\omega = (\omega_2, \omega_3, \ldots)$; i.e., $x_n(T\omega) = x_{n+1}(\omega)$,
P: any probability measure preserved by T.

PROPERTIES: Never invertible; ergodicity and mixing properties and values of entropies coincide with those of the two-sided counterparts.

Example 3.3 (p. 33).

A specialization of the general two-sided shift (Example 1.2) in which the outcomes are independent but each is repeated.

PROPERTIES: Invertible; ergodic (p. 34); not mixing (p. 34); $h(T) = -\frac{1}{2}\Sigma_i p_i$ log p_i (p. 86).

Example 3.4 (p. 34). *The r-adic transformation.*

$\Omega = [0,1),$

$T\omega = r\omega \pmod 1,$

P: Lebesgue measure.

PROPERTIES: Not invertible; ergodic; mixing; $h(T) = \log r$.

Example 3.5 (p. 34).

$\Omega = [0,1),$

$T\omega = r\omega \pmod 1,$

P: any probability measure preserved by T.

PROPERTIES: Not invertible.

Example 5.1 (p. 55)	*Example* 10.1 (p. 108)
5.2 (p. 56)	10.2 (p. 108)
5.3 (p. 56)	10.3 (p. 109)
5.4 (p. 56)	10.4 (p. 113)
5.5 (p. 57)	10.5 (p. 114)
9.1 (p. 99)	11.1 (p. 118)
9.2 (p. 100)	11.2 (p. 119)
9.3 (p. 100)	11.3 (p. 119)
9.4 (p. 101)	11.4 (p. 119)
9.5 (p. 102)	16.1 (p. 158)
9.6 (p. 102)	16.2 (p. 159)
9.7 (p. 104)	16.3 (p. 159)

General Index

Some entries refer to footnotes.

Abbreviations, a.e., 8
  dr., 2, 8, 98
Adler, 162
Alphabet, 146
Aperiodic, 33
Atom, 60

Baker's transformation, 56
Bernoulli shift, 6
Billingsley, 145, 152
Birkhoff, 29
Block codes, 175
Blum, 93
Borel set, 6, 68
Breiman, 129, 136, 162
Brown, 90

Cantor function, 36
Cantor measure, 36, 143
Cantor set, 138
Capacity, 160
Chain, 72
Change-of-variable formula, 9
Channel capacity, 160
Channel, compound, 163, 166

Channel (*cont.*)
  lossless, 159
  noiseless, 147
  noisy, 152
  without memory, 153
Chung, 134
Closed, 31
Code, 148
Coding, 66, 146
Coding theorem, noiseless channel,
    converse, 151
  direct, 151
  noisy channel, converse, 163, 164,
    166
  direct, 163, 164, 176
Complete invariant, 59
Completeness problem, 90
Compound channel, 163, 166
Conditional entropy, 77, 123
Conditional expectation, 106
Conditional probability, 95
Conjugacy, 57, 66
Continued-fraction transformation, 40
Coordinate function or variable, 3,
    146

cummings, 64
Cylinder, 3, 140

Daniell, 3
Decomposition, 60
Dimension, 136
Diophantine approximation, 45, 47
Direct product, 89
Dobrushin, 179
Doeblin, 50
Doob, 99, 106, 115, 116, 120, 121, 122
Dunford, 69
Dyadic transformation, 7

Eggleston, 139, 145
Entropy, 60, 77, 123
Equipartition property, 135
Equivalence of sets, 66
Equivocation, 157
Ergodic capacity, 160
Ergodic theorem, 13
Ergodic theory, 2
Ergodic transformation, 7
Experiment, 62
Extreme point, 38

$\mathfrak{F}$-decomposition, 60
Feinstein, 152, 157, 159, 162, 175, 179
Feinstein's theorem, 168
Feller, 30, 33
Finite subfield, 60
Franck, 93
Fundamental interval, 42

Gauss's measure, 43
Gauss's problem, 49
Generates, 172
Good, 145
Graves, 5
Guest, 64

Halmos, 2, 4, 12, 19, 74, 77, 90
Hardy, 40
Harris, 39, 77

Hat function, 17
Hausdorff dimension, 136
Hilbert space, 20
Hopf, 19
Hurewicz, 145

Indicator, 8
Individual ergodic theorem, 21
Information, 62, 156
Information source, 63, 147
Input-output measure, 154
Invariant function, 13
Invariant set, 8
Invariant of a transformation, 57, 59
Invertible code, 149
Invertible transformation, 2, 5
Irreducible, 31
Isometry, 20, 74
Isomorphism, 51, 52, 150

Jacobi, 10
Jacobs, 19, 77
Jensen's inequality, 112

Kac, 19, 50
Kernel, 153
Khinchine, 40, 50, 152, 154, 162, 179
Kinney, 141, 145
Kolmogorov, 2, 59, 64, 65, 77, 94,
　　106, 116
Kolmogorov's existence theorem, 3, 6,
　　35, 37, 90
Kolmogorov shift, 92
Kolmogorov-Sinai theorem, 65, 84,
　　126, 151
Kuz'min, 50

L^1, 22
L^2, 20
Leader, 27
Letter, 63, 146
Lévy, 50, 122
Lipschitz condition, 134
Lossless channel, 159

Markov shift, 30
Martingale, 121
Maximal ergodic theorem, 20, 25
McMillan, 129, 136, 162
Measure algebra, 67
Measure-preserving transformation, 2
Meshalkin, 91, 94
Message, 147
Meyer-Eppler, 179
Mixing, 12
Monotone class, 4
Morse, 63
μ-ρ-covering, 141

Noiseless channel, 147
Noisy channel, 152
Nonanticipating channel, 153
Nonanticipating code, 150
Normal number, 15, 34

One-sided shift, 33
Orbit, 7, 11

Pinsker, 168, 179
Pitcher, 141, 145
Pointwise ergodic theorem, 21
Probability measure, 4
ρ-sequence, 172

r-adic interval, 34, 140
r-adic transformation, 34
Radon-Nikodym theorem, 99
Randomness, 61
Rate of transmission, 155
Rényi, 50, 145
Respects, 17
Reza, 179
Riesz, 29
ρ-covering, 136
Rohlin, 50, 90, 128
Rosenblatt, 39
Rotation, 7
Ryll-Nardzewski, 50

Schwartz, 69
Shannon, 59, 64, 77, 129, 136, 152, 162, 179
Shannon-McMillan-Breiman theorem, 129
Shift, 5, 18, 33
σ-field, 2
Sinai, 65, 77, 90, 91, 94, 128
Singular measure, 36
Source, 63, 147
Spectral equivalence, 73
State space, 1
Stationary, 5, 148, 153
Stationary capacity, 160
Stochastic code, 166
Stochastic matrix, 30
Stochastic process, 5
Strictly invariant set, 8
Symmetric difference, 8

Tail σ-field, 49
Takano, 154, 179
Thin cylinder, 3
Thomasian, 136
Time-0 field, 63
Transformation, 2
Triple for isomorphism, 53
Trivial σ-field, 49, 93
Two-sided shift, 33
Tyche, 5

Uncertainty, 62
Uniformly distributed, 16
Uspenski, 49

Version, 97, 107
von Neumann, 29, 77

Wallman, 145
Wolfowitz, 175
Wright, 40

Zygmund, 112

ENTROPY: DEFINITIONS AND PROPERTIES

$\eta(t) = -t \log t$

$H(\mathscr{A}) = \sum_A \eta(P(A)) = -\sum_A P(A) \log P(A)$

$H(\mathscr{A} \mid \mathscr{B}) = \sum_{A,B} P(B)\eta(P(A \mid B)) = -\sum_{A,B} P(A \cap B) \log P(A \mid B)$

$h(\mathscr{A}, T) = \lim \sup_n n^{-1} H(\bigvee_{k=0}^{n-1} T^{-k}\mathscr{A})$

$h(T) = \sup_{\mathscr{A}} h(\mathscr{A}, T)$

(A₁) $H(\mathscr{A} \vee \mathscr{B} \mid \mathscr{C}) = H(\mathscr{A} \mid \mathscr{C}) + H(\mathscr{B} \mid \mathscr{A} \vee \mathscr{C})$

(A₂) $H(\mathscr{A} \mid \mathscr{C}) \leq H(\mathscr{B} \mid \mathscr{C})$ if $\mathscr{A} \subset \mathscr{B}$

(A₃) $H(\mathscr{A} \mid \mathscr{C}) \leq H(\mathscr{A} \mid \mathscr{B})$ if $\mathscr{C} \supset \mathscr{B}$

(A₄) $H(\mathscr{A} \vee \mathscr{B} \mid \mathscr{C}) \leq H(\mathscr{A} \mid \mathscr{C}) + H(\mathscr{B} \mid \mathscr{C})$

(A₅) $H(T^{-1}\mathscr{A} \mid T^{-1}\mathscr{B}) = H(\mathscr{A} \mid \mathscr{B})$

(B₁) $h(\mathscr{A}, T) = \lim_n n^{-1} H(\bigvee_{k=0}^{n-1} T^{-k}\mathscr{A}) = \lim_n H(\mathscr{A} \mid \bigvee_{k=1}^{n} T^{-k}\mathscr{A})$

(B₁′) $h(\mathscr{A}, T) = \lim_n H(T^{-n}\mathscr{A} \mid \bigvee_{k=0}^{n-1} T^{-k}\mathscr{A})$

(B₁″) $h(\mathscr{A}, T) = \lim_n H(\mathscr{A} \mid \bigvee_{k=1}^{n} T^{k}\mathscr{A})$

(B₂) $h(\mathscr{A}, T) \leq h(\mathscr{B}, T)$ if $\mathscr{A} \subset \mathscr{B}$

(B₃) $h(\bigvee_{i=u}^{v} T^{-i}\mathscr{A}, T) = h(\mathscr{A}, T)$

(B₄) $h(\bigvee_{i=0}^{k-1} T^{-i}\mathscr{A}, T^k) = k h(\mathscr{A}, T)$

(B₅) $h(\mathscr{A}, T) \leq h(\mathscr{B}, T) + H(\mathscr{A} \mid \mathscr{B})$